What people say about this book

In reviewing the book, I felt overwhelmed by the amount of information that was included in the pages. But then I started looking at it from the perspective of a road map as to how this could work if my company had a culture that was up to the challenge of improving the organisation. This book not only highlights the steps to implement TPM but demonstrates the need for a solid cultural foundation. It is a book that, no matter what continuous improvement programme an organisation is trying to initiate, gives a clear path to what is needed from a people perspective. There is a wealth of knowledge captured in these pages, from case studies to charts and graphs, from the right metrics to be used to audit sheets, from assessments to leadership habits. It is a book that I certainly would recommend.
Bob Kerr, *retired VP of High Performance Solutions (AME-USA)*

I have been in the lean arena for over 35 years and travelled many countries to see operational excellence in practice. When it comes to TPM there are few that do it well. *TPM: a foundation of operational excellence* is a great bible if you really wish to transform your organisation. You will continue to pick this book up as a great reference guide to help you navigate through the modern challenges with culture, leadership, people and technology. The art of any sustainable process is habit and this book offers guiding principles to develop those habits. Congratulations.
Brett Griffiths *MSc MBA, CEO – Lean Transition Solutions Ltd UK*

After 25 years of implementing TPM, my frustration has always been sustaining the gains and moving through the various stages. This book explains in depth how this can be achieved in an easy to follow format with lots of real life experiences from the authors. It is very up to date, addressing the positive and potential negative impact of Industry 4.0 and the critical importance of leadership behaviours and making them part of Leader Standard work. A great read and reference book.
Chris Horton, *Vice President Operations, Weener Plastics, Netherlands*

While many books have been written and training courses taught on TPM, I have yet to find any that demonstrates as clearly as this book does, how the combined use of proven tools and techniques, applied within a framework, can create behaviours which support operational excellence. By continuously improving the way people think and communicate, the organisational culture shifts from a reactive or inactive mode to a proactive dynamic team. Peter's and SA Partners' work focuses on harnessing the diversity of thought locked within the mind of each employee. This book will influence the way you think about your workplace environment and how to improve it for the better.
David Riley *MSc, Partner, OAC Consulting, Interim Continuous Improvement Performance Manager, Dublin Airport Authority, Ireland*

I found *TPM: a foundation of operational excellence* to be up to date and comprehensive – it's certainly relevant to today's industrial challenges. It is a very useful mixture of both theory and detailed practice and as such can act as a practical field guide. I believe the various audit sheets and appendices, and the internal workshop

designs, will be invaluab
operational excellence j
challenge of people & cu
– with the Shingo Mode!
of TPM implementation. _
work and Peter, John and Andy should be proud of it.
Eamonn Dunlea, *CI Director, Princes Foods, UK*

It is indeed an exciting journey to travel through the ten chapters of this book and, reaching the case studies, to realize how much TPM is an enabling tool to help asset-based organisations achieve their operational excellence aspirations. I invite all operations and maintenance organisations, associations and academia to consider this book on the top of their list of knowledge resources.
Dr Zohair Alsarraj, *Chairman, International Maintenance Association (IMA) Switzerland*

The vision of our enterprise is producing and manufacturing superbly. Our success is demonstrated by our exceptional business results. We tap the experience and commitment of everyone who works for us." If this vision is close to what you want to achieve, you will be delighted to discover this book! Here is the 'how to do it manual' for manufacturing excellence – in a truly accessible format. This book is for companies that are great at producing valuable products for society. The deep practical knowledge of the authors shines through – you can feel the joy that they have in codifying and passing on their expertise. Thank you very much indeed for adding this knowledge to the world!
Les Thomson, *former VP Operations for BP*

TPM: a foundation of operational excellence is a fantastic practical guide to help chart your journey through the implementation of a structured TPM system model. The book provides a road map for success with practical guidance and first hand case studies that help bring the model to life and showcase the improvements that can be gained. The extensive experience of Peter, Andy and John is invaluable in making this book an essential resource. Many congratulations.
Michael Hempton, *Operational Excellence Specialist, Moy Park, Northern Ireland*

This book provides an authoritative account of TPM and its modern application in a way that is accessible and enjoyable to read. The book is rich in the 'art and science' of TPM, drawing on decades of experience, and shows how to align TPM to deliver business results in today's highly competitive markets. The style of the book is easy to follow and will be of great use to those starting off with TPM or businesses that have many years of experience and are seeking to improve their performance even further. The book contains many applications, reader self-assessments, business cases and illustrations that add greatly to the value of this book for managers in all industries. A 'must read' for anyone seeking operational excellence for their business.
Nick Rich, *Professor of Socio-Technical Systems, Swansea University, UK*

As someone who knows the power of TPM to enable Operational Excellence, this latest book by Peter, Andy and John provides a powerful insight as to the full extent of what's involved to achieve success with TPM. The 11-step process is the foundation on which the possibilities for success are endless, so for those who are looking for a practical guide on what's involved, reading this book is a great place to start.

Pat White, TPM practitioner, Molex Ireland

When I was first met Peter Willmott and deployed TPM at the Mylan Damastown site (formerly Rottapharm), I never realised the journey this powerful system of work would lead to in terms of both organisational and personal growth. The introduction of TPM and later the Shingo Model transformed the operation at Damastown in terms of business results and culture. TPM is not just an engineering maintenance tool, which at first I thought it was. It is an essential system of work that helps drive desired behaviour and as this book clearly illustrates can be a key driving force towards developing a culture based on the Shingo Model of organisational work behaviour.

Richard Hayes, Operational Excellence Director, Mylan Damastown, Ireland

A really excellent read that anyone in manufacturing would appreciate. The principles are sound and will deliver the improvements, as the many examples illustrate, to the readers who apply them. At Spirax we have followed a number of these with great success. However, your book has enabled me to reflect and refresh our thinking on our journey towards operational excellence. The is not only a great read cover to cover, but also a great reference guide. Throughout the book you have made excellent use of real examples, templates and visuals bringing complete clarity to the subject and application of TPM. I would not hesitate recommending this as a must-read for anyone in manufacturing that wants to make a sustainable difference.

Greg Godfrey-Williams, Plant Operations Manager, Spirax Sarco-UK

This book is an essential read for anyone wanting to understand how to implement Total Productive Manufacturing. The authors share many years of practical experience along with case studies, self-assessments and useful tips.

Chris Butterworth, Award-winning author (two Shingo publication awards), Certified Shingo Institute Master Trainer and Shingo examiner

As former Director for the MSc in Lean where Peter Willmott was the lecturer on TPM I have been aware of the large positive impact that Peter's TPM approach had on our executive students and on their organisations. For perhaps two decades I have regarded Peter as **the** top authority on TPM in the UK and Ireland. Peter and his colleagues' new book brings together and updates the well-known Willmott 11-stage model for TPM. A full no-holds-barred description is given and as such it is a wonderful self-contained instruction manual. This is no theoretical treatise, but a highly practical approach that has been proven at a range of organisations. It is an end-to-end model, from diagnosis to sustainability. With the Willmott model, TPM goes well beyond description of the 'tools' of maintenance. It includes much guidance for senior management, as well as a comprehensive approach to gaining the buy-in of operators and their team leaders. I have seen first-hand the transformation of staff attitudes at two Irish sites where the model has been implemented. Of particular note is how the model links in and supports the Shingo Prize system.

Guidance sheets and survey forms appear throughout the publication, all ready to use. I particularly liked

- the balanced advantages and warnings about the use of OEE.
- the comprehensive documentation about changeover reduction
- the range of applications that are discussed – from manufacturing and warehousing to water utilities, wind-farms, and airport material handling
- the case studies that are written not by the authors but by senior executives from organisations where the model has been applied.

I know of no other publication on TPM that comes close to the scope, detail and practical utility of this book. It is likely to become **the** standard text on the topic.

John Bicheno, Professor of Lean Enterprise, University of Buckingham

A big well done to Peter, John and Andy for putting their knowledge and experiences into this brilliant book. The walk through each of the steps on the journey to excellence is clearly mapped throughout. Wonderful examples and stories of Total Productive Manufacturing which I absolutely loved and can associated with. This is a compelling read and a must-have reference manual and guide book for all those driven by continuous improvement and personal development.

Tony Beck, Master BB and Site Manager, Lubrizol Mostyn plant

This book moves TPM from a 'maintenance thing' to a core operating system within a company, with a focus on the purpose, the process and the people. It provides the reader with the theory they require, plentiful case material and a roadmap for action. A must-buy for any manufacturing business serious about becoming world class.

Peter Hines, Founder, S A Partners and Visiting Professor, Waterford Institute of Technology

This book provides you with a short cut to what Peter has learnt over his lengthy career and thus is a must-read if you want to be at the forefront of TPM.

Richard Lloyd, General Manager European Operations and Supply Chain, Accolade Wines, UK

What a great read. Through this book, and with the 11-step Model, S A Partners have made what can be seen as convoluted and complicated, simple and practical. Peter, Andy and John have encapsulated their wealth of experience in supporting organisations to implement TPM through a structured approach, and this book is the perfect companion to navigate your way to TPM Operational Excellence.

Yousif Eltom, Group Lean Manager, ABP Food Group UK

Finally, an understanding on how and more importantly **why** the traditional view of TPM needs to be seen and executed differently. Peter, John and Andy bring a fresh and pragmatic means to generate real value and integration of the key business tenets of Operational Excellence and TPM. This book will become a reference on how it should be done. A paradigm shift to Total Productive Manufacturing Itis long overdue.

Greg Julich, Director Global Reliability, Integrated Manufacturing Excellence and Network Performance, Certified Maintenance and Reliability Professional, Pfizer Inc USA

TPM
a foundation of operational excellence

Peter Willmott

John Quirke

Andy Brunskill

Together, the power to improve ®

S A Partners, Caerphilly

TPM: a foundation of operational excellence

Published by S A Partners, Y Borth, 13 Beddau Way, Caerphilly, CF83 2AX, UK

© Peter Willmott, John Quirke, Andy Brunskill, 2019

First published 2019

A CIP catalogue record for this book can be obtained from the British Library.

ISBN: 978-1-9993748-1-5

Edited and designed by Text Matters www.textmatters.com

Cover illustration and many of the diagrams in the body of the text created by Alex Everitt

About the authors

Peter Willmott

Peter Willmott gained his foundational experience as a mechanical craftsman in the aerospace industry. He graduated with an honours degree in Production Engineering from Loughborough University and is a Chartered Engineer

While heading up five TPM study tours to Japan in the early 1990s, Peter was inspired by the team working and empowerment potential of TPM.

Peter is a world-renowned and respected authority with over 25 years experience on the application of Total Productive Maintenance (TPM). He has written two previous books on the subject:

- TPM – The Western Way (ISBN 0 7506 1925 2)
- TPM – A Route to World Class Performance (ISBN 0 7506 4447 8).

Peter's list of TPM current and past clients include three recent Shingo Award winners where TPM has been a foundation system for each recipient:

- DePuy Synthes Ireland (Prize 2014)
- Lake Region Medical (Bronze Medallion 2015)
- Mylan-Rottapharm (Silver Medallion 2016)

Over the years, Peter's other TPM clients have ranged across the complete spectrum of industry as these examples illustrate:

- Accolade Wines
- Arjo Wiggins Paper Mills
- BAA Heathrow, Airport Authority
- BNFL, Nuclear Power
- BP Exploration, Oil and Gas extraction
- Exxon Chemicals, Primary Chemical Conversion
- Ford Motor Co
- General Motors, Europe
- Linpac Packaging, Food
- Molex, Electrical & Electronic devices
- Pfizer Pharmaceuticals
- Rolls Royce Aero Engines
- Royal Mail, UK
- Royal Mint, UK
- Sony Television
- Zimmer, Medical Devices

In the recent past, Peter has delivered the TPM, and associated OEE, 5S and SMED modules for over 10 years as an External Lecturer for the University of Buckingham's MSc degree in Lean Enterprise, (previously based at LERC Cardiff Business School).

He is a member of the Advisory Board of the International Maintenance Association.

John Quirke

John Quirke originally graduated from the Maynooth University with an honour's degree in Chemistry and Biology. John subsequently completed a master's degree in chemical oceanography with University College Galway. A specialisation in metal chemistry led John to an early career as a chemical process engineer with Fujitsu Isotec, where he spent time in Japan studying Japanese manufacturing and engineering techniques.

John's knowledge of process chemistry and toxicology resulted in a move to safety and environmental management with a blue-chip life science corporation. John's frustration with poor equipment design and poor process performance resulted in him becoming an early adopter of lean thinking within this organisation. The success of subsequent programmes, giving rise to improvements in process performance and waste reduction, led to global roles as director of business excellence and twenty years' continuous improvement experience working across all business sectors.

John's friendship and work with Peter Willmott goes back many years. John has worked with Peter to develop a system and behavioural based approach to TPM which has been the root of many organisational transformational journeys.

John is a director and partner at S A Partners and leads the Global Life Science sector and the Irish business. John's other specialist areas include coaching and lean leadership, strategy deployment, process design for lean, and problem-solving. John is a certified Shingo Institute Facilitator and a Master Lean Coach from Cardiff University. In addition to BSc (Hons) and MSc, John holds a Law Degree from University College Cork.

Andy Brunskill

Andy graduated from Bradford University with an honours degree in Chemistry. He then joined GSK on a graduate management scheme. On completion he moved on to become manufacturing manager responsible for the processing of bulk products across all processing areas of the plant. Andy became involved in continuous improvement activities at GSK as far back as 1989 when the site embarked on a CI journey and led initiatives based on bulk product wastage reduction and changeover optimisation of blister packaging lines.

Andy was given the opportunity to join one of GSK's outsourcing contract processing plants as Production Manager of CCL Industries, responsible for all toiletry and aerosol production lines, and was instrumental in the initiation of CI activity across the site including a key process reliability programme on the aerosol line that involved TPM team activities and cross functional group working with the supply chain to eliminate losses incurred as a result of supplier defects.

Under Andy's guidance the site became the first plant to be approved under the Proctor and Gamble key element assurance audit and went on to establish an extremely successful CI programme culminating in CCL winning the most improved factory in the Cranfield institute/Management Today Best Factory awards in 1996.

Andy then became Factory Manager at Nichols Foods (now Aimia Foods) initially for the soft drinks factory and then extending his responsibility to the dry production factory and its confectionery packaging factory. During this time Andy helped nurture a fantastic CI culture at the Haydock site that achieved some remarkable sustained results in a relatively short time period. The site became a multi award winning site including Best Factory 1999, sharing its experiences with businesses through the IUKE (Inside UK Enterprise) initiative. Following popular demand it opened its doors to paying customers for site experience days that created a revenue stream which was invested back into the development of CI at the site and in its people development. This included a study tour of Japan in 2001 for a cross-functional group of staff. Andy has been back several times since then as a consultant to support Japanese companies with the application of lean and TPM, a somewhat paradoxical thought back in 2001.

Andy joined S A Partners in 2004 as a consultant and was let loose on the outside world. As the Japanese say 'the frog has left the well' and he has worked in many different sectors including pharmaceutical, medical devices, steel, electronics, food and drink, utilities and waste management. He has led and supported global CI and TPM programmes across all continents of the world, working extensively in the UK, Europe, China, Japan and India over the last fifteen years.

Andy has been a partner at S A Partners since 2015 and is the Lead partner for TPM in the business. Andy's other specialist areas include value stream management, coaching, strategy deployment and problem-solving. Andy is also a certified Shingo trainer and has a Cardiff University LERC Black Belt accreditation. Andy has worked closely with Peter Willmott since 2014 and together they have collaborated working with clients across the globe on TPM.

His past and current clients includes Pfizer, Abbvie, Welsh Water, Tata Steel, Vale, ABP Food Group, Boston Scientific, Burtons Foods and Suez among many others.

Andy is also a passionate football supporter and an avid music fan.

Contents

Preface

Customers expect manufacturers to provide excellent quality, reliable delivery and competitive pricing. This demands that the manufacturer's machines, processes and systems – and hence its employees who drive them – are highly reliable. But what does the term 'highly reliable' really mean?

Certainly, with manufacturing, process and utility service industries becoming progressively dependent on the reliability – and hence predictability – of fewer but more sophisticated machines and processes, it means that poor equipment operating performance is no longer affordable or acceptable. As such, the overall effectiveness of our machines, equipment and processes is paramount to provide consistency of product quality and supply at a realistic and competitive price.

Coping with both proven and rapidly emerging modern manufacturing technology – via the 4th Industrial Revolution, or Industry 4.0 as it is being referred to – is one issue. Delivering the company's vision, values and expectations as an aspiring and inspiring example of 'Operational Excellence' is another. Both issues are explored in detail in Chapter 2.

Over 30 years ago some 'world class' Japanese companies recognised that the effective application of modern technology can only be achieved through people – starting with the operators and maintainers of that applied technology, and not through systems alone. Hence the emergence of total, productive maintenance as the enabling tool to maximise the effectiveness of their equipment by setting and maintaining the optimum relationship between people and their machines.

The problem with the words 'Total Productive Maintenance' – and hence the philosophy, tools and techniques of TPM – is that to Western ears, they sound as though TPM is a maintenance function-driven initiative. But it is not!

TPM is driven by manufacturing & operations, which pick up production and maintenance as equal partners. It is no longer appropriate to say 'I operate, you fix' and 'I add value, you cost money'. What TPM promotes – and can deliver in the right hands – is a mindset that says 'We are both responsible for this equipment asset and, between us, we will determine the best way of operating and maintaining it in the firm belief that if you ask our opinion about that 'best way' and then incorporate it in our future ways of working, then we will stick with it because it's our idea!'

So a better way of describing TPM is to call it Total Productive Manufacturing to emphasise the team working and culture change implicit in this powerful enabling tool.

Based on our experience of helping companies to implement TPM over the last three decades, enterprises who have been most successful in sustaining the gains are those that focus on four key success factors from the outset. These are:

- You must enrol and secure the visible and consistent commitment of the corporate and site leadership team from the outset.
- TPM is seen to be led by manufacturing as a key enabler to deliver the company's continuous improvement/operational excellence (OE) programme.
- You will not achieve your OE aspirations without operational basics in place: TPM is therefore a foundational system of work of your OE programme in the sense that it is a practical application of team working which allows you to take the company's vision and values off of the notice board and hand it to the employees and say with conviction. 'Here you are then, this TPM enabling tool will allow you to make a difference, leading to a trouble free shift by working smarter, not harder'
- As such TPM is a practical and hands-on empowerment process which gives shared responsibility and ownership to employees at the sharp end of the business.

Remember also that the application of TPM is like a heart transplant: If you don't match it to the patient you will get rejection. You must therefore treat each company and local site recipient as unique and adapt the principles of TPM (without corrupting them) to suit both the industry type and local plant-specific issues, which also takes into account their CI journey to date.

Over the last ten years or so, the Shingo Institute and its associated Shingo Model™ and Shingo Awards™ has emerged as the leading authority and standard bearer for benchmarking an organisation's successful establishment of a culture anchored on principles of operational excellence and which are based on criteria embedded within the Shingo Model.

Based on our own direct experience of working with a wide range of industries and locations around the world of aspiring 'world class' companies, five of the key outputs of the book will be to:

- Provide a practical guide of how to deliver sustainable benefits using the TPM enabling system.
- Describe how TPM can deliver your own company's vision, values and aspirations.
- Position TPM as a foundational element of sustainable operational excellence and illustrate how TPM can align with systems thinking and the ideal behaviours implicit in the Shingo Model and its ten guiding principles.
- Recognise that the digital and technologically driven Industry 4.0 revolution is just a powerful enabler and that it is our people's individual and collective skills who will continue to make the difference.
- Help organisations understand the likely resource commitments of people, money and time of running your own in- house TPM programme and how to prepare a compelling cost/benefit business case.

As such the intended prime audience for the book is three groups within a particular business enterprise:

- the continuous improvement specialists, who in turn will act as the catalyst to encourage
- the business leadership team to gain top down support and commitment and then
- the 'practitioners' at the sharp end of the enterprise to use the TPM system as the bottom-up 'enabling tool' to help deliver the company's business drivers, vision, values and culture.

We also hope that appropriate institutions of advanced learning and academia will include this book in their recommended reading lists.

Peter Willmott
John Quirke
Andy Brunskill

Foreword

In an increasingly connected digital world, industries and services will need to continuously innovate and improve to ensure they remain competitive. Organisations that stand still cannot withstand the increased change velocity of the technologically driven Industry 4.0. Enterprises which have embedded a culture of operational excellence can survive and thrive in this new world of globalised markets.

We began our Operational Excellence journey in 2010 when Peter Willmott introduced to me the TPM system when I was Managing Director of Rottapharm (now part of the Mylan Group). At the time we had an urgent need to attract new products in the face of a mature product portfolio and stagnant growth. For a number of years prior to that we had been deploying lean tools with limited success. Improvements in the main were short-lived. Peter offered a way forward with a bottom-up approach focused on involving the teams on the shop floor. By contrast our previous initiatives were largely top down, project driven and led by managers. I baulked initially at the downtime involved but was persuaded that the benefits would more than compensate for the temporary loss of production capacity.

The concept of a structured approach to improving the performance and longevity of our assets, utilising the skills and knowledge of our employees, offered a compelling vision of sustainable improvement. The time and resource requirement were considerable but insignificant in the overall context of the payback in cost, quality and service. In a short period TPM provided us with the platform for a continuous improvement system that has transformed the operational efficiency of the site.

In effect TPM became an engine of change which unlocked the potential of our employees throughout the organisation. In time we refined the model for faster and more effective deployment using the experience gained as we rolled out the programme to all areas of the plant. Subsequently we adopted the Shingo model to embed principle based behaviours and underpin the TPM philosophy. The Shingo Silver medallion awarded to the site in 2016 had it is origins in the people centred approach developed in 2010 with our first TPM programme.

This book provides Operational Excellence practitioners with tremendous insights and many practical examples of TPM in action.

Pat Garrahy
Head of Oral Solid Dose
Mylan
Dublin

Acknowledgements

This publication is the result of working with a range of excellent companies across the complete spectrum of manufacturing industries. The common denominator is that these enterprises have a firm belief that the TPM System and philosophy is the enabling tool to unlock their installed productive capacity by unlocking the creative and innovative potential of their front line associates: the operators and maintainers of those manufacturing assets.

We would like to thank them all and the following people in particular who have either directly contributed to the writing and publication of this book or influenced the continuous improvement thinking of its authors:

Mohammed Abuljebain, Cormac Ahern, Gareth Appleton, Mark Barratt, Tony Beck, Chris Belcher, John Bicheno, John Bolger, Michael Bradley, Warren Burgess, Derek Cochrane, Peter Connett, Phil Conway, Paul Delahunt, Neil Enright, Alex Everitt, Alan France, Pauline Gaffney, Pat Garrahy, Angelo Gerada, Greg Godfrey-Williams, Richard Gray, Richard Hayes, Michael Hempton, Noel Hennessy, Duncan Hine, Wesley Horan, Chris Horton, Ray Hunter, John Hurst, Deidre Hynes, John Jones, Neil Ketteman, Bob King, Trevor Leake, Richard Lloyd, Paul Ludorf, Matt McCarry, Dennis McCarthy, John Moulton, John McTernan, Paul O'Malley, Ray O'Neill, Nick Rich, Dave Riley, Ian Ross, Les Thomson, PJ Tobin, Greg Walker, Tim Watts, Paul Wheelhouse, Pat White, Lynn Williams, David Willson, Alan Wilson, Dr Zohair Al Sarraj.

We would also like to thank the following organisations for their inspiration and contribution in the development of the TPM System of work through sharing their 'learning by doing' experiences:

Abbott Laboratories, Abbvie, Accolade Wines, BAA, BNFL, Boston Scientific, BP Exploration, BPL, Daikin Industries, Exxon Chemicals, Ford Motor Co, General Motors (Europe), Guinness, Hollister, J & J DePuy, Kraft Foods, Leo Pharma, Lake Region Medical, Linpac Packaging, Molex, Moy Park, Mylan Rottapharm, Pfizer, Premier Foods, RHM Group , Rolls Royce, Royal Mail, Royal Mint, Shell, Shingo Institute, Sony, Spirax Sarco, Teva Pharma, Text Matters, Vale, Warwick Chemicals Waters Technologies, Yeo Valley and Zimmer.

Finally a big thank you to the leadership and the wider team within S A Partners for their support for this project and their willing inputs.

CHAPTER 1
Overview: TPM and system thinking

1.1 The initials TPM – what's in a name?

In the bad old days an operator in conversation with his maintenance colleague might suggest – albeit mischievously – "I operate, you fix. I add value, you cost money – so watch out my friend!"

In order to begin to change perceptions relating to equipment its operation and maintenance, we strongly recommend you define (or badge) the initials of your TPM programme as **Total Productive Manufacturing** – as opposed to the original Total Productive Maintenance – without corrupting the well-proven founding principles described in Section 1.32.

By approaching TPM as a system backed by a philosophy of curiosity and learning, we encourage conversations based on learning by doing problem solving and improvement. So now when the operator is speaking to their maintenance colleague it would go something like "…I'm beginning to enjoy this TPM stuff, where we are both taking ownership for this asset which is helping each of us to have a hassle-free shift – not because we're lazy but because we are now able to work smarter as a team."

An emphasis on Total Productive *Maintenance* runs a high risk of implying that it is a maintenance department-driven technical initiative and therefore little to do with the operators and production.

1.2 The five founding principles of TPM

To remind ourselves of the founding principles of TPM, which mainly come from the early work of S Nakajima, T Suzuki and their colleagues from the Japan Institute of Plant Maintenance, let's take a look at each in turn:
1   Increase the overall equipment effectiveness (OEE) or equivalent effectiveness measure
2   Improved existing planned maintenance systems
3   Make routine front-line asset care part of the job
4   Increase skills (hand and operational, team working and problem solving)
5   Early involvement in new equipment specification.

Like time, concepts and ideas move on. Despite the fact the foundational principles of TPM have been in circulation for over thirty years we see many TPM initiatives that have started off with the best of intentions but have failed. The rocks that then cause the sinking of the TPM ship in our experience are likely to be a lack of sustained team engagement and leadership.

As a result, we have added another critical element which forms the basis of employee engagement and enables a leadership style focused on improvement…
6   Make performance visible.

By making performance visible (visual management) we allow the team to see the results of the efforts. It can focus minds on the basic question, are we winning or losing? If we are losing, good systems of visual management help the team identify the priority areas to focus on.

1.2.1 Principle 1 – Increase the true effectiveness of the asset which is often measured using the OEE

OEE (overall equipment effectiveness) is a measure of availability multiplied by the performance rate of the equipment while it is running and the quality rate that the equipment is producing. It is important to remind ourselves that while OEE can be used as a key performance indicator (KPI) this is not its only purpose. OEE is an enabler for focused and prioritised improvement activity. We will discuss OEE in more detail in later chapters but OEE (or an equivalent effectiveness measure such as yield and/or capacity release) is the way to focus teams on prioritised equipment improvement. The aim is to improve productivity of our people and equipment assets.

The common factors affecting OEE performance are often referred to as the six classic equipment losses:
- breakdowns
- excessive changeovers and set up times
- running at a reduced speed because the equipment is not quite right
- minor stoppages, which do not need a maintainer to attend the machine but cause the operator to have to intervene because of, for example, a jam or blockage
- scrap, poor yield or rework and quality problems
- start-up losses every time an unplanned stoppage or changeover occurs.

As such OEE is a vital measure (within a balanced scorecard), as it measures equipment-based waste in all its forms. As a measure it must be understood, trusted, easy to obtain, and integrated into the visual management process (see below) for that work centre. The TPM system drives toward a high OEE by enabling consistent focused improvement resulting in a trouble-free shift that allows people to work smarter, not harder.

1.2.2 Principle 2 – Improve existing planned maintenance systems

Focus on the quality of the maintenance means that the maintenance engineers decide what the mechanical and electrical PMs should include together with the essential spares needed to support the equipment and each planned procedure. Proper use should be made of the computer maintenance management system (CMMS) in this regard, because – as with a healthy body – prevention is better than cure, and the equipment becomes easier to maintain. In this way the maintenance team's focus is not restricted to maintenance tasks but also
- accessing the relevance of the maintenance task itself
- finding ways to make defined maintenance tasks easier, quicker, and safer
- working within the maintenance team to eliminate recurring problems with the maintenance function itself.

1.2.3 Principle 3 – Develop routine front line operator asset care as part of the job

The third principle or pillar of TPM, often called autonomous maintenance (or AM), is when the operator decides, together with their maintenance colleague, what the 'basic regular care' routines of look, listen, smell, clean, and adjustment should be and whether they should be carried out on a daily, weekly or shift by shift basis.

This principle is based on a simple but true belief that, if you seek an operator's point of view about the best way to operate and maintain equipment at this basic level, and that knowledge is embodied in the way they will do things for the future, then they will stick with it because it is their idea.

This total involvement approach means that most operators will take ownership for their actions and, therefore, the maintenance, as well as the quality of that maintenance.

If, on the other hand, you impose so-called 'new working practices' on them, they are more likely to tick a few boxes on your fancy log-sheet but not actually do the checks. In fact they may well tick the boxes at the start of the shift, because they have no sense of ownership of the content.

1.2.4 Principle 4 – Increase generic and specific skill levels

By carrying out the activities of measuring OEE, improving the PMs, and taking daily front line basic care of the asset, the operators and maintainers will also need to increase their skills – not only in terms of hand operational skills, but also team work, problem-solving and general information technology skills. Doing this will improve their process and equipment knowledge. This work-based experience results in sustained, on-going interest and care for the workplace.

1.2.5 Principle 5 – Early equipment management (EEM)

EEM is a systematic and structured way of using common sense in relation to new equipment design and installation. If you are going to design or invest in a new facility, equipment or machine, it is wise to gather existing experience and learning by involving your existing operators and maintainers in design and purchase decisions. For many companies daily new product development innovations – which not only reflect the voice of our customers, but also demand a rapid response time to market – means that the EEM philosophy comes into its own. This is so because EEM provides a structured approach to tap into their practical knowledge base at the earliest opportunity, ideally at the concept and high-level design stage and not when the equipment arrives on the manufacturing floor.

1.2.6 Principle 6 – Make performance visible

Whether electronic or manual (our preference is for manual backed up by electronic data) visual management must be present where the work gets done. The indicators plotted must be those that can be influenced by the team and the targets set must be set by the team. We will come back to visual management later in this book, but those companies that have achieved a level of sustainable enterprise excellence have a robust visual management process in place that allows the team to see if they are winning or losing and, if they are losing, what they are doing about it. In addition, if the team are consistently winning it allows the team to review and put in place a new challenge.

Leaders in these benchmark organisations have been carefully trained in how to effectively engage with visual management processes, such as visual management boards or huddle boards as they are often referred to. Their attendance at team huddle boards is an integral part of an agreed element of their leader standard work. Their presence at these meeting is not to solve problems or to berate the redness of the indicators, the leaders instead uses effective enquiry to understand how the team are approaching the issues. The leaders will also check that underlying processes such as how performance is being measured, how problems are being highlighted and prioritised, and team activity are aligned to the overall goals and objectives of the business. The leaders will also use these interactions to check for and confirm the presence or absence of agreed behaviours and call it out where agreed behaviours are not where they need to be. However, the leader must show humility and accept that there is lack of support or follow-up on his or her part; responsibility must be accepted and genuine steps taken to address the gap.

Each of these founding principles are explored in detail in subsequent chapters against the backdrop of TPM as a holistic enabling system to deliver a company's aspirations in relation to sustainable business performance and its supporting culture and behaviours.

1.3 Operational excellence and the TPM system model

Operational excellence and its associated 'lean thinking' is the speed and pace with which we receive a customer's order and convert it into profit by eliminating waste in all that we do.

TPM maintains that flow through the company's critical physical assets by focusing on their reliability and the predictability of their performance. On the other hand, workplace organisation/5S is aimed at creating the necessary flow around those same critical assets (see Section 1.10 below).

Recent thinking in relation to Operational Excellence focuses on systems and the ideal behaviour of the people working in those systems. When we think about this in the context of our equipment and machines, the concept of systems-thinking requires us to have systems and processes in place, in order to understand and validate the true performance of those key assets, and then stabilize and standardize that performance. Furthermore there must be a system in place to support the relentless focus on optimising the performance of these assets and ensure that, as a business, we remain truly competitive.

Through practice and input from our customer base during our consulting activity we have developed a model for implementing the TPM system within an organisation.

The 11-step TPM model (Figure 1.1) allows us to achieve this by
- providing a structured and systematic approach which is both practical and process-focused
- encouraging wide engagement with our equipment performance and the improvement of that performance at all levels of the organisation
- establishing clear roles, responsibilities and expectations at the three organisational levels of 'leadership', 'management' and 'associates'
- providing a framework and robust governance system to continuously improve the process into the future, delivering significant business benefits and which is proven to be sustainable in the right hands.

As in Figure 1.1, the measurement, condition and problem prevention cycles of the model contain eight equipment-focused activity steps which are explored and described in detail in Chapter 5.

The fourth cycle of sustainment (detailed in Chapter 7) focuses on the soft cultural issues and hence behaviours in order to realise the future state through a habit of continuous improvement.

If you believe TPM is just about equipment performance improvement then you are wrong! TPM is a philosophy focused on people. It is about establishing the correct relationship between people and their equipment to enable ownership, teamwork and personal development. It's about unlocking the productive capacity of your equipment by unlocking the innovative capability of your people.

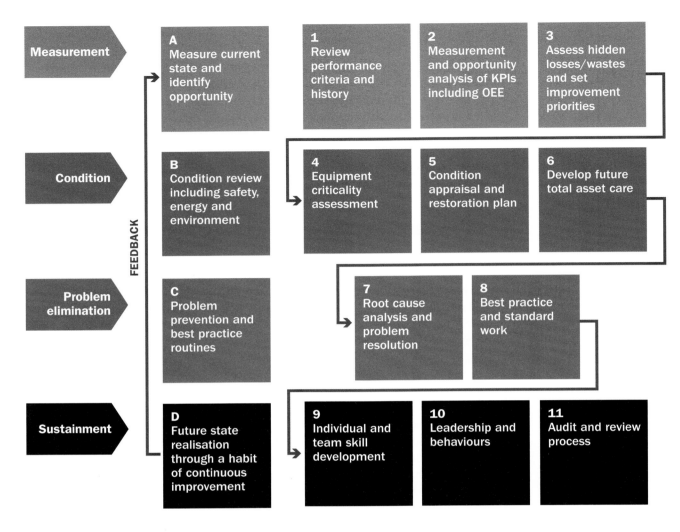

Figure 1.1: Four cycles and 11 steps of the TPM system

1.4 It's your people that make the difference

Central to the TPM philosophy is building on an operator's up-to-the-minute knowledge of their equipment to reduce the frequency of breakdowns and other unplanned events. If we can't work with our operators as a team, how can we hope to care for and maintain the assets of our business in an effective way? It's not about taking work away from technical and maintainer groups. It's about giving these groups more time and better information and allowing them to improve the technical performance of the equipment by working as an effective partnership.

In business if you don't improve you don't survive. We are often asked how we get people interested in improving their work environment where the work is so repetitive, mundane and boring. Our response is to suggest we not only focus on the work content but more importantly the *process* of work itself. To explain this we tell a story. A guy called Harry works in a warehouse. He takes things from shelves and loads them onto trolleys to be loaded and distributed on trucks to retail stores around the country. Unfortunately, his distribution business was taken over and due to consolidation, Harry is now out of work. We meet him attending his first interview and explore two scenarios here.

Scenario 1

Interviewer: OK, Harry, describe your last position and how you got on.

Harry: I worked in a warehouse picking products off shelves. We put them in designated trolleys and brought them to the dock for loading onto trucks. We worked at piece rate and I always met my rate. I also have my forklift driver and manual handling safety completed and certified as per these two certificates....

Scenario 2

Interviewer: OK, Harry, describe your last position and how you got on.

Harry: I worked in a warehouse picking products off shelves. We put them in designated trolleys and I then brought them to the dock for loading onto trucks. We worked at piece rate and I always met my rate. I have my forklift driver and manual handling safety completed and certified as per these two certificates....

I also got involved in some work study improvement activity where we looked at the best way to lay out the warehouse to make it easier to pick. As a team we increased our picking rate by 20 per cent without having to work harder. Part of that project was improving reliability and the availability of mechanical handling equipment by putting standard procedures in place for charging, pre-start up and end of shift checks and some planned maintenance checks. We had most of the root cause issues eliminated within two months. I got special recognition for my work on that team and here's the certificate I received from the CEO. For the first time I really felt we were being listened to and, more importantly, we actually were able to implement those changes ourselves and as a result work more effectively.

Interviewer: But didn't the improved pick rate mean you picked more for the same money?

Harry: Well, yes, but the business had been pushing for a new contract with a retailer and we won that. We were able to pick more easily, so in the end the money was the same. But our annual bonus got a big lift due to the increased volume turnover and improved profitability.

So who would you employ? More importantly what sort of employee are you currently developing in your organisation right now? No organisation can guarantee employment. What we owe our employees is employability through involvement. We should aim to make them the best they can be. By focusing on the *process* of work we give our employees the opportunity to become the candidate in the second scenario.

1.5 Three insights of the Shingo Model and TPM

1.5.1 Background

Summarised from 'Best Ways for Manufacturers to Boost Employee Engagement' by Dominic Bria, posted on blog. shingo.org on 21 March 2018.

The Shingo Institute carried out a research study involving four manufacturing companies to establish what conditions are the most likely to have the greatest positive impact on employee engagement.

This research study stresses that business leaders must pay attention to the positive impact an engaged workforce can have on everything from productivity to absenteeism and turnover.

The Shingo research study tested five conditions:

■ Employee perceptions of the opportunities available for personal development in the form of cross-training and other learning that might lead to job variety, value to the company, and possible advancement.

■ Consistent publicly expressed appreciation from leaders and managers for ideas, work, and other contributions from employees.

■ Employee perceptions of the relative availability of the tools, training, direction and knowledge required to meet the work demands placed upon them.

■ The extent to which an employee is able to make meaningful decisions regarding their work.

■ Understanding of how their tasks help the organisation accomplish its goals.

Figure 1.2 illustrates how five independent variables – as presumed prerequisites (or antecedents) – correlate to the dependant variable of employees' 'expressed feelings of engagement'.

1.5.2 Results of the study

A total of 594 employees from the four participating manufacturing companies completed the anonymous assessment, shared in agglomerated form with the leaders of that company.

The results were presented under the five headings of

■ **Development** – positive in the sense that it's a prerequisite for employee engagement to experience and know there are learning and personal growth opportunities

■ **Recognition** – higher correlation in service industry than manufacturing in the sense that manufacturing work content is more prescriptive and repetitive (i.e. standard work), hence employees less likely to receive 'public praise'

■ **Resources** – in the sense of access to tools, knowledge and materials to do the job. While this does not show particularly high correlation to engagement it is noted that to deny employees the resources to do their jobs efficiently is to invite disengagement, frustration and job burn-out

■ **Empowerment** – the inclusion of this prerequisite to engagement showed an even higher correlation than development as above. Much has been written in recent times about empowerment being a significant contributor to employee engagement. This particular study concludes that this emphasis and attention is well justified

Manufacturing/production employees

| Independent variables | | Dependent variable |

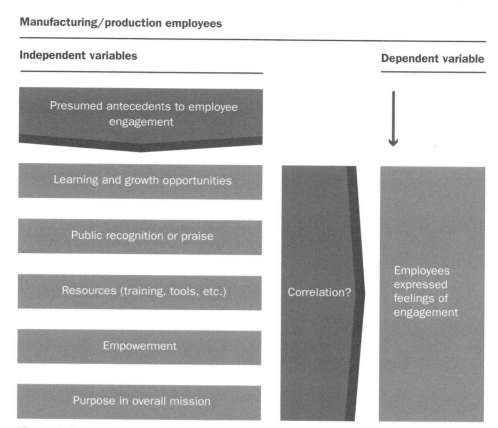

Figure 1.2: Independent variables to single dependent variable

- **Purpose** – this is described as an employee's understanding of how her or his job helps to accomplish the overall goals and business imperatives of the organisation. The findings, unexpected in some ways, did not show any significant correlation to employee engagement. However previous Shingo Institute research has indicated that understanding of purpose was indeed an antecedent of employee engagement and hence the topic suggests further research could be worthwhile.

1.5.3 Conclusions

The research study concluded that the variables with the most significant impact on employee engagement come under three main headings below.

- **Recognition** – praise and public recognition may not be as important to employee engagement in manufacturing settings as they seem to be in non-manufacturing settings. That is not to say that public praise is not important to the culture of the organisation.
- **Resources** – similarly, the information, training and equipment required to safely and efficiently perform the work may not contribute as much to employee engagement in manufacturing as it may in other settings. However, such elements are still very necessary to a culture of operational excellence.
- **Development and empowerment** – if a leader or manager of a manufacturing/ production facility wants to improve employee engagement, the antecedents/ prerequisites that seem most likely to do so are a) employee perception of opportunities for development and b) employee perceptions of their level of empowerment in their jobs, i.e. their freedom to make decisions about their work.

As authors we are convinced that as you read and apply the approach to TPM laid out in this book you will become aware of the power of a well defined TPM system to deliver on the three variables mentioned above. In addition we also believe that

TPM is a basis by which organisations can clearly identify what ideal behaviour will look like through the prism of the ten guiding principles of the Shingo Model.

The Shingo Model proposes three insights to sustainable enterprise excellence. We believe that the focus of TPMs cultural engagement is capable of helping to deliver those same three insights which are central (and in our view non-optional) attributes of Operational Excellence as described below.

Ideal results require ideal behaviours

The results of an organisation depend on the way their people behave. Whether or not an employee shows up to work in the morning will influence the results of that day. To achieve ideal results, leaders must do the hard work of creating a culture where ideal behaviours are expected and evident in every associate.

Also, results are the aim of every organisation, but there are various methods by which they are attained. Ideal results are those that are sustainable over the long term. Simply learning or applying new tools or systems does not achieve ideal results. Great leaders understand the cause-and-effect relationship between results and behaviour. To achieve ideal results, leaders must do the hard work…

Purpose and systems drive behaviour

It has long been understood that beliefs have a profound effect on behaviour.

What is often overlooked however is the equally profound effect that systems have on behaviour. Most of the systems that guide the way people work are designed to create a specific business result without regard for the behaviour that system consequentially drives. Managers have an enormous job to realign both management and work systems to drive the ideal behaviour required to achieve ideal business results.

Also it is important to recognize that many systems are de-facto systems that have evolved in response to a specific need for a particular result. Managers must shift from fire-fighting to designing, aligning and improving systems. TPM as described in this book is a system of work.

Principles inform ideal behaviours

Principles are foundational rules that govern the consequences of behaviours. The more deeply one understands principles, the more clearly they understand ideal behaviour. The more clearly they understand ideal behaviour, the better they can design systems to drive that behaviour to achieve ideal results.

Principles are foundational rules and help us to see both the positive and negative consequence of our behaviours. This fact enables us to make more informed decisions, specifically, about how we choose to behave. The more deeply leaders, managers and associates understand the principles of operational excellence and the more perfectly systems are aligned to reinforce ideal behaviour, the greater the probability of creating a sustainable culture of excellence where achieving ideal results is the norm rather than the aspiration. This is what the Shingo Model™ illustrates.

Excellence must be the pursuit of all great leaders. In fact, the passionate pursuit of perfection, even knowing it is fundamentally impossible to achieve, brings out the best in every human being.

Michelangelo apparently said in c.1450 "The greatest danger for most of us is not that our aim is too high and we miss it, but that it is too low and we reach it."

Our interpretation of this in the classic sense of the TPM philosophy is that we set our end game vision as striving for the Four Zeros of zero accidents, zero defects, zero breakdowns and zero interventions. Again, while we recognise the impossibility of achieving this goal (and hence the word 'striving') we do know that we will make huge progress on our journey of continuous improvement with the above three insights firmly in our sights.

A tool is nothing more than a point solution or a specific means to a specific end. Dr Shingo referred to tools as necessary but not sufficient techniques for problem-solving. He taught that tools should be selected to enable a system to perform its intended purpose. In many ways, a system may be thought of as a collection of tools working together to accomplish an intended outcome. A successful operation is usually made up of complex business systems that can be further divided into layers of sub-systems, each having embedded in them the necessary tools to enable the successful outcome of the system.

Perhaps the largest mistake made by corporations over the last three or four decades has been the inappropriate focus on a specific tool-set as the sole basis for their improvement efforts. Tools do not answer the question of 'why', only the question of 'how'. Knowing the 'how' without understanding fully the 'why' leaves people waiting for instructions and powerless to act on their own.

Conversely, when team members understand how the tools they use serve the larger system and its purpose, they are better able to use the tools toward the desired outcome. In other words, if they understand why the tool is important to the system, they can use the tool in alignment with the purpose of the system. It then becomes a vital part of empowerment for team members.

In Chapter 7 we will explore in detail behavioural alignment with the four maturity milestones within the TPM journey, which have evidence-based criteria to assess progress and any points of weakness that are inhibiting that progress towards sustainable levels of operational excellence.

1.6 **Individual and team skill development**

A detailed understanding of the needs of the equipment (as regards regular operator asset care checks, condition-based monitoring and planned maintenance checks, along with standard ways of working such as a precision change over) allows the team to define clear areas for skill development and knowledge transfer. In each relevant work area, the team develop a defined skills matrix which can be used to measure progress, identify gaps and then bridge those gaps.

It is not unusual for the TPM process to highlight particular skills within individuals which can then be harnessed and developed to benefit the company. Some operators become technicians, supervisors or trainers. The maintenance technicians have the potential to develop into engineers or equipment and process designers.

This relentless focus on the control and standardisation of the detailed elements of the process through the creation of standard work documents such as the single point lessons, as well as the development of individual skills, are the most potent antidotes to the 'withering humanity' phenomenon explored in Chapter 2.

1.7 **Leadership and behaviours to ensure TPM sustainability**

While Step 10 is towards the end of our TPM system model, questions about inappropriate and appropriate behaviours arise all the way through the TPM process. We want people to work in teams – not silos. We want people to be interested in their work process and what they do. We want leaders to support and enable this interest! We want an environment that is safe, where people's opinions or ideas can be both respected and valued. We do not want an environment where ideas are ignored or shot down. Where visual management boards are feared rather than seen as an engagement process to promote a system of improvement!

We want behaviour that is open, honest and based on trust, where data is visible and shared to enable the effective identification of issues, as well as quality problem solving.

The TPM process highlights the kind of behaviour that will enable or disable a sustainable culture of continuous improvement. In Step 10, the leadership team, along with other colleagues, define the ideal culture for their business and articulate clearly how these ideal behaviours should be expressed at all levels of the business. They also review whether the systems in the business currently enable or disable these ideal behaviours. The organisation also needs to define key behavioural indicators which can be reviewed to ensure that the ideal behaviours are actually being implemented in the business rather than remaining only aspirational.

In Chapter 4 we will explore the scoping study process as the essential front end planning phase to secure local site leadership 'buy-in'.

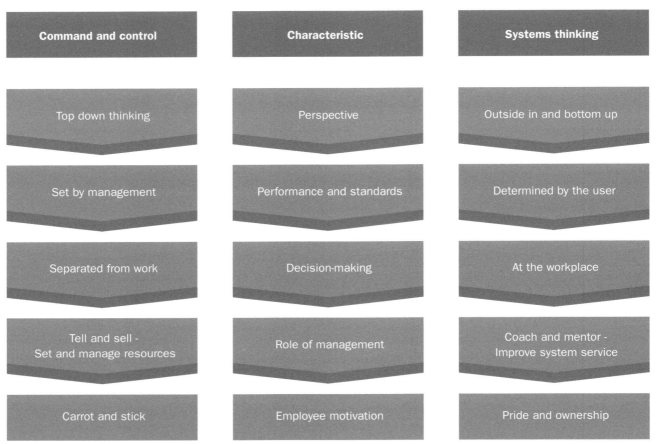

Figure 1.3: From command and control to systems thinking and empowerment (adapted from Seddon, J, *Freedom from Command and Control*, Vanguard Education, 2003, p11)

In order for Operational Excellence initiatives like TPM to thrive, leadership and management usually have to consider a new way of working which drives behaviours that are centred on

■ understanding the purpose of the system and managing the organisation as a system, with trust and delegation rather than command and control
■ designing the system to meet real demand and deal with demand variety
■ deriving measures from the actual work – not arbitrary targets

- modifying traditional management thinking of set, 'measure and monitor' resources, to one where the role of management changes to set the standards and provide the necessary resources
- then delegate and trust your staff to act on the system with pace and responsiveness when deviations occur from the standard.

Figure 1.3 illustrates this fundamental shift in management style from command and control to one of systems thinking via the five main characteristics shown. Suffice to say this journey is evolutionary (rather than revolutionary!) and is reflected in a journey of four maturity milestones over time, secured via a robust evidence-based audit process (detailed in Chapter 7).

1.8 **Audit and review processes**

For any system to be sustainable it needs to have checks and, where necessary, rebalances to ensure it stays on track. The TPM audit and review process – which is evidence-based and described in detail in Chapter 7 – combines with activities such as leader standard work and visual management to ensure that what we think is happening is really happening! The review process also allows us to clearly identify progress towards defined world class standards through specific maturity milestones. The audits – or 'honesty checks' as we like to call them – within Step 11 enable the appropriate improvement conversations. It is vital that leaders and supervisors have the skills to deliver effective conformance (not punishment!) conversations. This is a critical leadership skill which enables a sustainable and continuous improvement work environment. Punishment is personal, opinionated and hence judgemental and potentially very damaging, whereas conformance focuses on the process and the defined standards.

The audit and review process both defines how we measure progress along the TPM and overall operational excellence journey, and how we maintain and continue to improve on the standards that the teams have achieved. Their knowledge and experience is enhanced through 'learning by doing' and result in a real and sustained interest and care of the workplace.

1.9 **How do you ultimately measure success in TPM?**

Over the years we have often been asked the salutary question "How many successful applications of TPM have you been involved in?"

Before we answer the question we need to seek clarification by asking "By success, do you mean having helped say 100 companies over the last several years to get their TPM programme up and running and you then go back after say five years and see if TPM is still part of the way we do things around here?"

If so, then the answer is "probably in the range of one in five to ten".

So why is this the case?

It is too easy to glibly say something like, "Ultimately the success and sustainability of the TPM process will depend on the degree and extent of management commitment and their visible and pro-active support".

Yes of course that is part of the story but it is far more complex than that.

Over the years, it's been our privilege to be involved in many debates – whether ad hoc or through research-based studies – over why change programmes or continuous improvement initiatives in general (including TPM) 'wither on the vine'. The results can be summarised as follows:

- Lack of clear, consistent leadership and direction
- Lack of thorough planning, preparation, measurement, and feedback

- The change programme has no clear vision or endgame
- Lack of a thorough risk assessment and countermeasure definition from the start
- Poor, inadequate, inconsistent and ineffective communication
- Unclear roles, responsibilities, accountabilities and expectations.

The above are consistently reoccurring themes which we will explore more fully in Chapter 7, explaining how each one's impact and potential risk can be minimised via a relevant and robust CI/TPM infrastructure and governance system.

1.10 5S workplace organisation and TPM

1.10.1 Competing or complementary?

Finally a word of caution and explanation around the apparent dilemma of where the 5S and TPM boundaries reside, because this nearly always gives rise to some initial confusion.

It is important to stress that 5S focuses on workplace organisation (WPO) and is aimed primarily at **creating flow around** a particular physical asset.

The eight equipment steps of the TPM system are aimed at **maintaining that flow through** those same critical manufacturing physical assets, by eliminating reasons for poor performance and attacking the six classic equipment-based losses itemised in Principle 1 above. This includes the '100 fix year' solutions and countermeasures to prevent recurrence.

Principle 3 above – *Develop routine front line operator asset care* – emphasises the 'cleaning is inspection' principle and hence routines both in and under the machine to spot and prevent contamination and spillage – and of course includes visual indicators to make it easy to do the task correctly and difficult to do wrong – and finally not forgetting that safety is the number one priority on all aspects of TPM and WPO.

Below are highlights for each of the steps.

Step 1. Sort – the art of throwing things away

- Zone the area – 'Traffic light' every item where
- RED – clear, obvious and unnecessary items not used in the last three months, not useful/not needed
- AMBER – identify items which need review for possible use elsewhere
- GREEN – definitely needed, but maybe not in the right place (Step 2)
- Clean and develop initial standard. Communicate that standard to all shifts
- Identify sources of contamination (contain and progressively eliminate in Steps 3 and 4).

Figure 1.4: Sorting out: red for throwing away (surprising how much rubbish you can find in a workplace); green for finding a place where you can find and use it easily; orange for useful, but not here

Step 2. Set limits and locations – create a world class workplace where everything is to hand

- Analyse current practice
- Decide where things belong
- Decide how things should be put away and/or stored
- Aim to reduce obtain and/or put-away time to 30 seconds or fewer
- Use photos of visual standards x √.

Step 3. Shine – a commitment to be responsible for the things we use

- Decide what has to be cleaned/checked and what to look for
- Refine method to make it easy to clean/check
- Set standards for cleaning level and inspection
- Define responsibility for who does what
- Agree cleaning and inspection rules, including frequency.

Step 4. Standardise – making it easy to do things right

- Audit against standards and coach to improve ease of operation, maintenance, reliability and safety across all shifts
- Refine visual indicators for each standard to avoid human error, information of equipment settings, coordinate suggestions made/evaluated, problems solved
- Develop proposals to address areas of weakness
- Agree priorities for implementation.

Step 5. Systemise and sustain – make 5S part of everyday life.

- Agree new rules to secure the improved system as part of life – make it self-managing and sustainable
- Train everybody to follow the same rules and standards
- Continually re-visit work areas and review for ongoing improvement
- Formal problem solving to deal with implementation problems.

1.10.2 Putting 5S into action

Here is a typical one day agenda to launch your 5S programme as a 'learn by doing activity'. It is focused on Step 1 – getting rid of everything unnecessary – and Step 2 – thinking about the implications of 'creating a right place for everything you need for the future'. This will include proposals for storage facilities, shadow boards and floor markings.

5S awareness training workshop objectives

- Remind ourselves of the principles and application of the 5S philosophy to create and then sustain a world class workplace – initially focusing on the selected 5S pilot areas
- Identify the strong links of safety and environment issues with effective workplace organisation practices and setting 'best practice' standards
- Provide some additional tools and techniques to enhance our future safety performance especially to reduce slips, trips and falls rates towards zero over the next twelve months
- Develop local action plans to deliver the vision of a 'world class' workplace that enhances safety performance.

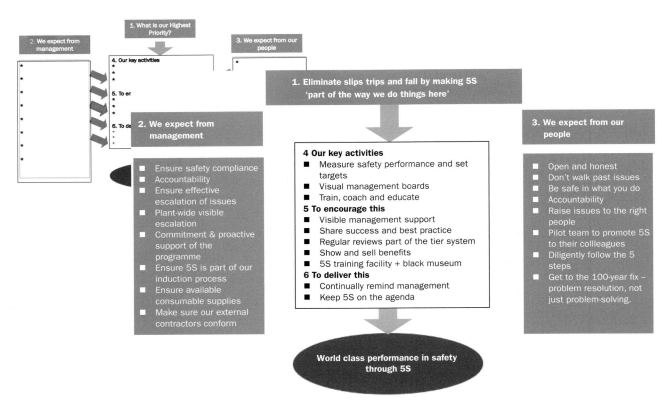

Figure 1.5: 'Spark to start': create, and then populate by consensus, a template to help you understand what you need to do and what you need your colleagues – including your managers – to do

5S training day agenda

Timings	Activity and timelines
09.00 – 09.30	Introduction, expectations for the day. Icebreaker using the Numbers Game in pairs.
09.30 – 10.30	Linking safety performance with workplace organisation and best practice standards (presentation), including a 'what is our end game vision?' exercise.
10.30 – 10.45	Coffee break & briefing for Step 1 and 2 practical activity.
10.45 – 12.15	'Go Do' Step 1 – get rid of everything unnecessary – exercise in the selected 5S Pilot application area in two syndicate teams. Start discussing/thinking about Step 2 – see Figure 1.4.
12.15 – 13.00	Syndicate teams feedback in the training room on Steps 1 & 2 plus safety, environment checklists and via 5S workplace organisation audits.
13.00 – 13.45	*Lunch break*
13.45 – 14.45	Syndicate teams swap areas and do Step 1 & 2 audit of their colleagues' area.
14.45 – 16.00	Revisit & finalise 'What is our end game vision?' exercise (Figure 1.5) to develop the framework of a local area 5S action plan. This includes the 'what, how, who and when', plus today's key learning points & way forward.

Key points during the session

You cannot achieve operational excellence without operational basics in place. This means the fundamentals of

- best practice workplace organisation/5S to create flow

- a disciplined, self-determined, TPM/asset care regime
- standard (and safe) operating procedures
- basic manufacturing process control & capability (CPK)
- reliable data collection & interpretation
- continuous development and training of our people.

1.10.3 Learning by doing: seven key learning points for 5S

1   5S-workplace organisation is about creating flow (it is not just about good housekeeping)
2   5S-workplace organisation is about obsessive attention to detail
3   What we have done is used our given senses to look, listen, discuss ,think of options, agree, and then prepare to do
4   Even the smallest thing wrong can develop into a major issue. At best it will stay as it is. At worst it will deteriorate. It certainly won't get better on its own
5   Spotting what's wrong is only half of the solution. Correcting the problem with a permanent solution is the other half
6   Many WPO problems have safety and environmental issues and some will impact on our operational efficiency and hence cost
7   In the real 5S cleaning is inspection... is spotting deterioration... is catching it before it becomes catastrophic... is pride in the workplace... is a hassle-free shift... resulting in pride of ownership.

1.11 Case studies

In Chapter 10 we describe two detailed case study examples plus a further four cameo examples to illustrate the potential power of the TPM system to deliver your operational excellence aspirations. These are
- Mylan Rottapharm – a Shingo Medallion Award winner from the pharmaceutical industry
- Welsh Water Authority – an award-winning public utility.

The four cameo case studies are taken from
- Warwick Chemicals – process industry
- Automated warehouse application
- Two medical devices industry examples (both Shingo award winners).

CHAPTER 2
The challenges facing the maintenance function

In this chapter we share
- three stories to illustrate our personal experiences and hopes for the future
- the impact of Industry 4.0 emerging technologies – both now and in the near future
- the continuing need to change the perception of maintenance from a 'necessary evil' to being about adding value to the business
- an exercise for you to answer the question: 'Where are you now with your maintenance practices?'

2.1 Personal experience stories

As joint authors of this book we would like to set the scene by each of us telling you a story from our personal experience, all three quite different, but hopefully relevant to this book.

2.1.1 Peter Willmott's story

While heading up a TPM study tour of Japan in 1992, we visited a recognised world class manufacturer – an exemplar Japan Institute of Plant Maintenance TPM-award-winning company. As we entered the plant on our tour bus we saw that the outside factory wall had been painted with a colourful mural of trees, bushes, flowers and plants. There was a message written in both Japanese and English: 'Welcome to our Park within a Factory' (not, you will note, a 'Factory within a Park'). So we – dare I say slightly sceptical – 'European bastions of industry' went on with our tour of the factory. The visual impact of that tour was indeed memorable. Three things in particular stood out:
- There were dedicated rest areas in several parts of the plant that had natural wooden seating, real grass, mini-waterfalls, flowers and yucca plants galore
- There were large windows in the roof above those rest areas to enhance a feeling of space and light
- Everyone appeared to be working harmoniously as opposed to hastily.

The TPM facilitator and a small group of operators and maintainers gave a short presentation in the debriefing room after the factory tour which highlighted what TPM had helped to deliver to the business over a six-year period:

Key performance indicator	Start point reference	Six years later
Breakdowns per month	250	5
Overall equipment effectiveness	65%	88%
Productivity index	100	180
Return on investment	$1.00	$4.50

I vividly remember the Japanese managing director walking up to a flip chart and writing: "In the 1950s and '60s we had 'M' for Manufacturing. Then, in the '70s we had 'IM' for Integrated Manufacturing…And then in the 1980s we had 'CIM' for Computer Integrated Manufacturing." He paused for a moment, added an H between the C and I, and wrote the letter H above it. He said:

"For the remainder of this decade and 2000 and beyond, our company is going to be pursuing 'CHIM' – Computer Human Integrated Manufacturing…" He added, "We have decided to re-introduce the human being back into our workplace!"

As Figure 2.1 below suggests, CHIM is no longer just a dream. It is a pressing reality. Today, over 25 years later, my interpretation of that powerful message is that it represents a challenge for all of us to develop and harness people's skills in parallel with advancing automation, data capture and technological innovation, in what is being referred to as the Fourth Industrial Revolution or Industry 4.0.

The bottom line is that it's our people at the sharp end of the business who will continue to make the difference.

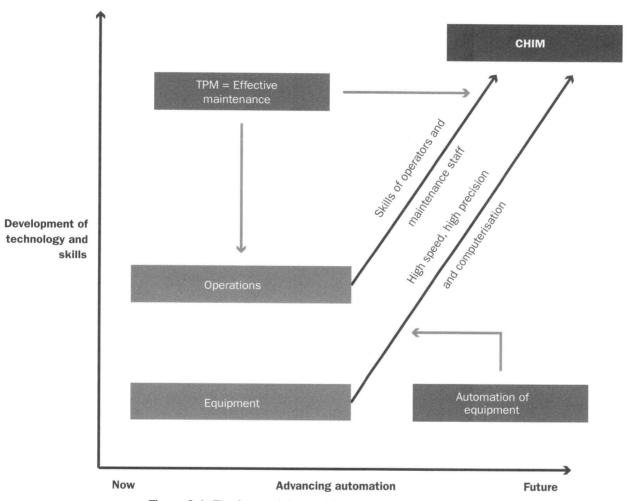

Figure 2.1: The future vision and impact of TPM on operational excellence

The biggest – and often false – assumption nowadays is that regular visible and physical 'human' inspections and maintenance are grossly undervalued and the technological tail is left wagging the dog.

The tail is an important part of the dog – but in this analogy the dog is the human being.

Although we have to embrace technology, there will always be some principles of work that will remain embedded in the philosophy of TPM. Of course we will need to be agile, flexible and innovative in how we adapt to the challenges that Industry 4.0 is bringing – for example, *the Internet of things, big data and advanced analytics, artificial and virtual intelligence, robotics and automation, simulations, 3D printing and augmented reality.*

Against this backdrop of reality and acceptance, we are also convinced that competitive manufacturing capability will come from those companies who focus on the judicious and innovative application of available automation and technology.

Already we are seeing that the fundamental and under-pinning people engagement practices, through teamwork, goal alignment and deployment, depend on a leadership style that is able to progressively trust to delegate. This factor will become even more important as technology becomes more multifaceted.

However it is also my firm belief that maintenance in the sense of using spanners and screwdrivers will be here for some time yet!

2.1.2 **John Quirke's story**

It was a beautiful day. One of those very rare days in Ireland where you step out of the car into an environment that is warmer than the one you have just left in the car! It was high summer and I had what promised to be a very pleasant day ahead. I was at a large maintenance facility spread out over multiple buildings in a picturesque part of Ireland. I had an enjoyable and enthusiastic meeting with my site contacts and then proceeded with my initial site review. The plan was to walk through the facility, review activities, meet some of the team and use this to provide an overview of what might be the core elements of this business's lean transformation programme.

The review started well but it quickly became clear that despite assurances that the business had a continuous improvement programme in place, the reality did not support this.

I make a point during my reviews to meet with and talk to as many of the front line team as I can. I have developed a number of techniques to allay their initial defensiveness and invite good, open dialogue. One encounter in particular had a profound effect on me and fundamentally changed the way I approach continuous improvement to this day. I talk about this meeting a lot with clients, because I see and hear the same thing as I travel and visit various companies around the world. I have also given it a name.

One of the philosophies often put out there in relation to an individual's engagement with their work is that ninety-nine per cent of people come to work to do a good job. There may well be the odd spanner in the works 'but in general it is accepted that the majority of individuals, given the appropriate training and skills (often even without these!), will endeavour to do a good day's work. Which makes my term for what I observed that day in Ireland even more disturbing. I refer to it as 'withering humanity'.

The situation went something like this: I observed an employee engaged in the repair of metal parts using a well-defined welding technique. The repairs were critical since, if the parts were not repaired or were repaired incorrectly, it could result in serious injury to the operator as well as process disruption and possible damage to the equipment.

I introduced myself and explained what I was doing and asked permission to observe the process. The employee had no issue, so I stayed and observed. The process consisted of fixed arc weld continuously fed by a raw metal feed wire which made the arc on the continuously moving part and contained the new metal to rebuild the original part dimensions. The arc weld was smothered in a carbon bead which fell from a hopper over the welding point and onto the floor where it was gathered and fed manually back into the hopper by the operator.

Employees are generally familiar with some of the bigwigs observing them for a short period of time. They might last as little as fifteen seconds! But that's not what I do anymore. After twenty minutes of observation, some basic questions and lending a helping hand where appropriate, I expressed my thanks for his time and asked if I could ask a few more questions before I left him. Without stopping what he was doing the operator allowed me to proceed with my questions. He said he had been doing this same job for over twenty years. I asked if the metal in the wire feed had the same properties as the part's base metal? Was it harder and more durable? He did not know. I asked what the black powder used to cover the welding point was made of and why was it needed. He did not know. I asked did he have busier or quieter times? His response was 'I just do what I do'. It was clear that it was time for me to move on. I took another look around the dark, untidy metal shed in which he was working, thanked him again, and continued on my troubled journey. This man's case was not an isolated one. I walked through the facility and returned to my hosts. I was given some time to gather my thoughts and prepare for the 'feedback' session.

The idea was that I give my opinion on how much productivity could be improved based on the implementation of a cultural change and continuous improvement programme. This company was in a serious financial situation; they needed a magic wand/bullet/potion. Needless to say, there was some disappointment when I gave my opinion that they were wasting their time. Job number one, I offered, was to rebuild trust and begin to respect the people who worked for them. The management's response was that it was their employees who were the problem, unwilling to change and adopt new practices, unwilling to embrace what continuous improvement could bring and help secure their jobs. Suffice to say, we did not go beyond this initial visit with the organisation. I understand they subsequently invested in a lean training programme (green belts, black belts, etc.) a lot of which was delivered online. I'll leave it to the reader to surmise how that went down.

The operator I observed had just been left to wither. Whatever spark of engagement or willingness to learn there had been slowly diminished over time. This gentleman was no 'spanner in the works'. He was a nice man. He lit up during conversations about the local environment and the history of the area and how things were in the 'old days' of this business.

I have seen examples of my friend above in many businesses. Even in the most modern medical device manufacturing organisations, buzzing with 'patient value offerings' and bulging 'new product development funnels'. In these organisations the need to constantly engage employees in the detail of work and the improvement of that work is neglected or at best given token attention. The excuses I'm given for this situation include:

'The real focus here is getting product out the door'

'With all the compliance requirements we don't have time'

'We don't want to get the operator involved in change, the process is validated'

'Change control is a nightmare'

'We do loads of training, first aid, GMP, safety and lean! Sure, I think one of the team even got a green belt this year'

These excuses are all too common. Even the last point, while there would seem to be an active training programme in this organisation, well-resourced and funded, it was clear training was happening for training's sake. When I spoke to these employees and asked how much of their training was relevant to the actual work they did, the percentage ranged from ten to 15 per cent relevance. The training programmes in this organisation were viewed by employees as just another example of how disengaged the management were from the reality of their day-to-day work.

The important point about withering humanity is that it is not just an affliction of front line operators. I see it among senior teams too. Leaders and managers who see fear as a legitimate means to achieve what is needed. Leaders and managers who have not taken the time to look inside at their own 'self'. To assess whether their 'self' is being nourished or starved by the environment in which they are working. Can they use the realisation of what is wrong as a starting point to understanding what leadership is really about?

As I said I retell this story a lot all over the world. It never ceases to have an impact. It gets my audience asking questions: what sort of employee are we creating right now? How are we helping them grow and achieve their potential? Is that person me?

To link this story to what we are about here in this book, it might be useful to discuss what I believe are the five key roles of a leader. Five is easy. Five fingers on one hand, so go ahead and tick them off:

1 Keep my team safe, both physically and mentally
2 Use the resources entrusted with me to deliver the necessary results –especially the human capital
3 Find ways to improve the effectiveness and efficiency of the resources entrusted to me to make it easier, faster and cheaper to deliver the necessary results
4 Develop the skills and capabilities of my team
5 Understand myself, my strengths, my weaknesses and my personal goals.

Another question I often ask leaders is this:

Can you describe one of the proudest and most personally gratifying experiences you have had as a leader?

I give the group a good bit of time to think and reflect on this. The vast majority of responses go something like:

> '…There was this employee working for me. I always knew she had something special about her but she was forever underselling herself. I gradually gave her more and more responsibility, helping and coaching her along. She really took it on board and became very successful. She is now running global operations for a major multinational. We still keep in touch…'
>
> or
>
> '…We were under pressure to meet an increase in production from our customer. One of our competitors had let them down and the customer had come to us for help. We pulled a team together and they communicated to all the staff how important an opportunity this was for us. We had to deliver at cost, on time, with no compromise on quality or safety, at margin. We asked the team to put a plan together and suggested that they present this to the customer. I helped the team with the plan but they did the bulk of the work. The presentation to the customer was fantastic. The customer questioned the team hard and they responded well. It was a real turning point for the business…'

2.1.3 Andy Brunskill's story

Writing down this brief story has given me the opportunity to reflect on my time in industry and the application of the principles of TPM. As I write this I am currently travelling back from a TPM practitioner's workshop that I have been supporting in Nagoya in Japan for the last week. This scenario is somewhat surreal based on the fact that TPM has its origins in Japan, and who would have thought that exactly thirty years to the month since I entered industry – a fresh faced undergraduate working in the pharmaceutical industry – I would be providing guidance to the Japanese on the principles and application of a process they invented. It's a humbling thought and experience.

This 30-year anniversary triggered a memory of something that happened to me three to four months into my then first role as a Beecham's (now GSK) graduate management trainee based in St Helens, England. Back in the good old days, before the onslaught of the digital revolution, a graduate production manager wouldn't be staring at a computer screen for seven or eight hours a day, they'd be on the shop floor at the 'coal face', learning what actually happens in the process.

We in the western world now call this 'look, go and see', but back in those days, if you wanted to learn, this was one of few options available. Because of the highly sensitive unionised environment and a management philosophy that was out to appease the trade unions without recognizing that true collaboration was surely the right approach, it was not possible for me to do the operator's job to gain a real and true understanding of the process.

At that time there was a concern over the potential risk of exposure to a material in Diocalm tablets. This meant that for about three weeks I had to make the product in the granulation department, as the trade unions had refused for their members to work with the materials until the required extraction had been installed in the dispensary area.

I had misgivings about the task ahead, about doing 'manual' labour for three weeks. However, with the appropriate personal protection equipment, I set about the job at hand. This opened a totally different outlook on the process and an appreciation from an 'operator's point of view'. It also helped me recognise very early on that it is the person doing the job that is the real expert in the process, not the manager who spends most of their time in the office and tends to only visit the 'value adding' area when there is a problem. Moreover, that manager's first point of advice is a supervisor who themselves only have second-hand, subjective knowledge of actual processes.

I recall a conversation I had with Joe, the foreman of the tableting suite, in charge of compression and tablet production. It's important to remember this was before the transformation to a value stream organisation when foremen became team leaders.

Anyway, there was an issue with tablet thickness and Joe came to me for advice. He came to me because I was a manager – albeit on the line making product as an operator. I was certainly not a tableting expert as I had only been working in industry for a couple of months. The thing was that Joe, who had previously been an operator, knew how to resolve the issue, but lacked the confidence and maybe the conviction to do so without first seeking permission from the manager, i.e. 'the boss'.

The key lesson I took from those early days was that the business I was working for didn't recognise that the person doing the task is in the best position to solve problems given the correct support, encouragement and resources. In the company culture of that time it was easier for Joe to escalate an issue and not accept responsibility or ownership of the problem. The management were ultimately responsible for creating this embedded culture, driven by fear of retribution and not allowing the realization of people's potential. Which is exactly the opposite of what the TPM System can deliver in the right hands.

My story is a constant reminder to me, and chimes with a saying attributed to US Navy Rear Admiral Grace Hopper (1906-1992), a pioneering computer programmer who said:

'It is easier to ask for forgiveness than it is to get permission'.

I interpret this wisdom to mean that: a good idea based on experience should be encouraged and served, not hampered by, at best, red tape or, at worst, complete disapproval by those in charge. It's better to try – and then have to apologize later if it doesn't work – than to have to ask for permission to try, and waste time in doing so!

2.2 Industry 4.0 – the impact of emerging technologies

Many observers believe we have gone through three industrial revolutions – the commercial steam engine to support the birth of the textile industry, followed by electricity enabling mass production, followed by the computer after WW2.

According to Professor Klaus Schwab – founder and executive chairman of the World Economic Forum – we are well underway with the Fourth Industrial

Revolution (4IR), now also referred to as 'Industry 4.0'. This revolution encompasses major innovations in technology that are coming to maturity at the same time and at a relatively rapid pace. These are being embedded by companies around the globe, integrating the virtual and physical worlds to bring about powerful ways of working. Examples of this technology include

1 **The Internet of things (IoT)** – the integration of software, sensors and electronic items with internet and machine-enabled data collection and transfer in real-time. This means that traditional supply chains can become more digitised, connected and transparent. Machine sensor technology has huge implications for asset management and hence those machine operators' and maintainers' skill sets.

2 **Big data and advanced analytics** – with the IoT comes a huge amount of data. The way manufacturing businesses read, analyse and act upon the data at the micro level – for example from product development to equipment design to build, test and install for production – is potentially very powerful for decision-making effectiveness and reduced lead time to market.

3 **Artificial and virtual intelligence, robotics and automation** – robots are already being used extensively in manufacture and distribution, and their development and use in 'smart' factories will have a massive impact on the skill sets of those taking care of and maintaining those physical assets. For example, the role of the operator will evolve to become more of a machine supervision role where the operator will oversee an automated process consisting of machines being loaded/unloaded by robots/cobots and automated guided vehicles. Likewise the maintainers will need to be trained to become highly-skilled technicians in the art of robotic maintenance, embracing electronics, precision maintenance and PLC fault-finding. This is in addition to machine-to-machine communications, which are all part of a wave of converging technologies.

4 **Simulations, 3D printing and augmented reality** – these are already becoming commonplace today, so that complex goods and their component parts can be rapidly designed at remarkable speeds and at much lower cost. Products can be designed and that same design then sent to multiple sites, via email, anywhere in the world for local manufacture. This same technology can then be integrated into plant and equipment design (and associated on-the-job employee skills training and development) to enable augmented reality equipment spares – more effectively than with paper or monitors (see also the Mylan Rottapharm case study in Chapter 10).

With the ongoing debate on the use of plastics and the damage to the environment, the 3D printing of machine parts, traditionally machined from solid blocks of plastic, could greatly reduce the amount of waste product ending up in landfill sites or worse.

2.2.1 The problem and hence opportunity facing businesses

Understanding what Industry 4.0 can offer is a far cry from being able to take advantage of it.

A recent survey of over 400 UK-based businesses carried out by the Institution of Engineering and Technology highlighted the following:

- 68 per cent are concerned that the education system will struggle to keep up with the skills required for technological change arising from implied in Industry 4.0

- 62 per cent are specifically concerned about the availability of relevant graduate skills

- 59 per cent feel the content of engineering and technology degrees does not suit the needs of their organisation because they do not develop relevant practical skills nor do graduates have a background of prior work experience

- 91 per cent agree, however, that to improve the supply of engineers and technicians, more employers need to provide work experience for those in education or training
- 76 per cent of employers agree that compelling all engineering and technology-dependent companies to provide work experience would improve the pool of engineering talent
- 68 per cent of employers say they are concerned that the education system will struggle to keep up with the skills required for technological change – again implicit in Industry 4.0 – but only 51 per cent report that they are taking steps to influence the content of degrees and the technical training engineers undertake.

These findings mirror closely a recent survey by McKinsey which found that seven out of ten companies have not formally defined their Science, Technology, engineering and Mathematics (STEM) skills gaps and only one in ten are implementing a plan aimed at bridging the skills gap impact.

We can conclude from the above that we need to be asking and answering at least five pertinent questions of companies that depend on physical assets to add value and deliver their customers' requirements in full.

These questions were stimulated in part by a recent article by a long term colleague Dennis McCarthy – we have expanded his commentary on each of the questions. (See 'Skill shortage or learning challenge?', *Maintenance Engineering* August/September 2018.)

Q1 – Is your company keeping pace with these emerging technologies?

The pace of technological progress is so rapid that traditional academic education cannot keep pace with developments in, for example, memory capacity, sensors and artificial intelligence. This is an area where in-house learning using practical hands-on 'learning by doing' projects is essential. Organisations that do this well will also focus on pockets of automation using multi-disciplined teams – including and especially front line operators as well as the maintainers and engineers, plus of course their team leaders.

Experience shows that cultural change through proactive involvement of the equipment users and maintainers invariably exceeds initial expectations and overcomes the most daunting of 'technology' driven challenges.

It is also important to remember that simple to use, cost effective devices such as digital process indicators (DPI) can be added to existing physical assets to show changes in performance in, for example, the variables of temperature, pressure and electrical current. The European experience shows that front-line operators with training, combined with routine cleaning and inspection checks, pay big dividends – and act as the early warning system for their maintenance colleagues to take preventive action and avoid catastrophic breakdowns. This approach is at the heart of the well proven TPM philosophy.

Q2 – What percentage of time spent by your current staff is fully productive and hence 'value adding'? And the second part to this question: do your systems of work and supporting processes systematically improve on your answer to the first part?

In one company where we diagnosed the effective use of a typical equipment maintainer's time the event sequence and profile emerged as illustrated in Figure 2.2. When looking specifically at responding to equipment breakdowns we found that only 15 per cent of time spent by the maintenance engineers was fully productive in the sense of 'value adding'. In our experience, this is often the norm rather than the exception.

With the interactive nature of real time data collection within Industry 4.0 digitalisation, this allows our CMMS systems to report each of the 11 sequential steps below. This fact then enables us to produce a current state map of what happens now and then use this information to 'Value Stream Map' every element in the 11 steps as either an operation, movement, delay, storage, inspection or electronic data entry. The operation elements are the only 'value adding' activity. The other five elements are either non-value-adding or they may be essential (for traceability purposes) but still non-value-adding.

We can then use the current state map to challenge each element by asking the ECRS question: can we **E**liminate this step? If not, can we **C**ombine it with another step upstream or downstream? Or **R**eplace it with something smarter? Or at least

Simplify it? The result of this challenge process then becomes our future state which is implemented as standard work once proven. It is our experience that if you get the right front line people involved in this value stream mapping and challenge process then the total response and repair times can be reduced by up to 50 per cent of current practice by working smarter (and definitely not harder!).

How much of a maintainer's time is actually 'value adding'?

- An equipment breakdown occurs. The clock starts ticking...
- Breakdown is reported to maintenance planning
- Planning allocates a 'maintainer' & informs the resource
- Maintainer goes to see equipment broken down at its source
- Isolate, initial Inspection, appraisal, discussion, decision
- Leaves source equipment to get necessary tools, parts, kit
- Return & **carry out repair** (this value-adding step is typically only 15% of total elapsed time)
- Test/check/start up & adjust
- Confirm the user as satisfactory
- Formally hand back to 'asset owner'
- Sign off job as complete to maintenance planning

Key learning point: as a performance metric traditional Mean time to Repair (MTTR) metric needs to become MTTR&R (mean time to respond & repair).

Figure 2.2: Equipment breakdowns are typically only 15 per cent value adding

Q3 – How well does your organisation encourage a positive attitude to learning in the workplace?

Skilled personnel are not usually tempted to change jobs for personal development opportunities and/or financial reasons alone. They tend to be motivated by in-house opportunities for self-development and job satisfaction. European surveys show that training and development are key job satisfaction factors for nearly 70 per cent of STEM workers. Food for thought if you want to keep the engineers you have!

Q4 – How well defined is the ideal engineering team skill profile, where are the gaps and how good is your company at developing the skills it needs?

This includes transferring lessons learned and helping engineers to acquire new capabilities. Organisations that do this well can reduce the time to achieve local site-specific competency levels by as much as 75 per cent.

It is important to reflect here on the European experience of skills capability development over the last 40 years or so as illustrated in Figure 2.3. This have been driven by enlightened attitudes from both trade unions and management **working in partnership** rather than the adversarial confrontation of the singled skilled craftsman of the 1960s and 1970s.

During the 1980s and 1990s we saw the advent of multi-skilled craftsmen – especially (but not exclusively) between the mechanical and electrical trades.

Throughout the early 2000s to the present day we have seen strong evidence in many manufacturing and utility companies of using '*Enabling Agreements*' to build flexible team-based working involving not only maintenance engineers but also (and most importantly) their operator colleagues – where it's no longer appropriate for the operator to say to their maintainer colleague "I operate, you fix...I add value... you cost money... so watch out!"

On the contrary, these enlightened enterprises build a culture which believes that effective team-working between the core operators and maintainers working in harmony is the best way to create maximum product flow through their physical assets.

The challenge now for these enlightened enterprises is to embrace the appropriate technologies that Industry 4.0 presents us with to build versatile, purposeful and innovative teams who are progressively encouraged and trusted by their managers to become self-managed teams within clear boundaries and rules that they have had a clear say in setting and will continuously improve.

It may come as a surprise to some that all four of the above areas are within the scope of Total Productive Maintenance (TPM) principles and techniques.

The TPM road map systematically removes the causes of reactive maintenance to release maintenance engineering time to focus on higher value-added activities. Within the TPM process, education and training is used to ratchet up equipment effectiveness, by refining working methods and standards to prevent breakdowns and systematically remove the causes of common problems. Through this process, cross-functional front-line teams become engaged with learning through their involvement with task simplification.

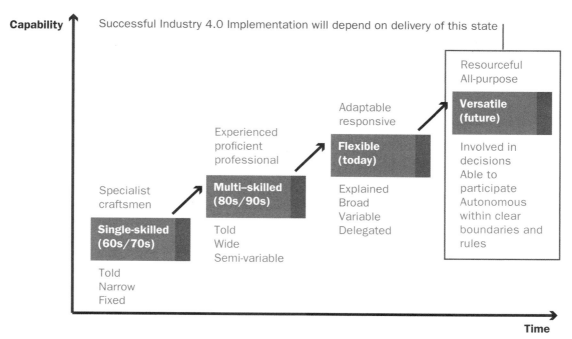

Figure 2.3: The history and developing future skills requirements

Such cross-functional team-based projects not only develop engineering skills, but also provide a vehicle to develop innovation, project management and leadership competence. The investment in time results in a bottom line return worth many times the cost. Perhaps the biggest benefit is the impact on the way skills are applied and future capabilities are developed.

There is no doubt that without skilled workers, it is hard for a business to grow, especially in the manufacturing and technology sectors. These are challenges that TPM and aligned tools like fast-track reliability-centred maintenance (RCM) are designed to overcome.

It is fairly certain that more new machines, processes and systems than ever before will be created. They will need to be repaired and eventually replaced: in other words, maintained!

This will create an opportunity for maintenance to be considered as a value-adding activity, rather than 'a necessary burden' as has been the case in the past.

For far too long the maintenance function in many business enterprises has been regarded as a non-value-adding direct cost burden – and hence a regular annual budgeting target for cost cutting, in the sense of doing the same with fewer people.

Fortunately, over recent times the advent of lean thinking and the emergence of Industry 4.0, together with the aspiration to achieve operational excellence, means that the more enlightened businesses view the maintenance of their strategic physical assets as a value-adding system and process.

Operational excellence is about striving to eliminate waste in all its forms in order to maximise value-adding activity. It is about the speed or velocity with which we can convert a customer's order into money in our bank account. This is surely sound common-sense and as such we need to be excellent at it.

However, on top of all this we are having to cope with the fourth industrial revolution via Industry 4.0!

2.2.2 What can Industry 4.0 offer to manufacturers and utility providers?

The fourth industrial revolution's arrival via Industry 4.0 is evolutionary. It will not arrive in a flat pack at the factory gate with instructions to build and immediately use.

Among many other developments smart sensors will be an essential building block of Industry 4.0 as the 'all seeing eyes' of the smart factory.

The opportunities are huge, ranging from the simpler and well-proven applications of measuring dynamic, physical attributes of process and product (positioning, timing, counting, measuring, flows, pressures, temperature and light), to the advances in chip technology that enable advanced intelligence in the sensors themselves.

Sensors traditionally collected a wealth of data but only at a local level. Now Industry 4.0 is allowing that same data source to be shared, compared and exploited between sites, across the globe.

Maintenance engineers are by nature practical people. So in a perfect world they need sensors that are quick and easy to install, easily adjusted when installed and easily replaced when needed – with minimal need for specialist skills to programme, commission and teach.

For the manufacturing business smarter sensors will aid the ongoing drive to improve

- continuous monitoring and diagnostic interpretation
- product tracking and traceability
- agility and flexibility on batch production changeovers
- reduced spares inventory
- process and linked assets end-to-end reliability tracking.

This is all potentially good news – it enables manufacturers to increase their ability to make real-time decisions leading to a more proactive and prevention-driven maintenance approach.

These new systems and their associated hardware are more complex and yet highly interactive and, in all probability, very much more customised than the previous generations of hardware. That affects the skills needed by the maintainer: more problem solving (knowledge working) than the more traditional follow-the-training-manual fixing or replacing a component part maintenance.

Judging by recent history, a probable consequence of the adoption of this digital age is the likelihood of hardware failing more often and being less reliable, leading to being maintained even more frequently.

The implication of this is that company CEOs, CTOs & CIOs will need to be very clear on the specification of their 'digital transformation' strategy before cascading it out into a deployment policy.

At a management level, delivery of Industry 4.0 will require individual asset-based businesses to think about and specify their particular new skills requirements. This will require strong and consistent management to support up-skilling of existing staff. It will also necessitate the training of their staff to be able to deliver both the transition and then subsequently the maintenance of those new technologies.

In parallel those same manufacturers, utility service providers and their outsourcing partners will need to proactively collaborate with our universities and centres of further education to deliver the science, technology, engineering, and maths (STEM) skills they need for their future talent pipeline.

At the sharp end of the business, this will bring into strong focus that every maintainer (and indeed their operator colleague) will need to be a knowledge worker in the sense of

■ knowledge – knowing what it is
■ skills – knowing what to do with it
■ experiences – know when things go wrong and why
■ and capability– know how to fix it and – most importantly – how to prevent recurrence of that same issue.

Increasing automation requires less human effort in the actual operation of equipment. However, this does not necessarily mean reduced human error. On the contrary, automation itself usually involves more control steps and is increasingly complex, but still has to be managed and maintained by humans.

Our experience suggests that the more steps that need to be taken to achieve a work-based objective, both in human terms and the parallel use of automation, then the more likely there are to be errors. This raises the question of whether we have the right skill sets – both hand/operational and mental/intellectual – to manage unplanned events.

As will be explained in later chapters, at the core of the TPM principles is a firm belief that technology is just the enabler; it's the skills and the people we have that will make the difference. As the IoT floods the factory floor then the KISS philosophy of keep it simple and straightforward – via visual management, standard work and single point lessons –will become increasingly important.

One thing for certain is that the 4IR and hence Industry 4.0 is here to stay, supported and enabled by a fusion of technologies, it is here right now and manufacturers need to decide quickly when to join the party and reinvent their own businesses.

In the book *What's Next?* Naomi Climer, an engineer and consultant to the board of Sony's UK Technology Centre, says:

…Already, we're seeing smart (IoT) devices for fitness/well-being tracking, monitoring for specific medical conditions such as heart rate or blood sugar…

…Meanwhile, and less visibly, industries are beginning to test the waters, and these may be where the greatest economic benefits will come in terms of contributing to big, global and national challenges. For example, wind farms find that they can use information from sensors to continuously adjust the blades to make the most of the wind. It's like tweaking the sails on a boat to get a little bit more speed-it can increase the amount of energy generated by up to 25 per cent. Factories are beginning to connect their own data with their suppliers so that components are ordered just in time for production. Sensors around the production line can also help to predict problems before they happen and delay scheduled maintenance when the machines are fine, making sure the engineering effort is being used where it is really *needed.*

The above observations on the knowledge worker followed by these quotes will have significant impact and emphasis on the TPM principle that front line operators are the best condition monitors ever invented, using their given senses of look, listen, smell, feel and discuss.

….International manufacturing companies like Bosch or Airbus are able to share data between factories to make sure that issues and fixes are managed globally using expertise from any location.

The other feature that IoT allows for is the collection of data on extraordinary scales. Very cheap, low-power consuming, connected sensors can be added to everything to collect real-time data about…specific systems, allowing us to continuously check for leaks with sensors in remote water pipeline…

Again the TPM philosophy underpins the fact that equipment shows early signs of deterioration via leaks (visual), vibration (hear, feel) or overheating (touch, see and smell)

....One of the challenges of the IoT is how to turn these vast amounts of data from multiple sources into meaningful wisdom.

Whole new job categories are opening up around data science as we seek people who have the talent to help work out how to turn unlimited data into useful wisdom. What are the right questions to ask of the data? What are the important patterns?

The prevailing term around this is DIKW: data, information, knowledge, wisdom. TPM adds two missing words: standards and behaviours. TPM focuses on tapping into your existing 'minds of gold' – the operators and maintainers – because only they know the reality, based on daily experience.

Another way we're currently exploiting the Cloud and the IoT is virtual reality (VR) and augmented reality (AR). We've seen these in computer games and the commercial mainstream for some time, but now they are popping up elsewhere too.

Architects and estate agents are using VR to help visualize things that are yet to be built; companies building ships, airplanes and oil rigs can use the technology to visualise things before making a massive investment ;some factories are using AR as a way to overlay instructions on a headset for technicians in order to give them step by step guidelines on what they need to do.

Both VR and AR are still relatively young but this opportunity will bring the well-proven principles of early equipment management (see Chapter 8) into clearer reality. We for our part will need to be agile and adapt those principles to the emerging realities.

2.2.3 Impact of technology transformation on operational excellence (OE)

These technologies are designed to make manufacturing leaner and smarter, and we can expect that our future manufacturing floors will bear little resemblance to those of the recent past. Organisations with a sufficiently high level of operational excellence 'maturity' under their belt will gain more benefit, sooner, from this next stage of manufacturing evolution than their competitors who lag behind the OE maturity curve.

As OE practitioners already know, excellence can only be attained through an incremental, maturity-based approach to operational excellence as well as the fundamental and parallel people-engagement practices. Culture will continue to eat strategy for breakfast in this battle for survival.

TPM, carefully adapted to this new scenario and, where appropriate, aligned with the Shingo Model™, will help to facilitate the non-optional journey of continuous improvement and hence marketplace competitiveness.

2.2.4 Technology will no doubt simplify things, but will the technological tail continue to wag the dog?

Technology will undoubtedly simplify things, but will also create a level of abstraction that can be wasteful or even dangerous. Consider monitoring screens used in control rooms: they can keep operators away from the real equipment performing the task, lulling them into a false sense of security that all is well even if, for example, sensors don't function properly. Both product and energy could be flushing down the drain due to faulty valves or devices, creating huge wastage and cost.

Consider the modern control room. We have highly-qualified control room operators spinning around on swivel chairs watching mimic screens with green and occasional red lights flashing on and off. They have been lulled into a false sense of security, while out there in the real world the physical asset with that critical prime-mover, such as a pump or motor, is going drip, drip, hiss and eventually bang!

'Manufacturing Our Future – is the UK manufacturing industry geared up for 4IR?', Sunday Telegraph, 3 December 2017

'The Cloud and Internet of Things' by Naomi Climer in *What's Next?*, edited by Jim Al-Khalili, 2017 ISBN 978-1781258958

Maybe we need to rediscover some of our old values and behaviours and start walking the talk.

2.2.5 It's your people who will make the difference

Competitive asset management will come to those companies who focus on the judicious and innovative application of automation and technology available within Industry 4.0. Already we are seeing that the fundamental and under-pinning people-engagement practices are key and are delivered through teamwork, goal alignment and deployment, which depends on a leadership style that is able to progressively trust to delegate. This factor will become even more important as technology becomes even more multifaceted.

Figure 2.4 illustrates the vital importance that maintenance plays in delivering the core quality of your business purpose, product and processes.

Figure 2.4: Asset maintenance and product quality are tied partners

Finally, as Figure 2.5 illustrates, it is our firm belief that the careful and judicious use of Industry 4.0 technologies will enable your plant to be a world class facility where your people – not technology alone – will make the difference. Also remember that maintenance in the sense of using spanners and screwdrivers will be here for some while yet.

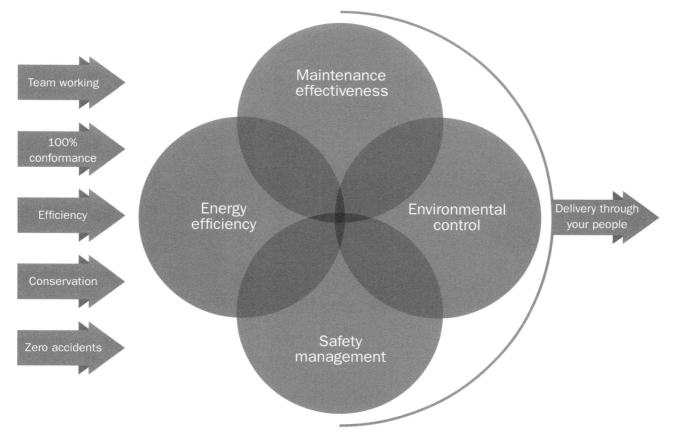

Figure 2.5: Delivering the vision through Industry 4.0

2.3 Changing the perceptions of maintenance

In the manufacturing sense, operational excellence is about striving to eliminate waste in all its forms in order to maximise value-adding activity.

Operational excellence is only as good as the reliability and predictability of our strategic physical assets.

Low levels of equipment effectiveness often result in those critical physical assets becoming the pinch-point in the customer service supply chain.

As a maintenance *manager* you will be under continuing pressure to cut the *direct costs* of the maintenance function now to be more *efficient*.

As a maintenance *professional* you will still be striving to increase the *effectiveness* of maintenance delivery. The bottom line is that you will almost certainly need to do more with less: that is the reality and therefore the challenge.

Our experience suggests that, in the maintenance sense, this all has to be achieved in parallel with yet more pressure and demands created by increasing environmental conformity, increasing energy costs and of course, zero accidents.

2.3.1 A health warning

Before developing the above themes further around operational excellence we expect that many of your in house continuous improvement programs will be tagged (some might say 'lumbered') with the term 'Lean', as in *Lean Thinking, Lean Manufacturing, Lean Maintenance* and so on.

You will know that 'Lean' is not about doing the same with fewer people, less money or less time, it's about doing more 'value adding' by eliminating waste – whether that is a waste of material, energy, space or time, or personal intellect. However, to the uninitiated, the word 'Lean' often means doing the same with fewer people. If we start off by sending out the wrong message we are not going to get too far with our *Lean Transformatio*n journey.

Hence our strong preference to use the phrase *operational excellence*

2.3.2 Is 'maintenance' still the poor relation in your company?

"If the jumper cables don't work, I'll pour more motor oil on the keys."

Figure 2.6: Are your maintenance processes keeping up with changing technology?

One of biggest problems still facing many of today's maintenance functions – and hence its managers and professionals – is one of poor image and perception. As the cartoon in Figure 2.6 suggests, this is not a new problem.

Let's imagine for a moment that you are the engineering director of a significant manufacturing plant. You go into the boardroom for the monthly site leadership team meeting and mention the word 'maintenance'. Does the chairman look at his watch and tell you that you have just three minutes to talk about this (frankly boring) subject?

Does the sales and marketing director simply look out of the window, because it's nothing to do with them? Does the finance director scowl at you as they see it as an unnecessary evil and damaging cost burden, and does the production director get ready for a slanging match because they see maintenance (or the lack of it) as the root cause of most of the company's production problems?

Is this an exaggeration? Sadly in far too many cases it may still ring true.

So why is there this poor perception?

Maybe it's because the engineering director has never sat down with their maintenance manager and thought long and hard enough about

- who is our internal customer?
- who are our key influencers – both positive and negative?
- how should we go about changing these existing poor perceptions?

The first two questions are relatively easy to answer:

The customer is production (or manufacturing) and the key influencers are your ultimate sponsors – the production director and the finance director and, ultimately, the managing director.

The essential first step to change these perceptions is for the maintenance function itself to reflect and define its own purpose and objectives. The team should make clear how these directly contribute to the business drivers, the operational excellence journey and the overall business transformation.

These outputs then need to be clearly articulated to the above three key influencers – not just in terms of maintenance efficiency (cost down) but also maintenance effectiveness in terms of what it can deliver via the elimination of waste in all its forms. Effectiveness typically includes the overall equipment excellence (OEE)'s classic six equipment-based losses, plus energy, environment and safety performance to the business. This can only be achieved by aligning maintenance's contribution to the company's operational excellence model.

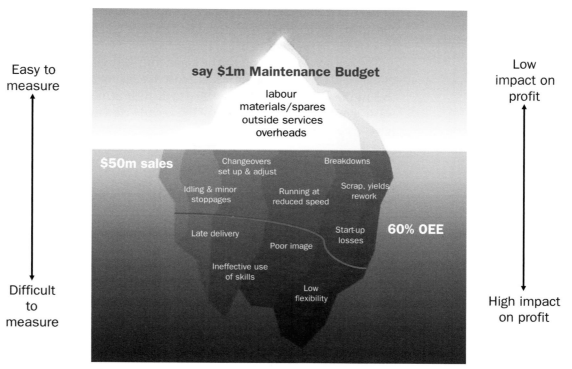

Figure 2.7: The true cost of maintenance is 7/8ths hidden

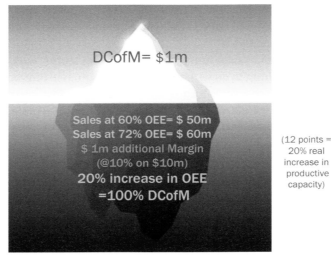

Figure 2.8: Efficiency v. Effectiveness

One way of visualising maintenance's potential contribution as a value-adding activity is to use the analogy of the iceberg. The tip of the iceberg is the visible direct cost of maintenance to the business via the annual maintenance budget, as illustrated in Figures 2.7 and 2.8.

In this simple example we have a business which has an annual maintenance budget of $1.0 million (which we will call 'direct cost of maintenance', DCofM). It is supporting $50.0 million sales, with a site average OEE of 60%.

If we can increase the site OEE to 72% through the implementation of a targeted and effective TPM programme the extra 12% OEE is equivalent to a 20% real increase in productive capacity without increasing our maintenance spend. If we can sell the additional output (a growth scenario rather than cost-down) our annual sales will be $60.0 million and the additional margin on those sales is worth $1.0 million to the business as illustrated.

In this example a 20% increase in productive and saleable capacity is equivalent to 100% of the annual maintenance spend. The message is, stop hacking away at the tip of your iceberg every year at budget time and instead concentrate on the less-visible opportunities below the surface.

The key point is that you can be apparently very efficient in your maintenance budget and spend (tip of the iceberg cost management) but totally ineffective (below the waterline) in its relevance to delivering the business drivers, where waste elimination should be top of the agenda. As a maintenance manager you have to be excellent at both.

2.4 **Where is your maintenance practice now?**

In order to position where you are now in your maintenance practices it may be useful to complete the following exercise as a joint evaluation with operations – your internal customer.

Maintenance assessment exercise

While we have developed structured, detailed and apparently cost-effective, approaches to our maintenance programmes here at our plant, we still suffer from significant backlogs. The results are unacceptable performance, risks, losses and costs. Why is this the case? Maybe the following ten statements can give us an insight:

So, from your own experience, based here at your operations, please rank each of these ten statements below as follows:

Very true/strongly agree	Score 3
True/agree	Score 2
Partially true/partially agree	Score 1
Not true/disagree	Score 0

		Score
1.	Our plant, machines and equipment are not fit for our current and future process/production demands	
2.	The tasks and routines defined by the maintenance programmes often conflict with the experience of the person actually carrying them out	
3.	Our maintenance staff were not involved in putting together these routines. So they have little ownership for the quality of the maintenance work carried out as described by the task	
4.	Our operators were also not involved in the decision process either, so their 'front-line' experience is not included and problems remain	
5.	Instead of measuring the reason why we do the task (to protect and/or improve the reliability/effectiveness of the asset) we only measure the direct cost of doing it. In other words, we are pre-occupied with maintenance 'efficiency' rather than asset 'effectiveness'	
6.	We know that plant and equipment reliability is affected by both design weaknesses and the way in which it is operated. However, designers and operators were not encouraged to view maintenance other than simply as 'a necessary evil' or function	
7.	Production demands and load conditions continually change, but the maintenance programmes do not change because our people are not encouraged, or given the time, to review and/or update practices	
8.	The link between our plant and equipment condition and its performance/effectiveness is not reviewed regularly	
9.	Production and maintenance seem to have different objectives and priorities and, as a result, resource and/or timing issues often conflict	
10.	The ease of carrying out maintenance is not looked at, so tasks that are difficult and take a lot of time are sometimes not done or left to a shutdown	
	Total (out of 30)	

We developed this list of ten checkpoints as the result of a one-day workshop we ran a few years ago for the offshore oil & gas industry. Towards the end of the session we asked the 50 or so delegates to list out and discuss the top ten reasons for gaps, omissions and weaknesses in their existing maintenance strategy and the statements above are what emerged.

The offshore oil & gas industry is regarded as being in the upper 10 per cent for well-defined and executed maintenance strategies – driven by the huge safety implications of getting it wrong and the significant costs of, for example, not having the correct spares on the offshore platform. So we see the list above as substantive and significant to industry as a whole.

TPM addresses each one of these ten fundamental reasons for the gaps in our existing maintenance practices and recognises that it is the person carrying out the tasks who is the key, and the way in which he or she is supported is vital to achieve true cost effectiveness.

So what is your benchmark score out of 30?

Score range	Significance
21 to 30	We have a major opportunity for improvement
12 to 20	We have significant scope for improvement
5 to 11	We are doing well, but can still gain some benefits
1 to 4	We are almost world class
0	We are the world's best!!!

In our experience, many companies initially fall into the top two ranges if they conduct the exercise with real honesty and healthy debate with both the maintenance representatives and their internal customer colleagues representing production/ operations.

Over the years we have also accumulated strong evidence that revisiting the same exercise two to three years down the road of pursuing a robust and relevant TPM programme produces scores in the 5 to 11 range and even one or two in the 1 to 4 range. We have yet to come across a string of ten zero scores – which is good, because we suspect that they would be less than honest if such perfection was achieved.

On the basis that this 'honesty check' or 'health check' has whetted your appetite, then you can look forward to the next chapter on TPM as an enabler of operational excellence, plus some myths and realities around TPM. For example, 'Is TPM a hidden agenda to get the operator to do the maintainer's job?' and 'Is an OEE of 85 per cent world class?'

CHAPTER 3

TPM as an enabler of operational excellence

3.1 TPM best practice and operational excellence

In our consultancy practice we are often challenged: what is operational excellence?

In response we first ask a number of questions.

- Is the future of your business likely to become more complex? By more complex, we mean greater variety in customer demand and more specialised customer requirements?
- Is the future marketplace likely to become even more cost competitive?
- Will there be pressure on your business to reduce cycle times and provide options for your customers to reduce stock holding?
- Will the future environment become more regulated with greater focus on high quality process performance data and product traceability?
- Will there be greater challenges in engaging and retaining your employees?

Almost invariably the answer to these questions is yes. Operational excellence is the core philosophy which will align the organisation to effectively and continuously address these challenges. A myopic focus on quality alone will not address these issues. There are many businesses who have lost competitiveness in the market due to an over-burdensome approach to quality control and compliance. An embedded culture of operational excellence focused on true customer value will enable each function of the business to align successfully to continually meet market challenges.

Let's also consider how operational excellence has influenced modern maintenance activity. In the past traditional manufacturing (at least in theory) made it easier to release equipment for maintenance through defined periods of planned maintenance downtime.

However, a culture of operational excellence requires equipment to be available on demand. The successful adoption of operational excellence will lead to revising the traditional maintenance of process equipment.

The focus on a consistent, reliable, flow of value in the operational excellence environment will require the maintenance function to consistently review and improve its contribution to ensuring that reliable process flow. Moving focus toward flow of value enables more valuable conversations around the effectiveness of the maintenance function rather than simply the efficiency of that maintenance work. Moving from conversations around how quick the response of maintenance to breakdowns is, to one with a consistent focus on the six equipment-based losses can often result in a 50 per cent increase in available productive capacity.

By enabling the maintenance function to systematically review the effectiveness of what they do, operational excellence helps the maintenance team deliver improved performance and lasting change. The broad focus that operational excellence provides also raises the profile of maintenance as a value-adding function and a key strategic enabler of business growth, rather than an overhead cost.

As such, maintenance practices must change and respond to meet the challenge of operational excellence. Table 3.1 shows some of the impacts.

Table 3.1 Impacts of operational excellence on maintenance

Activity definition	Operational excellence impact on maintenance
Value-adding activities which the customer sees providing a product or service of value	Stabilise and extend component life by controlling contamination, accelerated wear and causes of human error
Non-value-adding activities which do not provide product or service features which the customer uses (classic lean wastes).	Focused improvement to analyse and remove unnecessary work activity including unnecessary PMs, waiting time, and other wastes
Necessary non-value-adding activities which are difficult to remove but are essential to the running of the operation.	Analyse, challenge and then simplify non-value-adding activity. Engage front line operators in routine asset care and early problem detection. Improve ease of inspection and reduce time to repair. Improve equipment design and fixtures to reduce or eliminate change over time.

Let us now consider the impact of maintenance on operational excellence in terms of those same three categories of work as illustrated here in Table 3.2.

Table 3.2 Impacts of maintenance on operational excellence

Activity definition	Maintenance impact on operational excellence
Value-adding activities which the customer sees providing a product or service of value	Improve quality, cost and delivery capability
Non-value-adding activities which do not provide product or service features which the customer uses (classic lean wastes)	Stabilise process performance and define leading indicators to maintain optimal performance. Provide better and more-accurate data and process knowledge to predict and prevent defects and capacity loss
Necessary non-value-adding activities which are difficult to remove but are essential to the running of the operation	Simplify and then standardise necessary but non-value-adding activity

The key message in all this is that operational excellence and maintenance are both essential and tied partners.

An operational excellence mindset helps maintenance groups to regularly review their internal systems, processes, and tools – and their ability to constantly improve the asset management system's ability to add value by delivering

- stabilised process/equipment performance to reduce unplanned events and waste
- optimised performance and equipment design to reduce quality defects, cost, and delivery lead times
- better ways to interpret process performance to predict and eliminate problems.
- the ability to identify and address current and future skills gaps.

Operational excellence can help enhance maintenance effectiveness by using its proven tools and techniques to target waste reduction and non-value-added maintenance activities by

- stabilising and then extending component life through controlling contamination and accelerated wear, and minimising human error
- analysing and removing unnecessary maintenance procedures
- developing standard countermeasures to common problems
- reducing the time to respond and repair

- engaging operators in front-line asset care
- improving ease of inspection and early problem detection.
- constantly identifying opportunities to make equipment easier to use, easier to clean, easier to change over and easier to maintain.

In summary, the maintenance leadership team starts aligning effective maintenance to the operational excellence agenda, and presents this to its customer (production/operations) as an essential partnership for change.

TPM as a core philosophy can align equipment design, acquisition and ongoing performance into a defined system of asset optimisation. TPM also provides strong links with other core business systems such as

- continuous improvement
- management, through visual management boards
- learning and development in the organisation
- strategy development and the deployment of that strategy.

The visual management board, for example, is a common feature of most operational excellence programmes. The purpose and function of the board is often misunderstood. In the context of TPM within a manufacturing environment, the visual board is the focal point where many defined systems overlap. This is a good opportunity to review what would be considered as a benchmark visual management board.

The visual board should link the activity of this department and its team to the overall strategic objectives of the business by identifying critical success factors. A critical success factor (CSF) is a 'must win battle' which must be won if the business is to deliver on its objective (Figure 3.1).

A CSF may relate to the development of core skills, reduced lead-time or a reduced unit cost. Where the link is between a CSF and local team activity, then there must be some indication of how the team are doing. For example, if there is a stated objective to reduce cost per unit, then plot the percentage improvement, and similarly for key performance indicators (KPIs) such as output per head or increased product variety. If these objectives are articulated clearly with suitable progress tracked, the local team can directly relate their own improvement activity to these objectives.

A benchmark visual board will track the leading indicators that the team have identified as being essential to achieve their objective. It is vital that these indicators relate to factors within the team's control. Where external factors are affecting their performance, the team must be able to effectively escalate the issue and feel confident that it will be addressed and that they will be informed of progress.

There can often be confusion as to how a review meeting should be conducted at a visual management board. The expectation is that, for example, in the case of a shift startup huddle everything should be covered in five to ten minutes. This can certainly be achieved in a mature process where pre-startup checks have already been completed and the status is fed back to the team. Concerns and watch-outs in relation to safety and process issues and pending process changeovers are highlighted to ensure alignment.

On a cycle through the week the content of the huddle meeting should change with varying emphasis or updates from, for example, the safety team, improvement project activity, skills cross-training activity, business updates and team recognition.

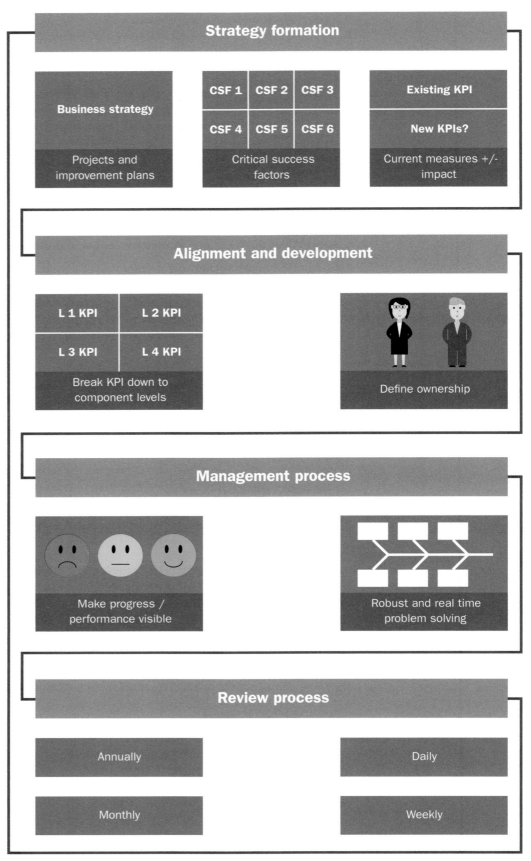

Figure 3.1: Effective strategy deployment

The visual board (see Figure 3.2) also provides a focal point for project team activity and updates. The board owner should also be able to review the board content with their manager to confirm alignment with overall business goals and objectives.

In the context of TPM the board should highlight current process performance with a clear analysis of the issues affecting that performance and what is being done about it. The visual board may indicate the progress on document development such as front-line operator asset care checks (FLOACs) and associated single-point lessons as a key part of standard work.

Figure 3.2: The visual board is ideally the intersection of many core business systems

3.2 **Operators and maintainers working as a team**

The whole philosophy of TPM is centred on teamwork between the operator and the maintenance technician by taking shared responsibility for the reliable health and predictability of their equipment.

As described in detail in Chapter 5, we encourage the analogy that healthy equipment is just like a healthy body. In this metaphor the operator is the nurse of the asset (the patient) and the maintenance technician is the doctor (and the surgeon in an emergency).

One way of describing the TPM journey, and the way in which a maintenance technician's use of time and skill sets are progressively developed to be more productive, is illustrated in Figure 3.3.

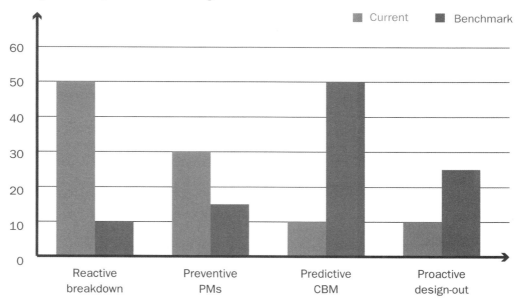

Figure 3.3: Maintenance time allocation: current vs. three-year benchmark.

Experience shows that before adopting the TPM philosophy, a maintainer's time and effort is typically spent as 50% reactive breakdown, plus 30% preventative fixed-interval planned maintenance, plus 10% predictive/condition-based. Only the final 10% is proactive design-out. By adopting TPM ways of working this profile progressively develops to a more value-adding productive role, typically over three years, to one of only 10% reactive breakdown, plus 15% preventative fixed interval planned maintenance, plus 50% predictive condition based, leaving the final 25% as proactive design-out.

The figures are relative rather than absolute, but they have been verified in practice.

3.2.1 What are TPM ways of working?

It can be hard to describe, but in practice you know them when you see them because they boil down to specific behaviours that you can observe, in the same way you might observe a waiter in a top-class restaurant adjust a table layout to the perfect standard. Similar observable behaviours reflect a shift towards an embedded culture of TPM.

Examples become evident when breakdowns become a rarity, because the '100-year fix' mentality becomes a reality. Asset teams don't just focus on solving current issues; they create their own 'legacy' as they use structured problem-solving to seek and assess suitable corrective actions that prevent re-occurrence.

PMs have halved, why? Because the team seeks opportunities to improve component reliability allowing the extension of the interval between PMs and removes unnecessary PM routines. We see a dramatic shift in observable behaviours towards condition-based inspection routines (including selective use of thermography, vibration monitoring and oil debris analysis tools) while recognising that the operator is the best condition monitor ever invented, using their given senses of look, listen, feel, hear and touch.

Teams develop, update and maintain front-line operator asset care checks (FLOACs) supported by the maintenance technician who takes on the role of the 'teacher'. Maintenance technicians encourage ever-increasing levels of equipment consciousness within the operator group, improving their understanding of the equipment and its operation.

As a consequence of increased front-line engagement, 25 per cent of the maintenance technician's time can now be devoted to designing out the equipment weaknesses as the 'engineer' he/she was indentured for rather than the 'quick-fix' person they have become.

3.2.2 Introducing new ways of thinking

As with most proposed changes to culture and work practice the age-old question still remains, 'so what's in it for me?'

To explain this, we ask the rhetorical question 'where would you prefer to use your skills?' – not in an arrogant way, but by showing some empathy for their current daily hassle and misuse of their capabilities. We also consider the opportunities for personal learning and the quality of the stories individuals can convincingly tell of their true level of experience and acquired skills.

The opportunity for developing and implementing effective FLOACs cannot be underestimated, as

- the front line tasks they identify probably don't get done by anyone at the moment – so it's not a hidden agenda to get the operator to do the maintainer's job
- these front line checks do not involve using any spanners, screwdrivers – far less voltmeters – yet they allow operators to increase their knowledge of the equipment and its use and take ownership of the development of support documents that work for them

- they are developed by the operator <u>and</u> the maintenance technician, who also helps train the operators to carry them out via single-point lessons and standard work. The approach fosters teamwork and mutual respect.

In essence, adopting the TPM philosophy enhances the skill sets of both the operator and maintainer rather than diminishing them, while delivering measurable levels of process improvement and employee engagement.

3.3 Dispelling six common myths about OEE

We find there are a number of misconceptions, misunderstandings and interpretations of how to apply and use OEE as a key performance indicator of the true productivity of our physical manufacturing assets and production processes.

However, before looking at the six myths it is worthwhile exploring the OEE concept in a little more detail.

Overall equipment effectiveness is a measure of 'availability' multiplied by the 'performance rate' of the equipment when running and the 'quality rate' that the equipment is producing. Negative effects that go against this being as high as it should be are unplanned events or 'non-conformity' such as

- breakdowns
- excessive changeovers and setup times
- running at a reduced speed because the equipment is not quite right
- minor stoppages which do not need a maintainer to attend the machine but cause the operator to have to intervene because of, for example, a jam or blockage
- scrap, poor yield, rework and quality problems
- start-up losses every time an unplanned stoppage or changeover occurs.

The first two losses above affect the availability of the asset or machine: the second two the performance rate when running and the final two the quality rate.

The above are referred to as the six classic equipment-based losses and are often described as floor-to-floor losses (F2F), whereby you pick up a product (or material) and process it through a machine before placing it on a pallet (or conveyor) for onward processing or to stores/assembly.

The OEE is a vital measure, as it is in effect a measure of equipment-based waste in all its forms. The TPM System drives toward a high OEE and being in control of the process through focused improvement, resulting in a trouble-free shift where people are working smarter and not harder.

A further important point to stress is one of targeting an improvement in the OEE.

Look at Table 3.3. If, for example, analysis of data shows a current OEE of 45% based on the average of the last four weeks, and the perceived wisdom of management is that it should be a 'world class' level of 85% then that represents an 80% real improvement in productive capacity ($85-45/50 \times \% = 40/50 \times \% = 80\%$). Your operators and maintainers will not accept such an improvement target as realistic, and you could hardly blame them – it's like suggesting everyone can run 100 metres in less than 10 seconds.

If however you look inside the data that has created the 45% OEE average over four weeks and see what is the best availability, performance and quality we have achieved in any particular week, and then multiply those three figures together, then the notion of an initial target based on a 'best of best' achievement of 60% becomes believable. Why is this the case? Well you can say with some conviction that if we just get control of the six losses (far less eliminate them), then we will hit the 'BoB' consistently week by week and by doing so create a new BoB which is getting nearer to that world class level of 85%.

Table 3.3 Setting an interim 'best of best' OEE target

	Availability %	Performance rate %	Quality rate %	OEE %
	Breakdowns, setups, changeovers	Running at reduced speed, minor stops	Scrap, rework, minor losses	
Current 4-week average OEE	64	70	90	45
4 weeks best of best (BoB)	75 (week 1)	83 (week 3)	96 (week 4)	60
World class	90	96	98	85

Myth 1: an overall equipment effectiveness level of 85% is 'world class'

It certainly is not if you are running, say, a flour mill or an off-shore oil platform! In this case if you're not hitting 90% + OEE then you'll soon be out of business. We didn't let the Japanese finish off the sentence when they told us 25+ years ago that *"85 per cent is world class…* (we then rushed out of the room, before they added*) … for a typical machining centre that has a significant number of changeovers".*

So, 85% is no golden goal.

It is necessary to look *inside* the OEE and determine world class levels based on the three elements of availability (uptime), performance rate when running and quality rate produced, then multiply the three metrics together to determine your world class target OEE. Depending on your industry, the result might be:

Packing line	80% x 96% x 97% = 75%
Flour mill	98% x 99% x 99% = 96%
Bottling plant	85% x 98% x 96% = 80%
Machining centre	90% x 96% x 99% = 85%

What can a TPM-driven approach deliver in improved overall equipment effectiveness? Some examples that we have witnessed and/or worked with are:

Application	From % OEE	To % OEE
Steel plant	74	90
White goods	79	88
Automotive	48	75
Flour mill	86	93
Chemical plant	82	95
Filling line	55	85
Packaging line	66	87

Myth 2: OEE is a management tool to use as a benchmark and comparator

This misses the point of the OEE being a manufacturing floor problem-solving tool.

If, however, 'corporate' insists on benchmarking, then beware of not comparing like with like – not just 'apples with apples' but 'Bramleys with Bramleys'.

Also five further questions to answer…

1   What is the impact of the number and variety of product changeovers?
2   Who sets the standards for performance rates when running – production planning, equipment supplier or engineering?
3   How big an impact do staffing levels and skill levels have on cycle time?

4 Are all minor stoppages recorded?

5 Are we measuring all aspects of quality including wasted packaging materials?

Myth 3: OEE should be calculated automatically

The computation approach is far less important than the interpretation. While initially calculating manually or inputting manually you can be asking 'why?' five times. Once you've proven the manual measurement process, then automate it.

Myth 4: OEE on non-bottleneck equipment is unimportant

OEE provides a route to guide problem-solving. The main requirement is for an objective measure of hidden losses even on equipment elsewhere in the chain – especially if it is generating controllable waste or non-value-adding.

Myth 5: We don't need any more output, so why raise the OEE?

Management's job is to maximise the value generated from the company's assets. This includes business development. Accepting a low OEE defies commercial common sense. If you are able to increase the OEE from say 60% to 80% by tackling the relevant six losses, you will have increased the productive capacity of that asset by 33% – which means you can produce the same output in two-thirds of the current time, or make 33% more in the same time. Either way it gives you a choice of flexibility at 80% OEE that you do not enjoy at 60%.

Myth 6: OEE is not useful because it doesn't consider planned utilisation losses and, for example, labour co-ordination/diversion losses or material supply starvation losses

The OEE is one measure, but not the only one used. Others will include productivity, cost, quality, delivery, safety, morale and environment. Often these 'door-to-door' or 'management' losses (as opposed to equipment-based manufacturing team floor-to-floor losses) are vitally important (see Section 3.4.5).

There is no one-size-fits-all approach to OEE .The challenge is to adapt OEE to your business (as opposed to blindly adopting it in the classic sense). What you must not do however is corrupt it, so it becomes unrecognisable and does not point you at the problems and hence opportunities

3.4 **Recognising different industry sector characteristics**

We in S A Partners aspire to help manufacturing and process industry to realise its full potential for customer service, cost, quality, safety and morale. TPM is a powerful enabling tool to help deliver this potential. Our experience suggests that, in the right hands, TPM is capable of unlocking your installed productive capacity by unlocking the potential of your people.

This statement is of course subject to two vital prerequisites.

Hardware considerations

When applying TPM to various industry sectors we need to take account of the type of manufacturing processes involved and whether, for example, it's a labour-intense or a capital-intense scenario; bulk processing or piece-part manufacturing and so on…

People considerations (see also Section 3.2 above)

We also need to recognise the differing impacts and hence the ideal behaviours the operator, the maintainer and the team leader need to exhibit in those different scenarios.

With both these considerations in mind, we are going to consider here a matrix of seven types of manufacturing process facility groups and six main factors that will impact the application of TPM.

The seven groupings are

1 process/bulk manufacturing (often capital-intense)
2 classic manufacturing (cell and/or linked assets)
3 packaging (sometimes labour-intense)
4 assembly (often labour intense and/or automated)
5 utilities & general services (often capital intense)
6 warehousing (pick and place + automation)
7 remote and dispersed assets (for example, wind farms, phone masts, reservoirs).

The six main factors we are going to consider are

1 the OEE measure (and other relevant KPIs)
2 operator impact
3 maintainer impact
4 5S workplace organisation and visual management
5 changeovers and setups
6 standard work.

3.4.1 Seven manufacturing process facility types and six characteristics

Table 3.4 illustrates a matrix of the seven types of facilities and the six main factors. Each of these is described in more detail below.

Table 3.4 Recognising the differences when applying TPM

Type of facility	OEE measure	Operator impact	Maintainer impact	5S – WPO & visual management	Changeovers & setups	Standard work
A) Process/bulk manufacturing (capital intense)	Campaign or batch OEE as a fixed repeating schedule	Significant – not just control room based	Major	Significant – contamination control + yields	Significant + cleaning in process & use of VSM & ECRS	Major
B) Classic manufacturing (cell and/or linked assets)	Running clock OEE	Major – can be labour controlled rather than machine controlled	Major	Major – to create flow	Major + use of VSM & ECRS	Major
C) Packaging (often labour intense + some automation)	Running clock OEE	Major – can also be partly labour controlled	Major	Major – to create flow	Major	Major
D) Assembly (often labour intense and/or automated)	Running Clock OEE	Major cycle or pulse rate often labour controlled	Major	Major – to create flow	Significant (& pre-kitting, VSM & ECRS)	Major

Table 3.4 Recognising the differences when applying TPM

Type of facility	OEE measure	Operator impact	Maintainer impact	5S – WPO & visual management	Changeovers & setups	Standard work
E) Utilities & general services (often capital intense)	? relevance of OEE vs. efficiency & MTBF & MTTR&R	Significant	Major	Housekeeping resulting in 'maintenance pride'	Rarely applicable	Major
F) Warehousing (pick and place + automation)	Running clock OEE	Major	Major	Major to create flow	Pre-kitting, VSM & ECRS	Relevant
G) Remote & dispersed assets i.e. windmills, phone masts, water reservoirs	Alarms freq, callout freq, MTBF, MTTR&R	Very little	Major	Some application	Rarely applicable	Major

3.4.2 **Process/bulk manufacturing**

This type of facility, which includes the acquisition and conversion of primary materials – for example metals and chemicals (both liquid and/or powder) and papermaking – often comprises major physical standalone and/or sequentially linked assets which are spread over a large area and/or multi-storey buildings. It is often capital intense, highly automated and employs relatively few staff. There is likely to be a central control room hub environment, often using a 24-hour, 7-days-a-week, 365-days-a-year shift pattern.

Because of this continuous full-time repeating 24-hour shift pattern where the manufacturing process is dictated by batches of bulk product following a specific process stream, it is often more logical to consider a batch OEE or, as it is sometimes referred to, a campaign OEE that has a defined standardised sequence each with its own standard time.

This pre-determined sequence can then be monitored and tracked through a series of gates which reflects the manufacturing logic for that specific batch. This is often referred to as a fixed interval repeating schedule OEE.

One of the central tenets of the TPM process and philosophy is that it encourages 'equipment consciousness' – this is how this process or mechanism is meant to work and these are the typical phenomena that stop that actually happening. The key learning points of the criticality assessment (Step 4 in the 11-step TPM process) is that it highlights the impact of safety, reliability, environment and its potential impact on the three elements that make up OEE as Availability × Performance rate × Quality rate produced. The criticality assessment also provides a focus on the parts that need to be kept in optimum condition as part of Step 6 – future total asset care – and Steps 7 & 8 – root cause analyses, problem resolution and standardised best practice.

Perhaps our overdependence on technology means we have lost the will and common sense to walk around a site/facility or plant and use our given senses of look, see, smell and touch. In other words, we have lost the ability to catch the status of an item early (as in a pump, motor or mechanism) due to over-heating, or perhaps a leak or vibration, before it becomes catastrophic. Often these out of sight, out of mind assets are also surrounded by unacceptable levels of 5S/workplace organisation, which result in inadequate safety, contamination control, spillage and hence low yields.

The principle of autonomous maintenance or, as we prefer to call the first part of Step 6, *front-line operator asset care* – recognises that the best condition monitor ever invented is the operator using their given senses of look, listen and discuss with their maintenance colleagues.

The above comments are also largely true of the other six types of facilities covered below.

A really good example of adopting a mindset based on knowledge and understanding is the adaptation of the OEE metric to suit an offshore oil platform in a hostile North Sea environment. Here the set of metrics developed by a TPM-driven asset reliability team are shown in Table 3.5, where APQ is Availability, Perfornace Rate and Quality rate.

Table 3.5 Example metrics

FREQUENCY		PARAMETER	MEASURE	RESPONSIBILITY	PERSON
Monthly	1	Subsea wells & reservoir (ORE)	APQ	Owner	Reservoir Engineer
Monthly	2	Field management effectiveness (OFE)	APQ	Owner	Reservoir Engineer
Weekly	3	Effectiveness of oil plant (OPE)	APQ	Operator	OIM
Weekly	4	Separation	AQ	Operator	Production Supervisor
Weekly	5	Flare minimisation	P	Operator	Production Supervisor
Weekly	6	Gas compression	APQ	Operator	Production Supervisor
Weekly	7	Overall gas compression system	APQ	Operator	Production Supervisor
Weekly	8	LP eductor equipment	P	Operator	Production Supervisor
Weekly	9	Produced water	AQ	Operator	Production Supervisor
Weekly	10	Fuel gas system	APQ	Operator	Production Supervisor
Weekly	11	Boilers	A	Operator	Chief Engineer
Weekly	12	Water injection	APQ	Operator	Production Supervisor

In the process and bulk manufacturing industries changeovers are often significant and often involve a 'cleaning in process' cycle between batches which is both lengthy and complex. In this environment value stream mapping can be used to develop an ideal future state. This in turn can be analysed to create 'one best way' which can then be standardised as a key part of Step 8.

We do this by getting the right people (especially the operators and maintainers) involved in defining each elemental activity of the current state via a systematic E,C,R,S challenge process, investigating which steps we can eliminate and, if we can't eliminate it, can we

- combine it with another activity upstream or downstream? If not, can we
- replace it with something smarter or at least
- simplify it ?

And then standardise that 'one best way' and train it out as standard work.

3.4.3 Classic manufacturing

Physical assets can either be singular (one machine/one operator) or cellular (more than one machine but only one operator), and/or coupled into a value stream comprising several linked assets and their associated dependency and inter-dependencies.

It is vital to fully understand and then assimilate those dependencies. For example one operator looking after more than one asset can become labour-controlled (as opposed to machine-controlled) in certain machine loading and changeover configurations rather than using the standard machine cycle time or nameplate performance rate when running. Line balancing becomes critical in these situations to optimise OEE considerations – whether a running clock OEE or batch OEE. The point is that the lost opportunity elements of the OEE are not always due to the classic six equipment losses, but can be based on a manning level decision (and hence a 'management' or 'door-to-door' loss). Figure 3.4 illustrates some of these issues that need to be fully understood, otherwise your performance measurement system will give misleading information because it is based on erroneous assumptions and standards.

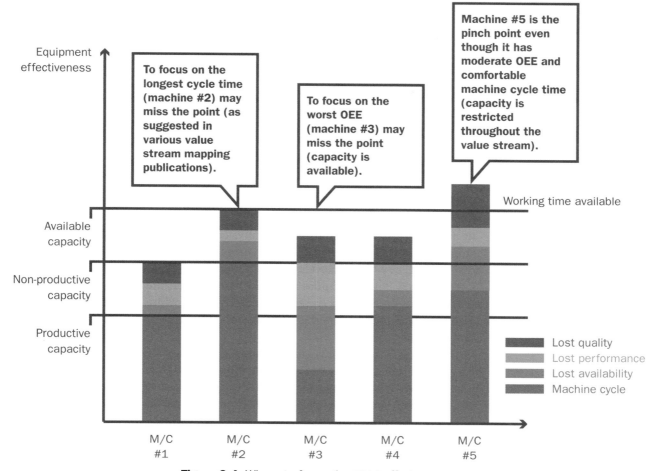

Figure 3.4: Where to focus the TPM efforts

The OEE says nothing about schedule adherence: it is pointless having a high OEE if you are making the wrong products.

So, OEE can be improved in good and bad ways. Good ways are to reduce unplanned breakdowns, minor stoppages and changeover times. Bad ways are simply to do fewer changeovers, or avoid making products with high defect rates or more difficult adjustments.

As such, OEE should not be used in isolation, but alongside such measures as customer request date, manufacturing promise date, schedule attainment, work in progress and inventory levels. Takt time (see Glossary) as opposed to cycle time also needs to be fully understood.

Similarly, your TPM efforts and the associated need for asset performance improvement (that is, the OEE) needs to take account of the top level business drivers and imperatives for the next, say, 12 to 18 months.

It is also a worthwhile exercise to stimulate discussion and more detailed analysis, by first setting down a simple but effective A,B,C categorisation of the physical assets where

A   Assets that are critical all of the time
B   Assets that are critical some of the time
C   Assets that are never or rarely critical

3.4.4 **Packaging**

Packaging is like classic manufacturing in the sense that both operators and their maintenance colleagues can have a major impact on asset effectiveness because all six classic equipment losses come into play. Many packaging lines have a combination of labour-controlled elements as well as islands of automation (conveying, weighing, filling, inserts, sealing, palletising and shrink-wrap). Minor stoppages corrected by the operator are often more significant as lost time and hence lost opportunity than breakdowns requiring the presence of a maintainer. Similarly, changeovers can be significant as can the need for excellent 5S/ workplace organisation to create flow around those assets, together with relevant use of equipment-based visual indicators.

3.4.5 **Assembly**

This might be a stationary but complex physical asset into which are fed several components, often at high speed, using complex tracking, sequencing, insert and pressing devices with high levels of automation.

Alternatively it may comprise a moving line or 'pulse line' assembly for larger more complex products (home entertainment goods, white goods and vehicles). Again the man/machine interface and interaction may be more labour controlled than machine controlled.

In both cases internal and external supply chain co-ordination will be crucial. Also the resultant internal pre-kitting, kanbans, line balancing and takt time will be just as important as the equipment reliability issues themselves.

This is where a broader view of the OEE is worth exploring.

Figure 3.5 illustrates three levels of measurement focus:

- The floor-to-floor (F2F) OEE, which focuses the core team's TPM efforts on the classic six equipment-based losses by tackling breakdowns, changeover times, running at reduced speed, minor stops, scrap, yield, rework losses – plus startup losses every time we get a breakdown, changeover or minor stop. This is where a product and/or raw material is fed to a 'value-adding' machine, physical asset or process and then placed on a pallet or conveyor for onward routing.
- The door-to-door (D2D) effectiveness which is within management's control (and is not an equipment-related loss). Typically these losses might be
  - labour co-ordination losses (that is, no operator available, or the maintainer is diverted to other priority)
  - product supply starvation
  - no work order
  - no packaging materials
  - consumable stock outs
  - awaiting QA clearance Instructions
  - new product introduction trials
  - machine upgrade and hence out of production service.
- The value chain effectiveness embracing suppliers through to customer delivery.

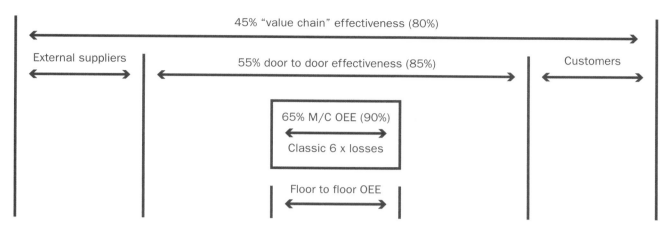

Figure 3.5: The OEE as an enabler across the end to end value stream

In Figure 3.5 the current and target levels of effectiveness are shown at each level. There is little merit in increasing the F2F OEE from 65% to 90% if the D2D effectiveness stays at 55%. Likewise, there is little merit in getting the D2D effectiveness up to say 85% if we are getting inconsistent supplier responses and we are making product that sits in the finished goods warehouse for six months. By concentrating on the F2F losses we will also be highlighting the D2D losses and in turn the supply chain effectiveness.

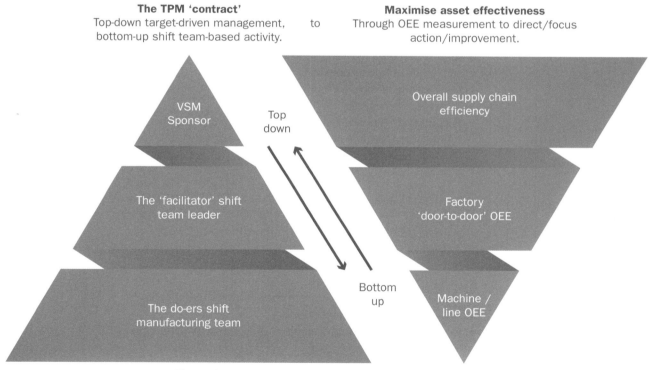

Figure 3.6: A three-level site performance 'contract'

This three-level model can then be aligned to the plant organisation structure to reflect accountabilities and expectations as illustrated in Figure 3.6.

This approach allows us to pinpoint commitment and accountability at the right level in a plant's organisation structure such that, in this example:

■ The value stream manager is the *sponsor* of the TPM routines (making TPM a non-optional part of 'the way we do things here')

- The shift-based team leaders are the *facilitators* of the TPM routines, ensuring that the routines are carried out to the required standard at the right time and frequency and are therefore part of leader standard work
- The shift manufacturing teams of operators and maintainers – the *doers* – carry out the TPM routines that they themselves have designed and specified during the TPM pilot project phase.

All of the above becomes a key part of the application of standard work which will be central to the TPM activity.

3.4.6 Utilities & general services

(See also Chapter 10 for a detailed case study taken from a public water utility)

This grouping includes public utilities such as water, gas, electricity and nuclear. We also include docks and airports in this category.

Likewise there are in-plant local services such as on-site combined heat and power (CHP) energy-raising (steam, gas, electricity and air) and its distribution to the point of use. Also effluent control and disposal.

There is often a very significant element of outsourcing of maintenance activity. This can range from specialist condition monitoring services to the total outsourcing of maintenance. In the past, outsourced maintenance agreements were governed by service level agreements (SLAs), which tend to generate the wrong behaviours – to the extent of them eroding over time to become adversarial and confrontational. Today the TPM philosophy is becoming more attractive as a trend towards 'enabling partnership agreements' becomes a reality.

In terms of measurement, the classic OEE is not always relevant and other KPIs need to be thought through and used. A few examples that we have seen in this category are

- **Airport baggage handling system** Number of lost bags per day. Number of false sensor alarm resets per shift
- **Mail sorting office** Number of mis-sorted items per shift. Number of interventions per day
- **Water treatment plant** Mean time between failures and mean time to respond & repair. Maintenance cost per 1,000 litres of processed clean water.
- **In-house plant services** Air pressure distribution loss. Energy cost per unit of output.

Obviously the possibilities are immense and it's perhaps worthwhile setting down the five measurement principles within TPM to help you decide on the correct measures to drive the right behaviours within your facility.

These correct measures will

- improve the quality of problem solving
- help set fast track priorities
- maintain management commitment to the TPM approach
- help deliver the business drivers
- focus on driving out non-value-adding waste in all its forms.

3.4.7 Warehousing and materials handling

Warehousing

This category is again an opportunity to be creative by the careful tailoring and adaptation of the more classic TPM application.

In Chapter 10, Case studies (10.5.1) we describe an example of an in-plant highly-automated storage and retrieval system (ASRS) characterised by

- six cranes servicing 12 racks over 13 levels, each with 100 spaces
- 13,000 pallet spaces

- 1200 pallet movements per month
- 100+ alarms per week caused by…
- misaligned sensors
    - dirty and/or damaged sensors
    - twisted pallets (variety of reasons)
    - random mixture of plastic v. wood pallets (good & bad points)
- significant number of conveyors and transport mobiles
- 'hundreds' of sensors
- very good visual process flow maps (photos and graphics)
- many linked critical assets
- new integrated process logic system bedding in
- need for high-level criticality assessment to focus improvement opportunities via TPM and develop future state via ECRS challenge and then standardise.

Materials handling

In a more mature application of TPM in a materials handling environment of a highly automated multi-sourced material stock feed system to 60 moulding machines, the following results – as articulated by the team of operators and maintainers at Milestone 2 of their TPM journey – have been achieved:

- '…The material handling system area has become an easier place to work in and is presentable to both customers and suppliers. Safety is now our number one priority.
- Current average alarms are 76 per week which represents an 80 per cent reduction from 463 per week before we started TPM.
- Average weekly downtime as a result of the material system improvements and feed delivery to all 60 moulding machines has gone from 68 hours down to just three hours a week…' This represents a huge financial benefit to the business.'

3.4.8 **Remote and dispersed assets**

Typical, but not exhaustive examples include wind farms, telecommunications masts, water reservoirs (both above and below ground) and their associated pumping and metering stations.

In the technical sense we might call these peripatetic maintenance assets, where the business is responsible for multiple and geographically diverse assets which are largely unmanned facilities requiring central 24-hour monitoring. The biggest – and often false – assumption in this scenario is that regular visible and physical human inspections and maintenance are of little value. The result is that the technological tail is left wagging the dog.

Maybe we need to rediscover some old behaviours and start walking the talk.

The OEE metric is not usually relevant in this category. More relevant asset reliability metrics would include

- alarms frequency
- callout frequency
- mean time between failure
- mean time to respond and repair

Operator impact is minimal, but maintenance impact is major and standard work and standard approaches are critical.

Standard work will range from how company vans are laid out to ensure equipment, tools and spares are close to hand and present to the development of standard work activity to ensure maintainers' safety and ease of equipment maintenance.

As each individual maintainer becomes more familiar with the assets the combined knowledge and learning of the team must be 'harvested'. The obvious reason is to improve the overall effectiveness and quality of maintenance activity, but also to ensure the connectedness with the team. New communications and video conference technology make it easier to stay connected with a remote team and speed the transfer of images and videos of the good, the bad and the opportunities to improve asset performance and ease of maintenance. However, despite the advances in communication technology the authors strongly recommend the facilitation of group face to face activity to review and improve how the maintenance work 'works' in a remotely distributed asset environment.

CHAPTER 4
The purpose of TPM

4.1 Overview of the TPM system

Our model centres on the three Ps of Purpose, Process and People with the overlapping elements of align, improve and engage. Companies striving for excellence clearly define core business systems and component processes within each of the six elements. The team as S A Partners have noted that those companies achieving excellence give equal if not more focus to the overlapping elements of align, engage and improve.

Figure 4.1: Enterprise Excellence Model

Our approach, while recognising TPM as a standalone system to manage and improve the performance of an organisation's assets, also enables robust interfaces with other critical systems such as the system of improvement: the system by which we engage our teams and clearly align their activity with business strategy and purpose. An effective system-based approach to TPM must also align with efforts to develop individual skills and career opportunities. Adopting such a holistic system-based approach to our asset performance, which supports the principles and behaviours we need in relation to our assets, ensures that we focus on sustainable operational excellence rather than an 'efficient' maintenance system. Taking a principle- and behaviour-based approach to TPM ensures both an efficient and effective approach to the maintenance and improvement of asset performance.

With this holistic approach in mind we have developed a defined approach to the development or relaunch of a cultural and principle approach to asset optimisation outlined in Figure 4.2.

The TPM programme is applied via an introduction and deployment process within the business unit called the *purpose,* which is the focus of this chapter. It includes

- a scoping or planning phase diagnostic study
- measuring the cultural temperature with a focused perception survey made up of one to one interviews with operatives, equipment maintainers, engineers, support teams and leaders
- how to prepare a compelling business case
- securing the site leadership team's 'buy-in' before the TPM programme launch.

The development of a TPM system begins with the application of our 11-step TPM model made up of a sequence of defined team-based 'learning by doing' activities as a four-cycle 11-step process (which is the focus of Chapter 5).

The outputs of this 11-step application are then used in a progressive and evidence-based assessment process to assure the team's progress in developing a holistic TPM system supporting the necessary ideal behaviours. This is the essential approach to the people development part, and is the focus of Chapter 7.

Purpose: Our TPM programme is applied via a defined introductory and deployment process within the business unit.

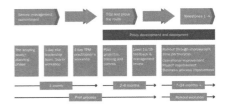

Process: Our TPM model is applied through a defined sequence of *learning by doing*.

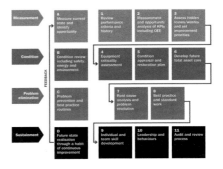

People: The outputs of this application are aligned to an evidence-based assessment process linked to the team's progress through the model.

Figure 4.2: The TPM system model

The four 'maturity milestones' shown in the people development element above are linked to a roll-out over time as illustrated below in Figure 4.3 supported by clear evidence-based bottom-up audits at each milestone that must be passed before proceeding to the next one.

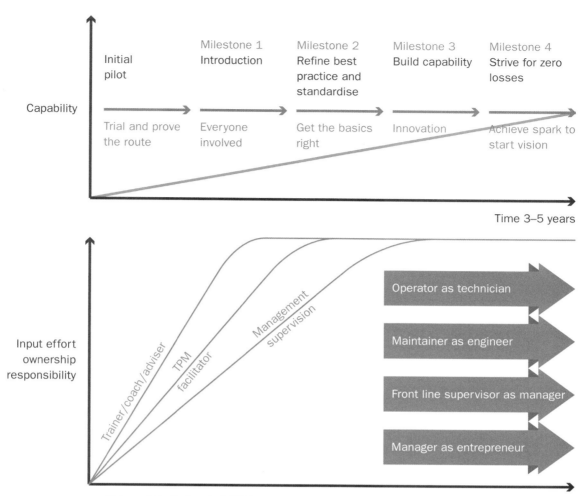

Figure 4.3: Roll-out of TPM

4.2 **The TPM purpose**

The ultimate purpose of TPM is to maximise business assets – to ensure shareholder return on investment and customer satisfaction – through employee engagement.

As a philosophy TPM falls under the umbrella of Lean thinking and team engagement. It brings together continuous improvement tools such as value stream mapping, SMED (single-minute exchange of dies), 5S, cost & loss deployment, centre lining, visual management and problem solving. When looked at in terms of a system it provides ample opportunity for effective coaching by leaders in relation to areas such as problem identification, prioritisation and resolution. Most importantly it provides a focus for the observation and reinforcement of agreed ideal behaviours. Examples of such ideal behaviours might include curiosity and process focus, information sharing and teamwork, and attentive and respectful listening. We will discuss and review such ideal behaviours in later chapters but for now we need to get the ball rolling!

Here we describe how to introduce (or possibly reintroduce) the TPM principles, philosophy and practicalities into an organisation in a structured, sustainable, common sense, step by step approach. This defines the TPM implementation journey or purpose. Within this element the leaders of the organisation gain clear alignment between the strategic objectives of the organisation and a system-based approach to TPM.

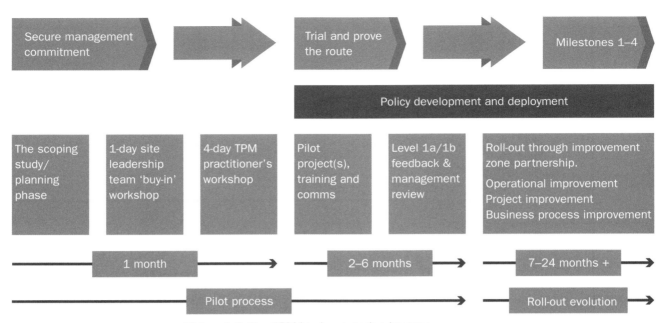

Figure 4.4: The TPM implementation journey

It is a journey which comprises
- securing senior management commitment at the front end via a detailed planning or scoping diagnostic study
- training up a critical mass of TPM practitioners through a hands-on four-day practitioner's workshop as a 'learning by doing' experience
- trialling and proving the 11-step TPM enabling tool through a series of TPM pilot projects. This is the key phase for moving from 'strategic intent' to 'making it happen'
- confirming progress and providing support through a series of four maturity milestones, based on selected TPM champions responsible for driving change through an agreed roll-out sequence of defined project activity.

Typical timescales shown will of course vary according to
- the size of the operation
- a current-state 'health check' to establish where you are on your operational excellence/continuous improvement journey
- the amount of resource – people, money and time – committed, and thus the pace at which you can initiate and absorb change
- The stability and consistency of leadership intent and focus.

These key questions – plus a first-cut cost/benefit appraisal – are addressed in the front-end scoping study or 'planning the plan' phase. Thorough planning – and the 'buy-in' from the site leadership team of that plan – are essential for a successful and sustainable TPM implementation journey.

4.3 The front-end scoping study

This includes the initial scope definition and potential financial benefits. It culminates in a site leadership buy-in session before running a four-day TPM practitioner's training workshop. The combined purpose of these three activities is to raise management and employee understanding of what TPM is and, equally important, what it is not. It is also to define what TPM can add to current initiatives and how it will support delivery of the business drivers and priorities.

Provided the scoping study is well planned, with a detailed hour-by-hour schedule, it can typically be completed in five days.

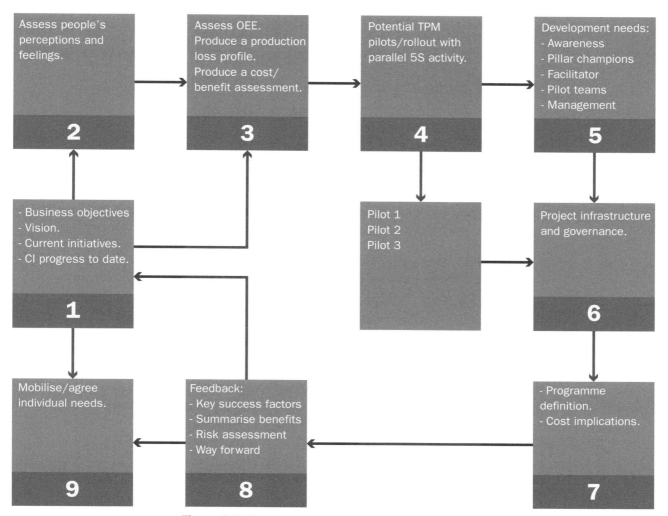

Figure 4.5: Plant-specific scoping study

The objective of the plant-specific scoping study is to address each of the above nine elements in order to

- check where this plant is on its continuous improvement journey – its business drivers and future vision, plans and intentions – as a 'maturity assessment'
- assess people's perceptions and readiness for the TPM programme
- assess equipment, door-to-door and supply chain losses, and the potential for improvement
- carry out a first-cut cost/benefit appraisal of the preferred first TPM application area
- identify TPM pilot opportunities and priorities within the application area
- identify the critical success and risk factors plus countermeasures to minimise risk
- develop a first-cut TPM site-wide roll-out approach
- specify full implementation, training and coaching plans to cover
    - potential pilot(s) and the likely benefits from those pilots
    - pilot project team size and membership
    - key contact people and roles
    - logistics and resource implications
    - an initial awareness, communication and training plan, including its timing
    - facilitator support requirements plus their personal development training
    - programme governance, including steering group membership and terms of reference
    - pillar champions and subject matter experts.

First we will look at four of the key considerations.

- checklist of information needed for the scoping study
- measuring the cultural temperature with a '28 perceptions' exercise
- how to prepare a compelling business case within the selected TPM application area
- site leadership buy-in session to sign off the scoping study findings and recommendations.

4.4 **Information required ahead of the scoping study**

There are two main documents involved, both of which need to be gathered and collated into a scoping study file ahead of the actual scoping study activity. These are

- 14 specific points of information for the particular company site/facility
- a production loss profile assessment for the likely initial application area(s).

Both of these documents help to ensure that the productivity of people's time involved in the actual conduct of the scoping study is maximised

4.4.1 **Fourteen points of information**

1 Site plan/map showing details of where safety procedures apply. Support this with information relating to any initial induction needs for scoping study team members who may access safety-restricted areas.
2 Total employees on the site
    - management
    - indirect support
    - direct.
3 Site leadership and senior management organisation structure with names and job titles.
4 Current process organisation structure for the likely application area(s) showing:
    - management (names and job titles)
    - supervision (names and job titles)
    - specialist support (names and job titles)
    - hourly-paid skilled and semi/unskilled by job title, by process location, by shift pattern
    - zoning and allocation of other central resources such as maintenance, transport and process quality assurance.
5 Working arrangements (including shift patterns, shutdowns, product changeovers, process control and QA checks).
6 Amount and reasons for any subcontract maintenance and/or outsourcing.
7 Amount and reasons for production and maintenance overtime and/or temporary labour.
8 Main/critical plant items/path in the plant value stream processes.
9 Examples of the plant operation's daily/weekly/monthly outputs including budget/targets/actual.
10 Typical shift log sheets and fault analysis data.
11 How is the plant area availability, performance and quality recorded and managed? By shift/daily/weekly ? Are any minutes produced?
12 Scheduling procedures specifically and between production & maintenance.
13 Best estimate of approx percentage split between predictive/condition-based, planned/fixed interval and breakdown maintenance.
14 Strategic, policy statements and 'pictures' of intentions regarding the company's operational excellence road map over the next three years,

especially those relating to specific tools & techniques, continuous improvement initiatives and lean transformation progress to date.

4.4.2 Production loss profile

Production loss profile for critical assets for [name of value stream/asset/ machine/line or process]

Please note: to help you complete the task below you should refer to the completed example in Table 4.1. The example also illustrates how it will be extended to build the business case during the actual scoping study.

What are the planned weekly core loading/attendance times and associated shift patterns for this asset?

What are the operations and maintenance team sizes and their immediate reporting structure? Are there formal shift handovers and at what times of the day?

If core weekly planned loading/manning time is **X** hours per week, please provide a best estimate of where the losses occur under these two categories:

Door-to-door losses per week, based on management decisions where the asset is unavailable for planned production
- Attending team briefings
- Rest breaks (lunch, tea breaks)
- Training (with the asset closed down)
- No labour available or diverted labour
- Planned maintenance
- Awaiting technical/quality assurance
- No work due to product starvation/waiting materials and/or product
- Doing 5S activity
- Other (please specify)

Six classic floor-to-floor equipment-based losses
- Breakdowns (estimate of number and hours per week)
- Changeovers (estimate of no & total hours per week)
- Micro/minor stops causing operators to stop the machine and clear a blockage/ make a minor adjustment (usually less than 10 minutes and <u>not</u> requiring the attendance of a maintenance technician)
- Running the line/process at a reduced speed/cycle time (is this possible and if so by how much?)
- Start-up product losses following a changeover, minor stop or breakdown as scrap or rework units
- Other scrap & rework units

Other considerations – please provide examples wherever possible
- Are there any regular front line operator asset care checks/inspection routines, per shift, per day or per week?
- What are the planned maintenance fixed interval schedules? Are they on a computer-based maintenance management system (CMMS)?
- Is any condition-based monitoring carried out (for example thermography, vibration, oil debris, other)? Please describe.
- What existing shift/daily/weekly performance/productivity measures/metrics are there? Show typical results (similar to, but not necessarily OEE-type measures). Are there daily/weekly formal reviews? What is the timing of these and who attends and for what purpose?

(Refer to the following example below to assist completion)

Table 4.1 Example: production loss profile for no. 6 fill and packing line

Worked example in RED	
If core weekly planned loading/manning time is 120 hours, can you estimate where the losses occur as:	
Door-to-door management losses	
Attending team briefings	10 x 15 mins = 2.5 hours per week
Rest breaks (lunch, tea breaks)	45 x 10 = 7.5 hours per week
Training	(covered by back fill)
No labour available	averages at 2 hours per week*
Planned maintenance	8 hours/month = equivalent 2 hours per week
Awaiting technical/quality	**zero effect on run time**
No work: product starvation or waiting materials/product	6 hours per week*
Doing 5S activity	done on the run if time
Other (please specify)	
Total D2D losses = 2.5 + 7.5 + 2.0 + 2.0 + 6.0 =	20.0 hours/week
At 120 hours manned hours D2D effectiveness = (120-20) /120 =	83.3%
Six classic floor-to-floor equipment-based losses for the remaining 100 hours production	
Breakdowns (estimate of no & total hours per week)	2 off = 6 hours per week
Change-overs (estimate of no & total hours per week	3 off = 12 hours per week
Micro/minor stops causing operators to stop the machine and clear a blockage/make a minor adjustment (usually less than 10 minutes/occasions and not requiring the attendance of a maintenance technician)-	Estimated at 4 hours per week
Running the line/process at a reduced speed/cycle time (is this possible and if so by how much ?)	95% of Planned running rate
Start-up product losses following a changeover, minor stop or breakdown as scrap or rework units	(see below – not captured separately)
Other scrap/rework units + see above =	4% (i.e. 96% FT quality rate)
In the 100 hours left for production 6.0 + 12.0 =	18 hours are lost to Availability
Therefore Availability = (100-18) ÷ 100 =	82%
In the 82 hours running time and Line speed is 95% so	4 hours are lost to Minor stops
Performance rate when running is (82-4) = 78 × 0.95% = 74.1 run hours. That is a performance rate of 74.1 ÷ 82 =	90.4%
Quality Rate produced = 100 - 4 =	96%
So F2F Equipment OEE = 82% × 90.4% × 96% =	71.2%

Summary

Current situation

At 83.3% D2D effectiveness we only secure 100 hours of our loading time

At 71.2% F2F OEE we only achieve 71.2 productive hours

Future challenge

If we could halve our no labour (2 hours) & no work (6 hours) from 8 hours to 4 hours, we would increase our loading time to 104 hours (D2D = 86.7%)

If we could halve our current F2F losses from 18 hours to 9 hours availability, minor stops from 4 to 2 hours, achieve a 97.5% run rate and increase quality to 98% then our potential improvement can be calculated as:
- Availability = (104-9) ÷ 104 = 91%,
- Performance rate = (95-2) ÷ 100 × 0.975 = 90.7%
- Quality rate = 98%.

Therefore F2F OEE becomes = 91% × 90.7% × 98% = 80.9%

80.9% of 104 hours = 84.1 productive hours per week – a gain of **12.9 hours per week** from the current 71.2 hours or **645 productive hours per year.**

What will this give the business?

A choice of flexibility at 80.9% OEE not enjoyed at 71.2% to either make more in the same time or make the same in less time.

The 'make more in the same time' scenario is **worth 645 productive hours per year to the business**.

4.5 **Measuring people's perceptions and feelings**

A key part of the scoping study phase is to gauge people's readiness for the TPM program. This is achieved by interviewing a small but representative number of employees which we group into three clusters of
- operators
- maintainers and
- their key contacts (typically managers, supervisors and specialist support staff who have a direct impact on the day-to-day operations).

The focus of each interview is to ask the individual to rank 28 statements as shown in Table 4.2. Fourteen of these statements relate to how involved the individual employee feels in their workplace decisions (as in Employee Involvement – the EI column). The other 14 statements (under the PM column) measure that person's perception of how Progressive the management are in creating a climate to enable that employee's proactive involvement.
   Some important points to note
- The statements are not handed out for completion prior to the interview
- Only the person's job title is noted - to respect the spirit of anonymity
- The interview is conducted across the table one to one, privately, using the 28 statements as a structured focus to promote open and honest discussion that can be subsequently analysed by response, strength of feeling and job role
- This also allows the interviewer to encourage clarification of a specific response or rating and gain useful insights as to why the interviewee feels that way
- The interviewer asks a final question of the interviewee: "If you were a member of the site leadership team, what would you try most to change or influence over the next say two years?" The responses to this question are often very enlightening!

Table 4.2 People's perceptions: 28 statements

	STATEMENT	EI	PM
1	In my view we still have an 'I operate, you fix' mentality		
2	In my area, lines of responsibility and accountability are <u>unclear </u>to me		
3	As a company we do **not** take training seriously		
4	In my area, groups do **not** get together to work on common problems		
5	In my view, people are reluctant to say what they really think		
6	From my position, production and maintenance people seem to **pull in opposite directions**		
7	I am **never asked my opinion** by my bosses about the job I do		

Table 4.2 People's perceptions: 28 statements

	STATEMENT	EI	PM
8	In my area, **skills are picked up** rather than learned systematically		☐
9	The company operates on **old ideas** rather than new ones		☐
10	When it comes to different on-site departments, the left hand doesn't know what the right hand is doing	☐	
11	Lessons learnt on one shift do **not** get transferred to others	☐	
12	As far as changing the way we do things, **attitudes are very fixed** in this company/organisation	☐	
13	Information regarding our equipment effectiveness in my section is **not** made visible or available to me		☐
14	We suffer from too many so-called 'Initiatives' which end up as **the flavour of the month**		☐
15	In this company people would **not** welcome more challenge in their job	☐	
16	Problems regarding our local work organisation and effectiveness are **not** faced openly and frankly	☐	
17	In my area the housekeeping and general cleanliness of the place is **not** what it should be		☐
18	In my area we are **not** supplied with the proper support 'tools' and equipment to do our job properly		☐
19	In my area, our spares stockholding for production equipment is **not** as good as it should be		☐
20	We should **not** be encouraged and trained to work in multi-disciplined teams, where we solve equipment and quality related problems.	☐	
21	We **don't work as a team** to improve the quality of maintenance	☐	
22	Most of my work is **unplanned**	☐	
23	Unit cost information is **not** made available to me		☐
24	The link between the business vision and what my department does is **not** clear to me		☐
25	The company **does not** take safety seriously		☐
26	Relevant technical information is **not** kept up to date	☐	
27	The company **does not** recognise the link between absenteeism & job content		☐
28	Standard methods are **not** important	☐	
	Total for PM		☐
	Total for EI	☐	

Each response is then analysed and fed back. Results are summarised as a grid matrix (Figure 4.6) together with the top perceived 'hinders' and 'helpers'. Tables 4.3–4.5 show four clusters (based on 7 each of the 28 statements): how the individual feels treated, how they feel the team works, how they feel the management works and how they feel the company works. This is followed by a summary interpretation of the result.

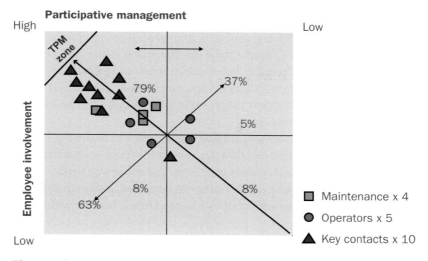

Figure 4.6: People's perceptions and feelings

Table 4.3 People's perceptions and feelings, what **hinders** progress?

By weighted strength of feeling	Maintainers	Operators	Key contacts	TOTAL
We suffer from too many initiatives	67%	100%	47%	**65%**
Lessons learnt on one shift do not get transferred to others	50%	73%	60%	**61%**
Production and Maintenance are separate 'Empires'	67%	67%	53%	**60%**
Inter departmental communication is poor	67%	80%	33%	**53%**
We don't work as a team to improve the quality of maintenance	50%	53%	53%	**53%**
Production and Maintenance tend to pull in different directions	67%	47%	47%	**51%**
Skills are picked up rather than learned systematically	67%	67%	37%	**51%**

Table 4.4 People's perceptions and feelings, what **helps** progress?

	Maintainers	Operators	Key contacts	TOTAL
We should introduce a CI/TPM approach	100%	100%	100%	**100%**
Standard methods are seen as important	100%	93%	97%	**96%**
The company does take safety seriously	100%	93%	97%	**96%**
The company encourages new ideas	83%	80%	90%	**86%**
I am asked my opinion about my job	75%	80%	90%	**84%**
Most of my work is planned	58%	80%	93%	**82%**
The company does take training seriously	92%	87%	73%	**81%**

Table 4.5 People's perceptions and feelings. How I feel that ...

How I feel that	Maintainers	Operators	Key contacts	TOTAL
I am treated	33%	42%	20%	**28%**
The team works	48%	51%	42%	**46%**
The management works	44%	47%	20%	**32%**
The company works	27%	45%	22%	**29%**
EI	40%	47%	31%	**37%**
PM	36%	46%	21%	**31%**

In this analysis, the lower the score the better – anything above 40% represents an opportunity for improvement. The TPM System will most certainly address the high ratings of how the team works.

Summary interpretation of above result

- 63% feel the participative management style is lagging behind the actual willingness to be involved (that is, they are positioned to the left of the diagonal)
- However, 79% feel both encouraged & involved
- Only 8% feel neither encouraged or involved
- The TPM programme will directly address six of the top seven perceived 'hinders'
- However, initially it may well add to the top hinderer of 'too many initiatives…'
- Most feel that the 'across the fence' communications and understanding of 'each others problems' has some way to go
- Most *expect* change to continue, although some may still resist it because they already feel they have too much to cope with.

4.6 How to prepare a compelling business case

During the scoping study it is essential to produce a production loss profile of the initial intended TPM pilot project (see Section 4.4 above). Often the required data and information is at best patchy, so it will be necessary to have several reiterations around this topic before a case can be made with justification and conviction.
The best way to illustrate this process is by way of a further example, shown in the tables Tables 4.6, 4.7 and 4.8 below:

Line 4: production loss profile and overall equipment effectiveness (OEE)

Line 4 has 136 hours per week of shift cover.

Table 4.6 Weekly door-to-door (D2D) losses

Description	Current hours per week	6 months challenge at MS1
Rest breaks & team briefs	9	9
Shift handovers	3	3
Planned maintenance	2	2
Product starvation	3	1
Total D2D losses	17 hours	15 hours (D2D = 89%)

This means currently we have 119 loading hours remaining (136-17) to make product (a D2D Effectiveness of 87.5%). During those 119 hours we have equipment-based losses (floor-to-floor) as below:

Table 4.7 Equipment-based losses, floor-to-floor (F2F)

Description	Current hours per week	6 Months challenge at MS1
Breakdowns	6	3
Changeovers	13	6
Minor stops	20	10
Running at reduced speed	Not possible	-
Scrap-yield – rework	2.5%	2.0%
Rework & start-up losses	Included in scrap above	-
Total F2F losses	39 hrs + 97.5% quality	19 hrs + 98% quality

The first table illustrates a current situation of 136 hours of weekly shift cover where 17 hours are lost due to door-to-door issues and a further 39 hours and 2.5% scrap lost to the six classic equipment-based issues as shown. We also set an agreed – demanding but realistic – target to be achieved within six months of launching the TPM pilot project, before it moves beyond this audited milestone 1 stage into a PDCA continuous improvement process.

Table 4.8 Current and target OEE

Availability	Performance rate	Quality rate	OEE
Current OEE			
(119-19) /119 x 100%	(100-20) /100 x 100%	100%-2.5%	
84%	80%	97.5%	65.5%
Milestone 1 target OEE (6months)			
(121-9) /121 x 100%	(112-10) /112 x 100%	100%-2.0%	
93%	91%	98%	83%

Using the data and figures from Tables 4.6 and 4.7 we can calculate our current OEE in Table 4.8 as 65.5% and an agreed targeted OEE at the rate of 83% at Milestone 1. This would be a 27% improvement in productive capacity on a base of 65.5%. We can now present this as a business benefit illustrated below.

Summary & challenge

Current state

136 Shift cover hrs - 17 Non-productive hrs. (D2D) = 119 Loading hrs.

@ 65.5% effectiveness = 78.0 productive hrs per week

Future state at Milestone 1

136-15 (D2D) = 121 Loading hrs.

When we achieve a F2F OEE of 83.0%

Then productive hrs become 100.5 per week

A gain of 22.5 productive hrs per week or 1,125 hrs per year

(equivalent to a 27% increase in productive capacity on a base of 65.5%)

Current Unit Cost of 23.0 c/kilo would become 18.4 c/kilo (validated by head of finance)

Plus the ability to absorb 20% planned volume increase

Based on 180 tonne per week this is worth $414k per year to the business

The key message to stress here is that this potential benefit of $414k direct contribution per year will give a basis for cost justification to cover project funding including likely refurbishment costs, training time costs, and any external costs. The other point to remember is that moving from an OEE of 65.5% to 83% gives a choice to make more in the same time, make the same in less time, or a combination of the two. This gives flexibility not enjoyed when you are stuck at 65.5%.

4.7 **Scoping study feedback to the site leadership team**

This is the final part of the scoping study where the objectives of the one-day site leadership 'buy-in' workshop are to review the outputs of this essential planning phase (as illustrated in Figure 4.5, steps 8 & 9 above) in order to

- gain the leadership team's commitment (and employee/trade union representatives if appropriate) to the TPM system in terms of priority, resource and likely pace
- familiarise the site leadership team with the principles of TPM and the implications of embarking on the recommended TPM programme
- review current plans and initiatives and how TPM fits into these and helps to deliver the business drivers
- define potential inhibitors to TPM and a statement of the resultant countermeasures to minimise these identified risks
- agree a future TPM vision for the site/plant/company
- set a policy framework to guide improvement and implementation
- define TPM programme governance & control system, including pillar champions
- agree to the immediate timing of the next steps of mobilising the TPM programme via the four-day TPM practitioner's workshop.

The final part of the site leadership team's 'buy-in' commitment to the TPM programme is achieved by getting the senior leadership team to address and answer two key questions:

1   From what we have learned today, what is TPM going to give us in terms of delivering our business imperatives that we are not already doing?
2   If it is significant, what is going to stop TPM taking hold and hence what are our countermeasures to minimise those risks?

Table **4.9** Impact of TPM on business drivers: Team A. *Impact: 0=none, 1=some, 2=significant, 3=major*

Business drivers	Potential impact of TPM –Team A
Profitability	3
Meet customer requests	3
Quality with compliance	2
Safety no 1	3
Enhanced reputation	3
Cost competitiveness	3
Increase market share	3
Reduce inventory	2
Increased OEE	3
Total score	25/27 = 93%

Table **4.10** Impact of TPM on business drivers: Team B *Impact: 0=none, 1=some, 2=significant, 3=major*

Business drivers	Potential impact of TPM –Team B
Reduced cost of production	3
Increased quality	3
Meet deliveries on time	2
Increased outputs/OEEs	3
Good safety record	2
Minimise inventory levels	2
Minimise lead times	2
Increased competitiveness	3
Total score	20/24 = 83%

Table 4.11 Key TPM blockers: Team A

Team A – Stoppers	Team A – Countermeasures
Lack of acceptance & buy-in	Engagement through education
	Building teams
Fear of change	Reassurance & involvement from start-up
Cost & people resources	Investment. Make resources available. Planning. Re-structuring. Have a budget & sign off
Unrealistic expectations	Milestone recognition
	Education, training & coaching
	Recognition for every improvement (big and small)
Poor communication/objective alignment	Ongoing communication
Ongoing communication	Put governance structure in place – regular SLT reviews

Table 4.12 Key TPM blockers: Team B

Team A —Stoppers	Team A—Countermeasures
People's attitude/ understanding	Relevant training & involvement: 'learning by doing'
Fear of change/new roles	Communication plan & cascade
Benefit not immediately apparent	Planning of work/publicise results
Poor teamwork	Improve understanding through coaching
Lack of perseverance/follow through	Persist through review and action + pillar champions
Lack of support/commitment from management	Provide necessary support/resources/budget v. compelling risk-assessed business case

Tables 4.9–4.12 are example outputs of addressing these two critical questions. We divided the senior leadership team into two syndicate groups and asked them to debate and then articulate the answers to the above questions and then share those responses with each other.

These two outputs are used as an essential reminder to senior leadership to continually revisit these 'statements of intent' at future TPM programme governance reviews, especially if there is evidence of programme drift or sub-optimal results as highlighted in the bi-annual top-down 30-point review process.

Some further important points to stress to the senior leadership team at the conclusion of this 'buy-in' workshop session are:

- **Plan for success**. TPM is not an 'add water and stir' initiative. The rollout plan has to be believable, with clearly identified resources of people, money and time linked to a properly thought-out and prepared business case. Failure to plan is planning for failure.

- **Understanding what TPM is – and equally, what it is not**. The subsequent four-day TPM practitioners event creates a critical mass of around 20 'disciples' who will then complete a 20-week TPM pilot project(s) cycle, audited and reviewed with the site leadership team before subsequent roll-out (see Chapter 5)

- **Badge the programme as Total Productive Manufacturing** to emphasize the need for teamwork between operators and maintainers rather than Total Productive Maintenance, which runs the risk of implying that it is a maintenance department-driven initiative.

- **Regular and relevant bottom-up evidence-based audit and review** processes set against clear milestone exit criteria. This is complemented by a twice-a-year top-down 30-point 'honesty check', each of which is pinned to a specific pillar champion – so there is no escape (see Chapter 7).

- **Recognize** that your business transformation programme may be revolutionary, but behavioural change is evolutionary. In our experience TPM in the right hands is one of the best examples of 'changing the way we do things here' and as such, we can accelerate behavioural change through involvement.

CHAPTER 5
The process of TPM

This chapter looks at the *Process* – the second of the three Ps – by explaining our 11-step TPM System, summarised in Figure 5.1.

The TPM System follows on from the scoping study and senior management 'buy-in' session described in Chapter 4. It is implemented via

- an initial four-day TPM Practitioners workshop,
- followed by launching initial TPM Pilots
- progressive plant-wide roll-out through four maturity milestones (the focus of Chapter 7).

Above all TPM is a practical 'learning by doing' activity including assessing the potential performance improvement opportunity, the current physical condition of the equipment –sometimes affectionately referred to as 'spot the rot' – and then, most importantly, how to *stop* the rot by restoring the equipment to an as-new condition and then keeping it in that condition for life by solving problems for good through recurrence prevention.

The outputs of this 11-step process are then used for an evidence-based audit and review assessment journey to validate the team's progress through the model – the essential people-development part, which is the focus of Chapter 7.

Purpose: Our TPM programme is applied via a defined introductory and deployment process within the business unit.

Process: Our TPM model is applied through a defined sequence of *learning by doing*.

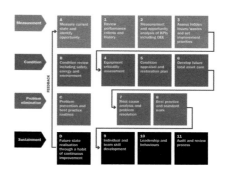

People: The outputs of this application are aligned to an evidence-based assessment process linked to the team's progress through the model.

Figure 5.1: The TPM System Model

5.1 **The need to develop effective teamwork**

The application of teamwork principles links to one of the core themes of this chapter: that the operator is the best condition monitor ever invented. Three everyday analogies may prove helpful:
- the motor car (using the senses)
- the healthy body (defining core competencies)
- the soccer team (creating the company wide team).

5.1.1 **The motor car**

A good analogy of using our senses, including common sense, is the way we look after our cars as a team effort between the operator (you, the owner and driver) and the maintainer (the garage maintenance mechanic).

As the operator of your motor car you take pride of ownership of this important asset. TPM strives to bring that sense of ownership and responsibility to the workplace.

When you, as the operator, take your car to the garage with a problem, the first thing the mechanic will seek is your view to what is wrong with the car (your machine). They will know that you are best placed to act as their senses – ears, eyes, nose, mouth and common sense. If you say, "Well, I'm not sure, but it smells of petrol and the engine is misfiring at 60 mph," they will probably say, "That's useful to know, but is there anything else you can tell me?" "Yes," you reply, "I've cleaned the plugs and checked the plug gaps." They won't be surprised that you carried out these basic checks, and certainly won't regard them as a mechanic-only job. "Fine," they might say, "and that didn't cure the problem?" "No," you reply, "so I tinkered with the timing mechanism!" "Serves you right then," says the mechanic "and now it will cost you time and money for me to put it right." In that final stage you, the operator, went beyond your level of competence and actually hindered the team effort. TPM is about getting a balanced team effort between operators and maintainers – both experts in their own right, but prepared to co-operate as a team.

As the operator of your car you know it makes sense to clean it – not because you are neurotic about having a clean car, but because cleaning is inspection, which is spotting deterioration before it becomes catastrophic.

The example in Table 5.1 shows the power of this operator ownership. In the routine car checks described, our senses of sight, hearing, touch and smell are used to detect signs which may have implications for safety, inconvenience, damage, or the need for repairs or replacements. None of the 27 checks in the table requires a spanner or a screwdriver, but 17 of them (*in italic*) have implications for safety. The analogy with TPM's 'condition appraisal and condition monitoring' activity is clear: failure of the operator to be alert to their machine's condition can threaten safety and lead to consequential damage, inconvenience, low productivity and high cost.

We are highly conscious of changes in our cars' conditions and performance using our senses. This is made easier for us by clear instruments and good access to parts which need regular attention. We need to bring this thinking into our workplace.

Table 5.1 Front line operator asset care (FLOAC). An example of using our senses

Routine checks	
Tyre pressure – extended life, safety	eyes
Oil level – not red light	eyes
Coolant level – not red light	eyes
Battery – not flat battery	eyes
Cleaning the car – using your eyes	

Table 5.1 Front line operator asset care (FLOAC). An example of using our senses

Spot rust	eyes
Minor scratch	eyes
Minor dent	eyes
Tyres wearing unevenly	eyes
Water in exhaust pipe	eyes
Worn wipers	eyes
Rubber perishing – trims	eyes
Oil leak	eyes
Suspension	eyes
Other conditions when driving	
Steering drag	eyes, touch
Wheel bearing	ears
Clutch wear	ears, touch
Brake wear	ears, touch
Exhaust	ears
Engine misfire	ears, touch
Engine overheat	nose
Petrol leak	nose
One driver to another	
Exhaust smoke	eyes
Front/rear lights	eyes
Stop lights	eyes
Indicators	eyes
Soft tyre	eyes
Rear door not shut	eyes

5.1.2 **A healthy body**

Figure 5.2 shows our second analogy, which is that healthy equipment is like a healthy body. It is also a team effort between operator (the nurse) and maintainer (the doctor). Looking after equipment falls into three main categories:

1   **Cleaning and inspection** The daily prevention or 'apple a day', which prevents accelerated deterioration or wear and highlights changes in condition. The operator can do most or all of these tasks where a technical judgement is not needed. In TPM these are front-line operator asset checks (FLOACs).

2   **Checks and monitoring** Measure deterioration or use the thermometer, which highlights trends or changes in performance. The operator supports the maintainer by acting as their ears, eyes, nose, mouth and common sense, so allowing the maintainer to concentrate on the critical diagnostic tasks.

3   **Planned maintenance** Treat before breakdown: prevent failure by reacting to changes in condition and performance. The maintainer still does most of these tasks under TPM because they have the technical skill and/or technical judgement required.

Daily prevention

Routine service
Clean
Adjust
Inspect
FLOACs

Measure deterioration

Monitoring & prediction
**Condition-based
monitoring**

Interject before breakdown

Timely preventative
maintenance
**Fixed interval PM
schedules**

Figure 5.2: Healthy equipment is like a healthy body

Under TPM the operator and maintainer determine the routines in each category. The central message of the necessary culture and behaviours to drive TPM is: 'If you ask our opinion as an operator or maintainer and that opinion is embodied in the way we do things for the future, then we will stick with it because it is our idea.'

In other words, with right guidance, those who do the work are in the best position to both define and then refine the work content and hence the core competencies required.

5.1.3 **The soccer team**

This third analogy of the football or soccer team emphasizes the critical aspect of teamwork. At every stage in the development of asset care and condition monitoring strategy, teamwork and total co-operation – without jealousy or suspicion – are essential to success. Figure 5.3 shows how teams can function at maximum efficiency with minimum losses.

The defenders are the maintenance technicians, the production operators are the attackers. However – as in any modern football team – the operators spend 80 per cent of their time in attack and the other 20 per cent of their time in defence, helping to stop a goal being scored. Similarly, the maintenance technician spends 80 per cent of their time in defence, but the other 20 per cent in attack, helping to score a goal. They are both experts in their respective positions but they are prepared and willing to co-operate – to be versatile and help each other.

There is no hidden agenda to get the production operator to do the maintainer's job –neither is it a hidden agenda to do the maintainer out of a job.

Both types of players are only as good as the proactive support they get from the outer ring – the coach, the manager, the physiotherapist, and so on. These key contacts are on the touchline waiting to support us as and when required. They are not up in the grandstand or – even worse – not turning up for the game. As such the core TPM team must have the proactive support of the designers, engineers, quality control, production scheduling, employee representatives and management.

The facilitator, or coach, is there to guide and to help the whole process work effectively. People are central to TPM. We 'own' the assets of the plant and we are, therefore, responsible for asset management and care. Operators, maintainers, equipment specifiers, designers and planners must work as a team and actively seek creative solutions which will eliminate both waste and equipment-related quality problems once and for all.

One thing is for sure in the modern world class game: if we do not co-operate, we will certainly get relegated. The core team of the operator and maintainer together with their shift team leaders will invite functional help onto the manufacturing floor when they need it and everyone will co-operate to maximize equipment effectiveness by eliminating waste. Without this willingness to co-operate and trust, the team will not win.

Figure 5.3: The TPM football team

By the way, you cannot play football on a poor surface or pitch. So in our game of TPM, the core team with help from the key contacts also take responsibility for the condition of the pitch – in other words the 5S workplace organisation to help create flow on the field of play.

Teams need a playbook. In TPM it's provided by the 11-step process shown in Figure 5.4.

5.2 **The 11-step TPM process**

Operational Excellence will remain an elusive goal if we don't have '*Operational Basics*' in place.

Operational Excellence and its associated 'Lean Thinking' is the speed and pace with which we receive a customer's order and convert it into profit by eliminating waste in all that we do.

To help achieve this, we adopt **5S workplace organisation** (WPO) aimed at creating the necessary **flow** around our critical assets. 5S and WPO are explained in detail in Chapter 1.10. TPM is about maintaining that flow through those critical assets by focusing on asset reliability plus predictability of performance. This means we need to have a system and process that allows us to validate, then stabilize, then optimize our manufacturing processes

It comprises a set of eight sequential equipment-based steps which are underpinned with a further three behavioural steps that the teams work through as part of their TPM activity.

The 11-step TPM system provides a systematic approach which is practical and focused on 'learning by doing'. It
- is time-tabled and scheduled (and hence non-optional)
- encourages wide engagement, both bottom up and top down
- has clear roles, responsibilities and expectations
- is proven to be sustainable in the right hands.

The TPM process allows us to take the vision and values off the notice board and hand it to the manufacturing staff and say with some conviction: "here you are – you can make a difference with this TPM enabling tool."

One of the best definitions of TPM that we encourage to be used is that it allows us to 'Unlock our installed productive capacity by unlocking the full potential of our people'.

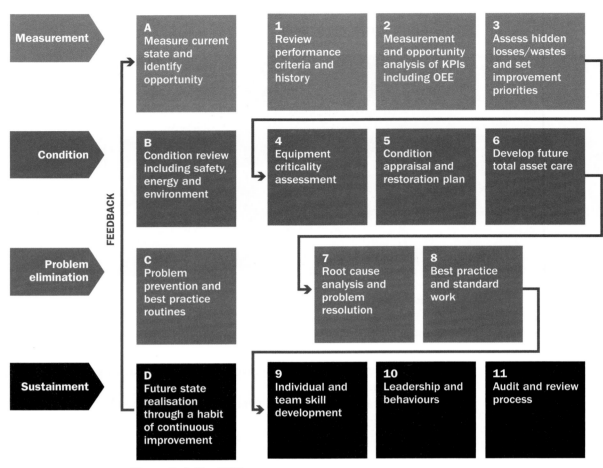

Figure 5.4: The TPM process

The initial eight equipment-based steps enable the operator and maintainer team to

- understand the equipment
- measure the opportunity for improvement and then, through analysis and debate, to
- fix and restore the condition of the equipment to an 'as new' condition
- keep it in that as-new condition as defined in the future total asset care routines and also
- resolve the underlying problems once and for all with the '100-year fix'.

Taking each of the eight steps in more detail:

5.3 **The measurement cycle**

The current state measurement cycle comprises three steps.

Step 1 – Review performance criteria and history

The TPM team collects process and equipment history and then ranks these sources of information according to their comprehensiveness, accuracy and trustworthiness. The TPM team also establishes if they need to design and trial an overall equipment effectiveness (OEE) shift log sheet.

Table 5.2 shows an example of the outputs together with the key learning points of this step.

Table 5.2 Example STEP 1 Sources of information
1 = Poor, **2** = Fair, **3** = Adequate, 4 = Very good, 5 = Excellent

Source	How comprehensive?	How trustworthy?
SAP	4	**1** to 5
Efficiency files (AO1 only)	**3**	**3**
Kissler monitor (E14 only)	4	4 to 5
Operator log book	**3**	**2**
Maintenance log book	**2** to **3**	**2** to **3**
Tool history log	**3** to 4	**3** to 4
Materials handling system	**3**	5
Robot history (E14 only)	**3**	Rarely used
OEM manuals	4 to 5	**2**
Operator knowledge	**1** to 5	**1** to 5
Maintainer knowledge	**1** to 5	**1** to 5
M/c history single page	**1**	5
SORT-suspect parts	4	4
Spares usage	5	5
Daily activity sheet	**3** to 4	**3** to 4
Daily management board	**3**	**1** to 5
Material cycle count	4	4
Process change management	4	**3**

Key learning points of Step 1

The operator and maintainer team brainstorm and review every different information source (see Table 5.2) in terms of their variety, their comprehensiveness and their integrity or trustworthiness. The number of 1, 2 and 3 rankings is surprisingly high with too few 4s and 5s.

They also subject each source to the ECRS (eliminate-combine-replace-simplify) challenge and ask

- what sources can we eliminate or combine and, if not,
- can we replace it with something smarter or at least simplify it ?

The final challenge is to ask

- can we extract the OEE metric from these sources or do we need to design and implement an OEE shift log sheet?

Step 2 – Measurement and opportunity analysis of key performance indicators (KPIs) and OEE

As shown in the example at Table 5.3, the TPM team define the OEE potential at three levels:

- Current average OEE, our reference or start point
- Best of the best OEE, an interim and believable target
- Future 'world class' OEE level.

Key learning points of Step 2

What is the best of the best and then world class levels of OEE worth to us?

In the Table 5.3 example, the asset is planned to be manned for 168 hours per week. So

- at 70 per cent OEE we only achieve (0.70 x 168)= 118 productive hours/week
- at 84 per cent OEE we can achieve (0.84 x 168)= 141 productive hours/week

This yields an extra 23 productive hours/week or 1150 hours per year – flexibility to make choices at 84 per cent OEE that we do not enjoy at 70 per cent OEE.

In other words, in a cost-down scenario we can make the same output units for 20 per cent less input, or in a growth scenario, we can make 20 per cent more output for the same input.

Table 5.3 Self-assessment example

	Availability %	Performance rate %	Quality rate %	OEE %
	Breakdowns Setups/ changeovers	Running at reduced speed Minor stops & idling	Scrap rework Startup losses	
Current 4 weeks average OEE	80	90	97	70
4 weeks best of best (BoB)	90 (Wk 1)	95 (Wk 2)	98 (Wks 1, 4)	84
World class	95	96	99	90
Difference between current average & BoB is (14/70) x 100% **= 20% real improvement in productive capacity**				

The notion of a best of the best (BoB) OEE is very powerful and in the example shown in Table 5.3, the BoB figures are 90 per cent availability (week 1), 95 per cent performance rate (week 2), and 98 per cent quality rate (weeks 1 and 4), giving a BoB of 84 per cent.

What is stopping us achieving the best of best consistently? The answer is… we are not in control of the six big losses shown in Figure 5.5.

By first gaining control and then stabilising the equipment processes through teamwork and problem solving we will hit our BoB consistently. This in turn will lead on towards optimising our equipment processes and hence move towards our world-class OEE level of 90 per cent through the progressive elimination of the six big equipment losses.

We can also calculate that when we hit world-class levels of 90 per cent OEE, the benefit is worth 1650 extra productive hours a year.

Based on our current sources of information and an analysis of existing data we have been able, through debate, discussion and reiteration, to

■ calculate a current average OEE
■ set an interim credible best of best OEE target
■ define our ultimate world class level of OEE
■ calculate the value of additional productive hours per week when our BoB is achieved (worth 1150 productive hours a year)
■ recognise that this potential value will help to make a compelling business case to implement TPM and justify the cost of completing our Step 5b) refurbishment plan.

Step 3 - Assess hidden losses/wastes and set improvement priorities

In this step we brainstorm the reasons why the OEE is at its current 70 per cent average level by populating the fishbone diagram as shown in Figure 5.5 under the six classic losses. The TPM team will revisit this step several times as they progressively build up their knowledge via analysis of the shift-by-shift and hence daily/weekly OEE data sheets. Event frequencies and actual time(s) lost or taken per event will be able to be added to the fishbone. Also, in addition to the six classic equipment-based 'floor-to-floor' losses, the team will be recording and hence differentiating the door-to-door management losses.

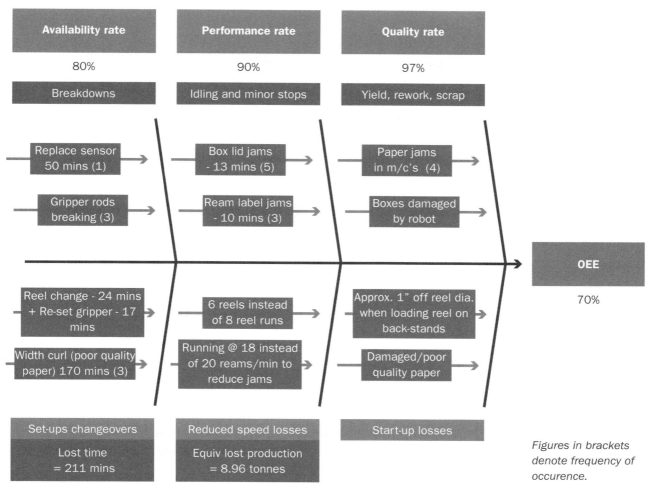

Figure 5.5: The classic 'floor-to-floor' equipment-based losses

5.4 **The condition cycle**

Let's now take a closer look at steps 4, 5 and 6 of the condition cycle to understand the key learning points – all of which centre on 'learning by doing'.

Step 4 – Carry out a criticality assessment of the equipment

See the example output sheet in Figure 5.6.

This step will help you understand how the equipment functions and which parts of the machine and process are the most critical.

In this step we go to the physical asset and list and assess all the elements on that asset from major sub-assemblies down to replacement part level. This lets us work out their potential impact on the classic six equipment-based losses – and therefore which elements need to be kept in optimum condition. The key outputs and learning points of this step include

- building teamwork between operators and maintainers
- better understanding of the equipment functionality (how it works)
- providing a checklist for the condition appraisal (Step 5a)
- give a focus for future total asset care (Step 6)
- highlighting safety – and environmentally critical items
- assessing the potential impact on OEE
- highlighting weaknesses regarding ease of operation and ease of maintenance

■ challenging the perceived wisdom of currently accepted inherent reliability factors.

EQUIPMENT DESCRIPTION	\multicolumn{9}{c}{1-3 RANKING AS IMPACT ON:}
	S	A	P	Q	R	M	E	C	TOT
1. Hoist	3	3	2	1	1	3	1	3	17
2. Matcon Discharge station	2	3	3	1	3	3	3	3	21
3. Vacuum Transfer system	1	2	2	3	1	1	2	2	14
4. Hopper & screw feeds	1	3	3	3	1	1	3	3	18
5. Stirring Motor x 2	1	3	3	2	1	1	1	3	15
6. Dosing Auger x 2	1	3	3	3	1	1	2	3	17
7. Vibrator	1	3	3	3	1	1	3	2	17
8. Dosing Funnel x 2	1	3	3	3	3	3	2	3	21
9. Aspirator	1	3	3	3	1	1	3	3	18
10. Top Sealing plate	3	3	3	3	1	1	2	3	19
11. Code block (Filling)	2	3	3	3	1	1	1	2	16
12. Foil cutting	3	3	3	3	1	1	2	2	18
13. Suction cups/Pick 'n Place	1	3	3	2	1	1	1	1	13
14. Toothed transfer belt	2	3	3	3	1	3	1	2	18
15. Green Belt transfer	3	3	3	3	1	3	1	2	19
16. Collator/Magazine	3	3	2	1	3	3	1	3	19
17. Foil Holder – loading foil holder	2	3	3	2	1	1	1	2	15
18. Foil Pulling & guiding system	1	3	3	3	1	1	1	2	15
19. Foil Perforation	1	3	3	3	1	1	1	2	15
20. Foil bottom seal	3	3	3	3	1	1	1	2	17
21. Foil separator	1	3	3	3	3	3	2	2	20

Where:

S = Safety
A = Availability
P = Performance
Q = Quality
R = Reliability
M = Maintainability
E = Environment
C = Cost

Rating Scale
1 = No or Little Impact
2 = Significant Impact
3 = Major Impact

LEGEND
A,P,Q over 3
Reliability over 3
Safety over 3
Over 20 total
Highest total

Figure 5.6: Example of a typical criticality assessment output sheet

As shown in Figure 5.7 the operators and their maintenance colleagues become far more equipment conscious. They now understand how the equipment works.

The assessment also highlights the impact of safety, reliability, environment and the OEE, and hence focuses on parts that need to be kept in optimum condition as part of Step 6 (together with Steps 7 and 8).

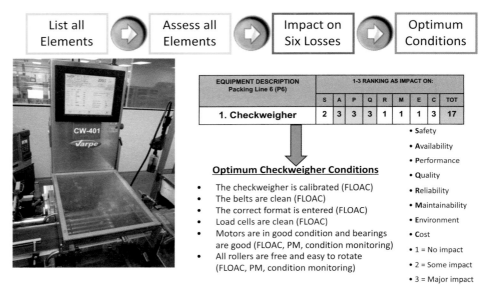

Figure 5.7: The criticality assessment output process

Step 5a – Carry out a conditional appraisal – affectionately known as 'spot the rot'

In this step the TPM team go to the machine/physical asset and systematically inspect every square centimetre for deterioration and refurbishment needs, looking particularly for

■ dirty or neglected equipment (debris and/or dust particles)
■ disconnected hoses

- missing nuts and bolts producing visible instability
- steam or air leaks
- air filters that need cleaning
- jammed valves
- hydraulic, lubricating and oil leaks
- measuring instruments broken and/or too dirty to read
- abnormal noises in pumps, compressors and motors.

The team pays particular attention to critical components identified in Step 4 above: they will need to be kept in optimum condition.

As well as the team seeing the equipment running in its operating environment the equipment itself also needs to be stopped for this exercise, with panels removed and electrically isolated.

The teams are encouraged to be obsessive (in a positive way) about attention to detail:

- If this asset was back in my home and my livelihood depended on it, would I allow it to be in this state?
- No matter how small, incidental or apparently trivial, if it's not as you would expect it or want, then list it!
- Take close-up photographs to illustrate your examples.
- Include the workplace organisation as well as the equipment itself.
- When you think you've finished, look again and find ten more things wrong it.

Table 5.4 is a typical condition appraisal/spot the rot summary of two syndicate teams' outputs from just a one hour visit to the equipment shown in the figure during the TPM four-day practitioner's workshop. Imagine what they found when they spent one whole TPM activity day during the actual comprehensive condition appraisal as a key step in the 20-week cycle of the TPM pilot project.

Table 5.4 Spot the rot summary

Asset	Total issues	Safety issues	Environment issues	High OEE impact	Medium OEE impact	Low OEE impact	Cum OEE impact
Line 1: input side	25	15	2	5	5	9	19
Line 1: output side	55	14	7	6	3	20	29
Total Line 1	80	29	9	11	8	29	48
Total of 80 issues of which... 36% are potential safety issues, 11% environmental issues and 60% perceived as having a potentially negative impact on the OEE							

During the on-the-job training, the key learning points from this exercise are to stress:

- TPM is about positive obsessive attention to detail.
- We are just using our senses of look, listen, smell, feel/touch *and* discuss.
- Even the smallest thing wrong can develop into a major problem. At best it will stay as it is. At worst and most likely it will deteriorate – and it certainly won't get better on its own.
- Use photographic evidence as a reminder of 'before TPM'.
- Spotting what's wrong is only half of the solution. Correcting the problem with a permanent '100-year fix' solution is the other half (see Steps 5b, 6, 7 and 8)
- Many small problems have potential safety and/or environmental issues.
- A significant proportion will eventually impact on the OEE.
- In the real TPM, 'cleaning is inspection ... is spotting deterioration ... is catching it before it becomes catastrophic ... is pride in the workplace ... is a hassle-free shift ... resulting in pride of ownership.

Step 5b – Carry out the refurbishment plan

The purpose of this step is to restore the equipment to an 'as new' condition.

This is achieved by setting up a repair and replacement plan, based on the condition appraisal (Step 5a).

The plan will provide a detailed summary of actions to be co-ordinated by the team and will include

- dates and timescales
- resources (labour, materials, time and hence money)
- responsibilities
- control and feedback (the management of change via PDCA).

To help plan and complete refurbishment tasks, it is helpful to categorise them into three work packages:

1   On the run (low cost/easy to do, requiring no outage of the asset/machine)
2   Minor planned outage (8 to 24 hours)
3   Major planned outage (involving redesign/fabrication/external vendors).

It is also useful to plot a weekly/monthly tracker chart as illustrated in Figure 5.8 so that everyone walking past the TPM activity board can see, at a glance, that real progress is being made.

The key learning points of this step are:

- Restore to 'as new' condition, before improving.
- The need for a progress tracker.
- Now able to justify cost/benefit via OEE best of best additional productive hours (see Chapter 4 section 4.6 for an explanation and example).

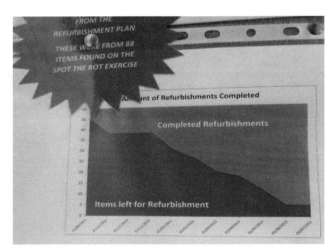

Figure 5.8: Refurbishment progress tracker

Step 6 – Future total asset care

The purpose of this step is to develop and implement relevant and comprehensive routines to ensure the refurbishment gains of Step 5b) are sustained and that it doesn't fall back into the same state. See Figure 5.9. This covers the three categories of

- front-line operator asset care checks (autonomous maintenance),
- condition based monitoring routines
- fixed interval inspections and planned maintenance schedules.

As stated earlier, the whole philosophy around TPM is centred on teamwork between the operator and the maintenance technician by taking shared responsibility for the health and reliability of their equipment assets.

So we need to view and consider both roles together in order to define who does what – and hence the why, when and how.

We also encourage the analogy that healthy equipment is just like a healthy body. In this scenario the operator is the nurse of the asset (the patient) and the technician is the doctor (and occasionally the surgeon) of the asset.

In order to keep the equipment to its restored state and standard, it is vital to divide the Total asset care into three elements:-

- **Front line operator asset care checks.** Abbreviated to FLOACs and carried out on a shift or day-by-day or even weekly basis-not requiring spanners or screwdrivers but making maximum use of visual indicators ,in order to make it easy to do right, and difficult to do wrong. The operator therefore starts to carry out the more interesting tasks and progressively expand their knowledge and capability. We will look at these aspects in more detail in Chapter 7 and how the four 'maturity' milestones of our TPM journey align to the classic seven steps of autonomous maintenance.
- **Condition based monitoring.** Abbreviated to CBM routines, selectively applied using the well proven techniques – now aided by the rapidly emerging technologies of the fourth industrial revolution – which are carried out to pinpoint significant equipment degradation trends. These techniques, referred to as NDT (non-destructive testing), can include, for example:
  - Ultrasonic inspection as vibration monitoring
  - Thermography
  - Magnetic-particle inspection as oil debris analysis
  - Leak tightness control
  - Eddy-current testing
  - Remote visual inspection
  - Dye penetrate inspection
  - Radiographic testing

The philosophy of TPM also recognises that the best condition monitor ever invented is the operator using their own senses of look, listen, feel and touch-(with the safety proviso that initially this excludes anything electrical)

- **Planned maintenance schedules.** Referred to as PMs: usually a combination of fixed interval and/or post inspections, and include spares provisioning

There are four major benefits of this overall asset care teamwork approach for the maintenance technician

1   They can now spend more time on design and engineering out problems.
2   Less work is outsourced.
3   More knowledge and ability is developed in-house.
4   The technicians themselves will feel more motivated and more valued.

There's a lot more detail of course, but this is the essence – and it's worth reminding ourselves also to stress three factors about those front line operator asset care checks:

1   They quite probably don't get done by anyone at the moment (so it's not a hidden agenda to get the operator to do the maintainer's job).
2   They do not involve using any spanners or screwdrivers – far less voltmeters.
3   The checks are developed by both the operator *and* the maintenance technician – who also helps train the operators to carry them out via single point lessons and standard work (Step 8).

The condition cycle can be summarised as Figure 5.9. This shows how Step 4, criticality assessment, Step 5a, condition appraisal, and Step 5b, refurbishment, are the essential inputs to formulate the future Step 6 – total asset care plan. It also shows how this links to the Step 8 best practice and the standard work part of the problem prevention cycle described in Section 5.5.

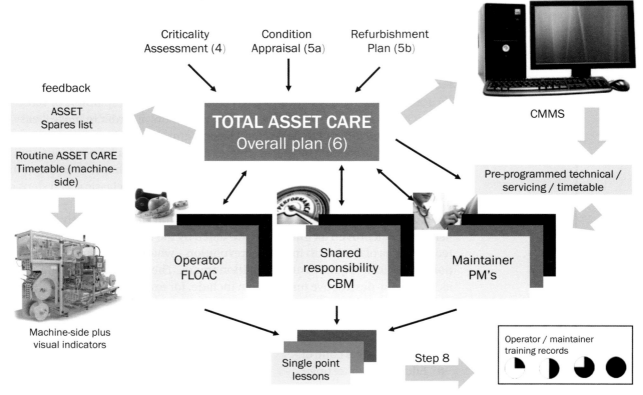

Figure 5.9: Developing future total asset care: asset care lists, inspection and planned maintenance

5.5 The problem prevention cycle

This cycle has two steps: root cause analysis and problem resolution, followed by developing best practice and standard work.

Step 7: Root cause analysis and problem resolution

Here the task is to identify and implement permanent improvements via root cause analysis and problem prevention. This will comprise low-cost/no-cost solutions and also technical and support solutions, which are then standardised with the '100-year fix' solutions so that it feeds back to Step 2 and becomes a sustained improvement in the OEE.

Among other classic problem-solving techniques, we encourage using a very simple, yet effective, event analysis format as illustrated in Figure 5.10.

This format can be used for breakdowns, minor stoppages or repetitive quality issues. It is a single page with a unique identifier which is owned by one member of the TPM team. It not only aims to solve the immediate problem via a 'five whys' format but also, and perhaps more importantly, changes to

- existing asset care routines (Step 6)
- single point lesson/standard work (Step 8)

as countermeasures to prevent recurrence of that same problem.

EVENT ANALYSIS FORM (inc SPL)

PLANT NO	*Rotor 101*	**LINE NO**	*7*
PRODUCT	*Gold 87*		

Opened Date/Shift	*06/07/17 Nights*
Briefing Date	*07/07/17*
Owner	*Jim Broadbent MT*

EVENT REF	BRIEF DESCRIPTION OF FAULT AND PROBLEM DEFINITION:	
R79	*Drive wheel seized, timing belt stripped as a result*	
HOW LONG AGO COULD THIS DEFECT HAVE BEEN DETECTED?		
Probably 1 month plus		
	REASON	**Notes/Clarification**
WHY? 1	*Lack of lubrication/fibres and material in bearings*	*Need to prevent fibres getting into panel*
WHY? 2	*Not routinely cleaned or lubricated*	*Belt condition not checked either although it is on PM list*
WHY? 3	*Components behind guard - Out of sight, Out of mind*	*Reduce time needed to inspect/ease of inspection*
WHY? 4	*Critical nature of belt drive not appreciated*	*Single Point Lesson needed here*
WHY? 5		
SHORT TERM ACTIONS :	*Replace bearing belt*	
PRIORITY FOR REVIEW	*Make it easy to check and look after drive gear*	

PROPOSED COUNTERMEASURE(S) TO PREVENT REOCCURRENCE		STATUS
MODIFICATION TO OPERATOR/ MAINTAINER PRACTICE/TRAINING	*Belt drive care/inspection SPL*	◑
IMPROVED Routine Activities	*Introduce routine cleaning*	◑
Check/Prediction	*Introduce daily Ammeter load plus stretch check*	◑
Planned Maintenance	*Only needed if condition is highlighted by Operator*	◑
Component Modification	*Transparent panel plus plunger to provide stretch check*	◑
OTHER	*Minor refurbishment required*	◑

◑ Agreed   ◐ Planned   ◕ Implemented   ● Confirmed

Figure 5.10: Event analysis example and format

Problem-solving and recurrence-prevention in TPM use a mindset referred to as P-M analysis as illustrated in Figure 5.11. The thought processes go like this...

There are four Ps of ongoing Problems with this equipment which are based on Phenomena which are Physical that can be Prevented because they are due to interactions of the five Ms of Materials & Mother nature, Machines, Methods and Manpower and, in order to make progress, we need a 6th M of Measurement.

The P-M Analyses process can be defined by these 11 logical prompts which the TPM team are coached to do during this step:

1. Understand how the mechanism is supposed to work (criticality assessment) (Step 4).
2. Restore before renew – solve existing problems before introducing new equipment which will have new problems (Step 5b).
3. Make all aware of the problem/opportunity.
4. Observe current situation <u>and</u> take measurements.
5. Define the problem in physical terms and identify factors which contribute to its occurrence.
6. Develop optimum solutions for all contributory factors.
7. Try out ideas first and check the results.
8. Apply proven low-cost or no-cost solutions first.
9. Implement ideas as soon as possible.
10. Standardise best practice with all those involved.
11. Monitor and review.

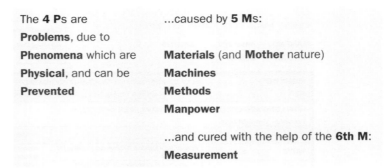

The **4 Ps** are	...caused by **5 Ms**:
Problems, due to	
Phenomena which are	**Materials** (and **Mother** nature)
Physical, and can be	**Machines**
Prevented	**Methods**
	Manpower
	...and cured with the help of the **6th M**:
	Measurement

Figure 5.11: The four Ps and six Ms of P-M analysis

The key learning points of Step 7 can be summarised as
- recognise the importance of the P-M mindset of the four Ps and six Ms
- use the event analysis form to not only solve the problem but also to prevent re-occurrence with the '100-year fix'
- use the strong links back to solve highlighted issues on the Step 3 fishbone
- use 'ask why?' five times or A3, DMAIC and FMEA tools to deliver the 100-year fix mentality.

Step 8: Develop best practice and standard work

Operate, maintain and support the asset across all shifts as standard work using single point lessons and associated skills training matrices.

In terms of developing 'best practice' we need to move from the typical 70 per cent firefighting to no more than 20 per cent through systematic continuous improvements, as illustrated in Figure 5.12.

Research suggests that in any company or operation, the 70 per cent fire fighting has two main causes.
- 95 per cent or more is due to lack of effective communication or a lack of adherence to standards. Perhaps no standards actually exist. Most likely there is no time to deliver the '100-year fix' solution.
- This leaves just five per cent or less of 'new' first-time-occurrence issues.

Einstein suggested that repeating the same behaviours over and over again and expecting a different result is one way of defining insanity. We need to break the cycle.

We can then set and consistently communicate best practices, shared knowledge and new standards to vastly reduce the firefighting of these unplanned events.

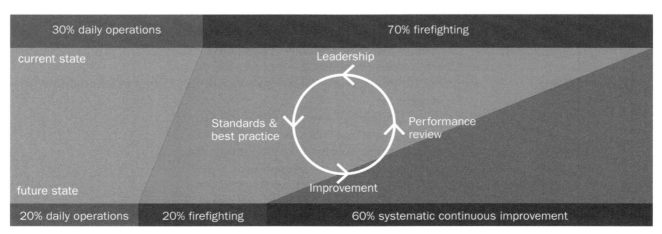

Figure 5.12: Developing best practice reduces firefighting from 70% to 20% of people's time

The key learning points of Step 8 are very simple to express:
- there is only one 'best way'
- visually describe that best way with single point lessons (see Figure 5.13)
- define your skill requirement for each best practice routine and produce a skills gap analysis to track progress via a skills matrix (see Figure 5.14)
- manage the whole process by adopting the standard work philosophy.

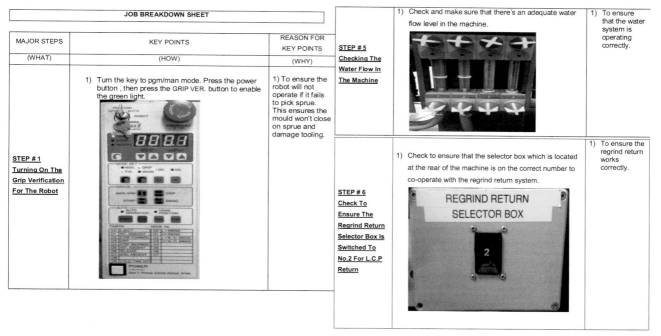

Figure 5.13: Single point lesson example

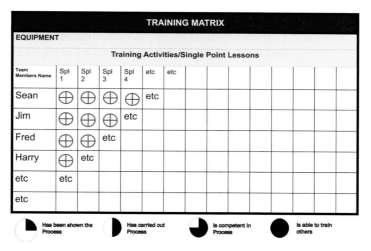

Figure 5.14: Skills training matrix capability tracker

5.6 **Eliminating unplanned events – the reality**

Within the 'TPM community' it is generally accepted that for every 100 unplanned equipment-related events, breakdowns, minor stoppages or quality defects:
- 40 per cent can be eliminated by refurbishing and restoring equipment to its optimum standard conditions (the second part of Step 5 above)

- 20 per cent can be eliminated by applying appropriate front-line operator asset care checks (the first part of Step 6) and best-practice routines of operation (underpinned as standard work in Step 8)
- 25 per cent can be eliminated by applying regular and relevant condition monitoring and planned maintenance (the second and third part of Step 6)
- 15 per cent can be eliminated by designing out physical weaknesses in the equipment (a key part of Step 7).

We often think that 85 per cent of our problem is that the equipment is out of date, outmoded and hence of a bad design. The reality however is that nearer 85 per cent of the problem is that we have not looked after it. This leaves just 15 per cent design improvement opportunities.

It is also essential to remember that you will not sustain the 40 per cent refurbishment gains *unless* you underpin it with your newly defined asset care regime.

5.7 Launching your TPM pilot project program

In Chapter 4 we described the essential initial scoping study and the senior management 'buy-in' session. The next step is to get a critical mass of TPM practitioners equipped to launch the initial TPM pilots and move towards subsequent roll-out.

We start this process via a four-day TPM practitioners workshop.

5.7.1 Practitioner's four-day TPM workshop

The objectives of the four-day TPM practitioner's workshop are
1 To provide a thorough understanding of TPM and how to put it into practice
2 To provide a framework and understanding for facilitators so they can work in, and influence the behaviour of, multi-discipline, multi-interest teams.

At least 70 per cent of the workshop is focused on carrying out the four-cycle, 11-step TPM improvement process on your own 'live' operations and assets on-site. Delegates experience the on-the-job reality of putting TPM techniques into practice, as a learning by doing activity.

It is vital for the delegates to appreciate that the purpose of the workshop is not to get an immediate kaizen-type result – it is to experience each of the eight equipment steps in detail. They will get some results, but the purpose is to fully understand what's coming over the next 16 to 20 weeks when we launch the TPM pilot projects and move towards a Milestone 1 audit.

Attendees should comprise
- team leaders and shift team members (operators and maintainers)
- proposed facilitators/trainers, pillar champions, unit managers process owners, group leads or similar, with executive responsibility
- change 'driver' – a middle manager or supervisor at the sharp end of the business, responsible for producing quality output from consistently highly reliable equipment
- specialists representing typically HSE, engineering, quality, production scheduling, HR and finance.

During the four days each TPM syndicate team (maximum of four teams) of about six people from multiple functions progressively builds a story board around the eight equipment steps as shown in Figure 5.15. The teams use this to feed back their findings and experience over the previous three days to their colleagues and to the site leadership team, who are invited to attend the feedbacks to show their visible support and commitment.

Figure 5.15: TPM activity board

5.7.2 **Launching TPM pilot projects**

The objectives of the initial follow-on TPM pilot projects are to
- prove the first eight equipment steps of the 11-step TPM process
- raise awareness of hidden losses, the techniques to eliminate them, and the value of doing so
- design, develop and implement a parallel clear and clean process using 5S philosophy to create flow, raise standards and begin the process of problem ownership
- establish performance and measurement to record progress for specific audit and review processes
- establish the infrastructure and governance to support eventual site-wide deployment of TPM, including pillar champion, subject matter experts and supervisory roles, responsibilities and expectations and hence TPM coaching needs.
- gain experience of the application of TPM principles and techniques contained within the TPM 11-step improvement plan including value stream mapping, precision changeovers, cost and loss deployment, and other focused improvement activities
- define the TPM continuous improvement master plan to guide priorities and transformation of the operation – often within the existing continuous improvement infrastructure (and certainly not instead of it).

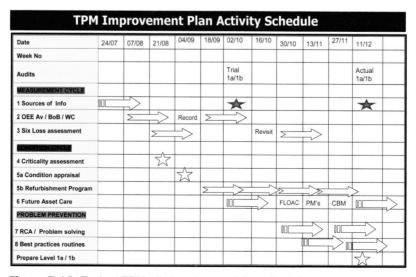

Figure 5.16: Typical TPM pilot project activity schedule

Figure 5.16 is an illustration of a typical TPM pilot project activity schedule. In this example the team has a fortnightly TPM activity day of eight hours covering 12 sessions over a period of 24 weeks, in order to progressively work through the eight equipment steps. The schedule includes a mid-term 'trial run' of the Level 1a and 1b evidence-based audit, so they know what to expect for the formal Milestone 1 close-out. Again, the site leadership team should be present at the close-out to celebrate the team's success, before moving on towards Milestones 2, 3 and 4.

5.7.3 OEE focused improvement project

You will probably need to set up a small working group for around three months to focus solely on how the OEE will be measured for the TPM pilot project. The group would typically be the manufacturing manager (as the OEE pillar champion) and the TPM facilitator along with representatives from plant engineering, production operations, finance and IT.

The group would use the pilot project learning experience to describe the why, what and how of a site-wide deployment of overall equipment effectiveness – at equipment level and as door-to-door management losses – as the principal metric within the TPM system.

OEE working group objectives

To analyse, evaluate, design and agree the parameters, data sources, standards, targets and procedures for regular recording and hierarchical reporting of overall equipment effectiveness for the individual key process elements and plant.

As a result of the outputs above, operations management should be better able to

- focus attention and action on the critical areas of process plant availability and productivity affecting unit costs and delivery performance
- focus on further and future potential project areas for TPM team leaders and their groups under the TPM programme.

Work programme and method

In order to achieve the above objectives it will be necessary to carry out the following programme of work (see Figure 5.17):

- Agree and set down the process logic and key sequences, dependencies and controlling factors affecting plant availability, throughput rates, product quality and associated costs profile from the beginning of the process through each key process element to completion
- Review, agree and set down common standards of terminology and definition regarding process operations, delay and fault codes and description
- Review, validate, agree and set down where necessary, standard operating procedures affecting process cycle times, ancillary operations and their frequencies
- Carry out a detailed reference period analysis covering a recent 3 to 6 month period, but excluding shutdowns (i.e. Christmas/New Year) or exceptional circumstances. This analysis will concentrate on data associated with 'delays to production report', weekly management meeting minutes and other relevant output, quality, adherence to schedules and other sources of information
- The above activities will allow a reference period data model to be built embracing all key manufacturing processes of 'actuals' compared to 'standards' and 'targets' which need to be agreed
- Define the data collection, analysis, presentation and review procedures for the specified individual plant/processes and overall equipment effectiveness measures

■ Pull all of the above together as a proposal for discussion, modification and subsequent adoption.

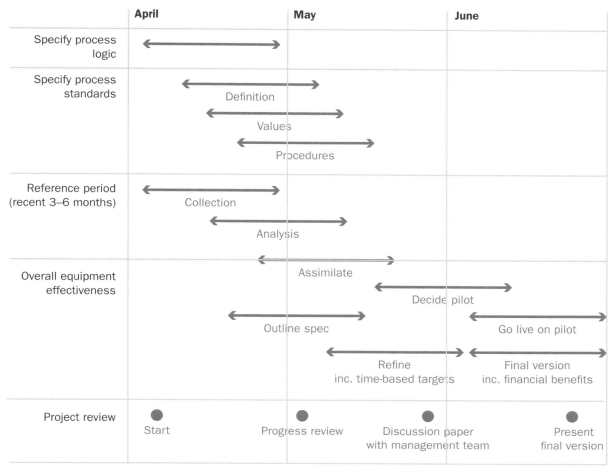

Figure 5.17: Typical OEE project definition programme

5.7.4 **Outputs and benefits**

As a result of the proposed programme of work, you will have specified and set out an agreed reporting system of overall equipment effectiveness which will

■ reflect the plant's performance in terms of availability (uptime/downtime), productivity (the efficiency of actual production running time) and quality (both in terms of yield and scrap and/or rework)

■ allow realistic target setting and performance trend monitoring to take place on a regular and highly visible basis

■ pinpoint areas of chronic poor performance and therefore facilitate effective TPM team-working

■ integrate into the site-wide policy deployment and performance targeting strategy as illustrated in Figure 5.17.

5.7.5 **What can TPM deliver by Milestone 1?**

Figure 5.18 illustrates the dramatic change in equipment condition before and after a successful TPM pilot at Milestone 1 over a 20 week TPM pilot project.

Figure 5.18: Before (left) and after TPM activity

5.8 **Roll-out evolution: from project to CI routine**

As we progress through the four milestones, the initial eight equipment-based steps – which are each comprehensively addressed in the TPM pilot project stage – move into a TPM routine phase, having successfully passed the Level 1A/1B evidence-based Milestone 1 audit.

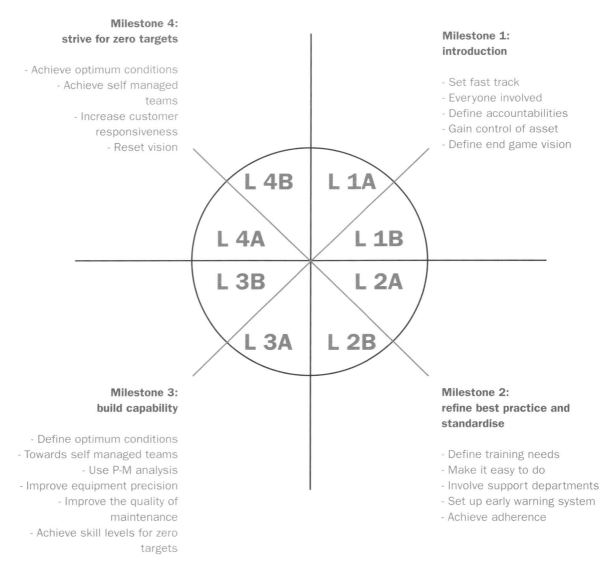

Milestone 4:
strive for zero targets

- Achieve optimum conditions
- Achieve self managed teams
- Increase customer responsiveness
- Reset vision

Milestone 1:
introduction

- Set fast track
- Everyone involved
- Define accountabilities
- Gain control of asset
- Define end game vision

L 4B L 1A

L 4A L 1B

L 3B L 2A

L 3A L 2B

Milestone 3:
build capability

- Define optimum conditions
- Towards self managed teams
- Use P-M analysis
- Improve equipment precision
- Improve the quality of maintenance
- Achieve skill levels for zero targets

Milestone 2:
refine best practice and standardise

- Define training needs
- Make it easy to do
- Involve support departments
- Set up early warning system
- Achieve adherence

Figure 5.19: The four maturity milestones of organisational learning

From Milestone 2 onwards the TPM activity becomes a regular routine following the typical PDCA cycle. The TPM team get together formally once a fortnight for a couple of hours to review the OEE (Step 2) and other metrics which will raise new problem prevention tactics and actions (as in Step 7). That may in turn modify or enhance the total asset care (Step 6) and best practice routines (Step 8). In essence just four of the eight equipment steps carry on as 'part of the way we do things here'.

The pillar champions have a vital and proactive role in showing their visible support for these TPM review activity sessions – not just in the initial eight-step TPM pilot projects but also for the ongoing PDCA TPM routine stage as roll-out progresses.

Figure 5.19 illustrates the bottom-up evidence-based audit review of the four maturity milestones and the key ways that progress manifests itself towards the four zero targets set at the launch stage: zero accidents, zero defects, zero breakdowns and zero interventions.

In Chapter 7 Section 5 we explore in detail how the bottom-up evidence-based audit process works in practice as a key part of the overall programme governance system.

5.9 What can TPM deliver by Milestone 2 ?

Table 5.5 is a cameo example of what TPM is capable of delivering in the right hands using the 11-step TPM system based on purpose, process and people at Milestone 2 – in this case achieved nine months from the TPM pilot launch date.

Table 5.5 Fill and packing line: Milestone 2 achievement

	12 months average reference point	Following 9 months 4-week moving average	Improvement
OEE	20.7%	49.5%	x2.5 increase
Equip failures	25.7%	4%	Down 85%
Idle time	38.0%	21.5%	Halved
No data	2.1%	0%	Eliminated
Line restraint	5.9%	0%	Eliminated
Minor stops	7.8%	2.7%	Down 65%
Actual vs target (production plan)	73%	100%	100% OTIF

5.10 Ensuring on-going success

As described above in Section 5.7.2 – Launching TPM pilot projects – each of the eight equipment steps are progressively worked through (typically in 24 weeks) to a successful conclusion, which is validated by passing the Milestone 1 Level 1a and 1b audit 20 checkpoint criteria before progressing towards Milestone 2 and beyond.

The TPM system application on that specific equipment, asset, line, or value stream moves from a project-based activity covering all eight steps to plan-do-check-act, where only four of the original steps carry on as a continuous improvement process. This transition is illustrated in Figure 5.20.

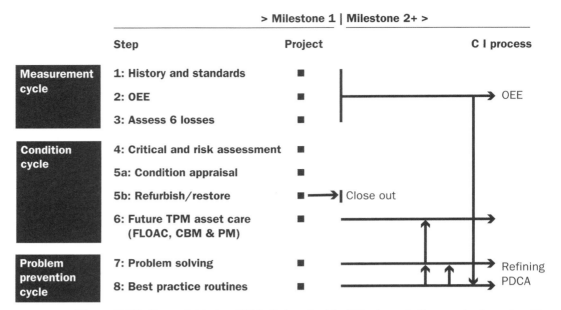

Figure 5.20: From eight-step TPM pilot project to Milestone 1, then on to four-step CI –PDCA process, to Milestone 2 and beyond

It is vital that TPM activity moves from project-based to process-based activity. Ensure that the ownership becomes 'part of the way we do things here' by embedding it into the leader standard work routines.

Ultimately the success and sustainability of the TPM process will depend on how much and how visibly your management is committed to progressively delivering team performance through your people.

The roll-out process builds on experience gained during the pilot process to ensure that the four development milestones of MS1 (introduction), MS 2 (refine best practice and standardise), MS3 (build capability) and MS4 (strive for zero losses), become a reality and that TPM becomes a way of life through self-managed teams.

The future state realisation cycle, comprising three steps

Step 9 Emphasise and focus on individual and team skill development requirements

Step10 Leadership and behaviours training, coaching and mentoring

Step 11 The audit and review processes via evidence-based criteria across the four milestones

This part of the TPM journey is the focus of Chapter 7.

In Chapter 10 three case studies and three further cameo examples illustrate the potential power of the TPM system to deliver your operational excellence aspirations.

CHAPTER 6
Precision changeovers (SMED)

In spite of advancing automation, SMED (single-minute exchange of dies) continues to be a huge topic and opportunity for waste elimination. As one of the classic six equipment-based losses within the OEE metric, a focused improvement attack on excessive changeover times is often central to the TPM system and application philosophy.

In the mid-1980s Shigeo Shingo, the guru of SMED, stated in his book *A Revolution in Manufacturing: The SMED System:* 'Every machine setup can be reduced by 75%'. What a challenge this has proven to be for manufacturers around the globe for over 30 years – SMED still merits a book devoted to the topic in its own right.

However in this chapter and within the scope of this book, we will highlight six areas which may improve your current and future changeover reduction endeavours.

1　What's in a name? The need to use the right language.
2　Be precise on your definition of a changeover's total elapsed time.
3　Be aware of some essential prerequisites and conditions for success.
4　Value stream mapping still has its place. Especially if you add the ECRS (eliminate, combine, rearrange, simplify), challenge and get the right people in the training room.
5　Ensure you sustain the gains through four 'maturity' evidence-based audits of changeover progress.
6　A focus on centre-lining can also yield significant benefits.

6.1 What's in a name?

A few years ago we were having a conversation with a site full-time trade union representative about the introduction of a SMED programme. We explained to him that because the site was essentially a bottling plant with many bottle size and label changes (but no dies to be changed) that we should 'badge' the programme as quick changeovers (QCO) rather than SMED.

After a few moments' reflection he responded by saying that in no way would he ask his members to buy into any programme that suggested they work quicker, and by implication probably less safely. He then added, "Why don't we call it precision changeovers in the sense that there is only one best way, as in standard work".

This was wise: we continue to call it PCO where there are no die changes involved. As this trade union representative recognised, language and vocabulary, and indeed their acronyms, are vital to send out the right messages from the outset. Another phrase we use – and indeed encourage – is 'changeover optimisation', which accurately describes our end goal as described in Section 6.3.

In this chapter we are also very aware that there is a risk of confusing the reader with different words to describe the activity of work and/or its content as one of many including activities, phases, steps, elements and milestones!

So for the purposes of this chapter we are going to define a cascade or hierarchy as follows

A changeover comprises…

■ a number of work **activities,**

■ which are sequenced and presented as discrete **phases,**

- each of which many contain a number of **steps**
- which in turn can comprise a number of work **elements.**

In addition, as the changeover improvement experience develops and matures over time, there are discrete **milestones** which are audited against evidenced criteria to ensure sustainability of the improvements for the long term as part of the continuous improvement process.

6.2 **Definition of a changeover**

We have also learnt that we need to define the precise elapsed time definition of a changeover as:

'From the last good product A to first good product B *at the standard production rate'*.

The last five words of the definition are very important. Analysis suggests that typically for every changeover there are four main categories of work as in Table 6.1. This, of course, needs to embrace the SMED principle of inside work (or internal steps) where the machine asset must be stopped, compared to the outside work (or external steps) of preparation and putting away with the machine asset running. However the biggest element of 50 per cent for trial processing and adjustment time can often cloud the true reality if we just consider the time element when the equipment asset is switched off between changeovers. Likewise, that same 50 per cent can include significant product yield, scrap and rework losses suffered until we are running at the standard rate.

Table 6.1 Adjustments as a percentage of total changeover time

Activity	Total setup time
Preparation of materials, jigs, tools & fittings	20%
Removal and attachment of jigs, tools & dies	20%
Centring, dimensioning	10%
Trial processing & adjustments	50%

6.3 **Prerequisites and conditions for success**

Over the years we have also learnt that the successful application of the SMED approach is subject to certain prerequisites and conditions:

- An attitude – in the sense that the team wants to score.
- Empowerment – the team has a budget of not only money, but also dedicated improvement time.
- Involvement – which starts from the bottom up.
- Commitment – management sets the target and then provides the resources to deliver.
- Philosophy – step by step improvement through a CI mind-set.
- Challenge – an agreed and quantified improvement potential to aim for.

This final point of setting a challenge can be illustrated by taking an example in which we were involved. The company concerned had a major machining facility, whose loading capacity equated to 6,500 hours per week, and where changeovers were consuming 20 per cent of that capacity (1,300 hours per week).

An initial machining centre pilot project application – using the value stream mapping model approach described in Section 6.4 and Figure 6.1 – delivered a 50 per cent reduction in changeover times in three months. This was based on a starting reference point of 240 changeovers per year of 3 hours average duration for the pilot asset = 720 hours per year. The saving of 360 hours was valued at $12,600 per year for the machining centre.

Based on this pilot success the company was able set a demanding but believable two-year rollout plan across a further 90 machining assets linked to a 'challenge' target to release 32,500 hours to production worth $1.13 million per year to the business.

An important point to note is that the selection of a changeover improvement project needs to be aligned to the site's strategic goals, targets and policy deployment processes. Companies that have traditionally struggled with excessive changeover times or setups have often

- compromised their inventories and held additional stocks of finished products to buffer for these excessive changeover times or
- deliberately extended production runs rather than run as 'on demand'.

This can often be the result of measurement driving the wrong behaviour where, for example, the operations/production manager is measured by production unit cost per case or product and as a result of this measurement runs the asset all week on product A and has the line changed over at the weekend ready to run the next week on product B.

The need to do 'quicker changeovers' can therefore be driven by the greater need to reduce inventories as it is the cost of working capital and ultimately poor cash flow that is really hurting the business.

Another key driver is often quality or right first time/yield. Changing the asset from producing product A to product B can often be the biggest trigger to increase defects, scrap, yield losses and rework. Depending on the type of process and industry, setup or changeover loss can be a significantly greater cost than the setup time alone and therefore a key driver in the business will be elimination of defects (towards zero defects as often referred to in many industries). Hence the term changeover optimisation or precision changeovers is preferable to changeover reduction.

6.4 Changeover analysis and mapping

A typical changeover optimisation/precision changeover process that will yield the improvements in the example above is a 'learning by doing' experience. This is a combination of theory and practical learning in the classroom followed by diagnostic analysis of the changeover on the shop floor and then practical application of the PCO technique using a PDCA (plan-do-check-act) improvement cycle. The changeover optimisation process would typically be split into four discrete activities and these are:

1 Preparation
2 PCO training event
3 Trialling improvements and embedding as standard work
4 Sustaining the gains through 4 levels of changeover maturity.

Each of these activities are described below.

Activity 1: Preparation

This focuses on the identification of the changeover optimisation opportunity and the link back to the strategic objectives and policy deployment for the site/business. To understand *why* we need to focus on optimising changeover we must clarify *what* is currently hurting us. We can do this in the same way that we get site management commitment and buy-in from the senior leadership team – by articulating the site/business objectives and then evaluating, across each of these objectives, what changeover optimisation will contribute to those objectives, on a scale from 1 (meaning low impact) to 3 (meaning high impact).

We use this method when evaluating the benefit of TPM for a site, but it can also be effective in helping to evaluate the importance of changeover optimisation – and help secure leadership buy-in and commitment. During this activity we will also decide on the scope of the changeover improvement process application and hence the focus and content for the initial changeover optimisation workshop. For example the type and profile of changeovers that we have on the asset/line may require the creation of a changeover matrix to evaluate the complexity of the different types of changeover/setups and their sequence, frequency and current times. All these considerations can have a significant impact on the actual losses incurred.

We can then determine the appropriate type of changeover to focus on during our 'learning by doing' workshop. We will also need to determine the resources required for our initial changeover optimisation workshop and ensure that we have representatives from both production and maintenance (the people who actually do the changeovers as they are the experts and will be closest to what really happens during the changeover – their involvement and buy-in is critical to success). We also require the presence of support functions for the initial workshop and follow-on activities. For example, if we do not have representation from QA, tooling and production scheduling we often find that we will not get the buy-in and ownership and, as a result, making changes to develop our future-state changeover just becomes a bureaucratic chore.

During the initial changeover practitioner's event (typically held over three to four days), we need to ensure that we have the appropriate type of changeover scheduled in – typically on day two – so that the team can all 'go, see, look and discuss' and video the changeover in its current state. Sometimes when changeover schedules are tight or difficult to plan for this to happen during the workshop, it can be done as a preparation and scripted step before the workshop. However our experience has highlighted the importance of doing this for real as a team effort at the point where the activity takes place. The team will then have had the benefit of understanding the principles of changeover optimisation through theory and a practical exercise in the classroom the previous day.

This is similar to the concept of 'go see and look' on the shop floor using our 'Muda'/waste glasses following a lean awareness/eight-waste session in the classroom. Various sources of data that will be useful for the changeover optimisation event are identified and collected. For example,

- a schematic layout of the asset /process in order to create a 'spaghetti' diagram during the changeover event to identify the wastes of transportation and motion
- a documented current changeover standard operating procedure to use as a guide during the event to ensure common nomenclature/terminology is being used.

Activity 2: The PCO training event

This is normally run over three to four days depending on the complexity of the changeover to be analysed. The workshop would include some theory element for the delegates to understand the background behind the changeover optimisation event and the historic development originating from Shingo's SMED six-step methodology and focus on *why* we need to have precision changeovers. This facilitated discussion does not give the delegates the answers but is a coaching session to draw the answers from the delegates. Typical responses can often be split into business reasons and team reasons. Examples for the business are improved equipment utilisation, reduced downtime and capital expenditure, reduced inventory, lower WIP, inventory and improved 'cash to cash' cycle, improved use of resource, reduced labour content and better use of specialist skills, enhanced flexibility, better response to market needs to supply niche markets and accommodate internal uncertainty, enhanced process control, increased process reliability and reduced scrap.

Examples from the team perspective might include giving us a standard operation (there is only one best way), repeatability of the job with less frustration of things going wrong, enhanced team working with coordinated roles and increased job satisfaction, improved safety, fewer near-miss and unplanned changeovers, and visibility of production schedules. Most importantly it can often increase team skills and tap into our unrealised human potential.

The SMED technique was developed by Shigeo Shingo to speed up press tool changeovers. In one of the first SMED applications Toyota shortened the changeover of a 1000-tonne stamping press from 4 hours to 3 minutes.

Although the PCO workshop is very much a learning by doing event the introduction of a changeover simulation is used as a key part of the theory element of the workshop. A four-step adaptation of Shingo's six-step SMED process (see Figure 6.1) is used. The team carries out a current-state changeover on a machine by reading from the current standard operating procedure for the changeover. Different roles are allocated as part of this exercise and the execution of these roles is key as this standard process is the one that will be used when analysing the teams' actual changeover. These roles include an operator (to carry out the changeover), some maintenance roles such as an electrician to disconnect the electrical supply, a stores clerk to issue raw materials for the next job, and quality control to issue the setup standards for the next job and to carry out initial product inspection.

These roles are allocated to team members and we would typically encourage delegates to take a role that they would not normally do (especially as the current-state changeover in this simulation exercise would typically take up to 90 minutes).

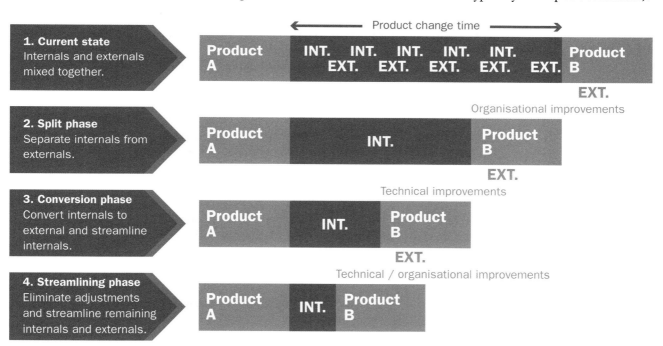

Figure 6.1: The four phases of the precision changeover process

Other delegates will take up diagnostic and observational roles (which we repeat when analysing the 'real' manufacturing floor changeover on day two). These roles include completion of a changeover study chart to record each step and the time taken for each step (or element) plus a timekeeper to record the time for each step/element. One delegate completes a spaghetti diagram to record operator movement (motion) and the movement of parts (transportation); this is carried out on a to-scale asset/line layout drawing. In our simulation this would entail the workshop room itself as well as outside where tool storage areas and QA have been strategically located. The remainder of the delegates are asked to observe the whole process and to identify what problems and issues there are with the current process – and what improvement ideas could be implemented. They do this individually, in silence, and their ideas are discussed at the analysis stage.

The current changeover will present many improvement opportunities including some obvious ones – location of tools and location of parts storage and QA samples for example. Other opportunities will be more subtle.

The team maps the current changeover on the wall chart (see Figure 6.2) starting with the steps split into elements, with a time taken for each step and the observations and ideas for each step noted on sticky notes in the appropriate spaces.

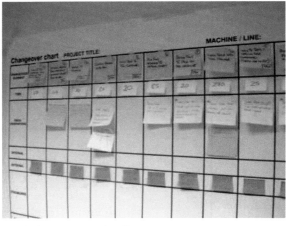

Figure 6.2: Changeover simulation and changeover charting

As a start point for the four-phase analysis process the team maps the current changeover sequence and the time it took (which is typically 90 minutes) and discusses how long a target changeover should take. Our experience of running many of these workshops in the last twenty years is that the targets set by the team will vary depending on the changeover expertise within the team. Typically, teams will opt for a 50 per cent reduction in the changeover time. Some teams often recognise reasonably quickly that two key elements in the changeover can be converted to external work with the machine running and therefore a 75 per cent reduction is possible. The debate is healthy as this will serve its purpose when we repeat the exercise of target setting on the 'real' changeover on the manufacturing floor, and can help break down some preconceptions.

The teams then follow the four-phase process (see Figure 6.1). Phase two is referred to as separate internal and external steps and we have come across different interpretations of this step over the years. This is quite simplistic in that it is asking whether the step is currently an internal step (a step that currently takes place with the machine stopped and therefore adds to the total changeover time) or an external step (a step that currently take place when the machine is running so is effectively a pre-prepared step).

The team then identifies the work elements that can be moved from internal to external purely by organisational improvements only. For example, tool and part location to reduce transportation and motion can be visually highlighted in the spaghetti diagram. The team will discuss and list improvements as part of phase two and then calculate the potential savings.

Phase three is the conversion of the remaining internal work elements to external work elements or elimination of the work element altogether. The focus of this phase tends to be towards technical improvements rather than organisational flow improvements that involve little or no capital investment. The discussion here is very much about 'Can we do things better? Or can we do better things?'

Figure 6.3: Chinese train innovation and military planes refuelling in mid air

Different analogies are used to coach the team to identify opportunities for the conversion and elimination of internal work elements. Figure 6.3 shows two such examples: military planes refuelling in the air and how the Chinese invented a way of getting on and off a bullet train without it stopping. There are 30 stations between Beijing and Guangzhou. So just stopping and accelerating again at each station will waste both energy and time. A mere five minute stop per station (elderly passengers cannot be hurried) will result in a total loss of 5 minutes x 30 stations or 2.5 hours of additional journey time. The innovative Chinese invented the non-stopping train concept. When the train arrives at the station it will not stop at all. The passengers at the station embark onto a connector cabin before the train arrives at the station .When the train arrives it just slows down to pick up the connector cabin mounted on the train's roof. While the train is still travelling away from the station, those passengers will board the train from the connector cabin. After fully unloading all of its passengers the cabin connector will be moved to the back of the train in order that the next batch of outgoing passengers who want to alight at the next station will board the connector cabin at the rear of the train roof.

When the train arrives at the next station, it will simply drop the whole connector cabin at the station itself and leave it behind at the station. The outgoing passengers can take their own time to disembark at the station while the train had already left. At the same time, the train will pick up the incoming embarking passengers on another connector cabin in the front part of the train's roof. So the train will always drop one connector cabin at the rear of its roof and pick up a new connector cabin in the front part of the train's roof at each station.

The team brainstorm ideas around the conversion/elimination step and then estimate the savings made if these ideas were implemented. This process again has proven to be extremely helpful in being able to evaluate payback and tangible benefits in terms of time savings or defect reduction on changeovers.

Phase four in the PCO/changeover optimisation process is to access all of the work elements that are left. For internal work that cannot be externalised the team looks at reducing the time taken and ensuring that they are right first time through, for example, mistake-proofing ideas. It is not only the internal factors that the team focuses on streamlining; it is also the work elements that have been externalised. Externalisation will reduce the changeover time but those external elements are still work that has to be done. We therefore focus on reducing the work content and waste from both internal and external elements.

Streamlining helps the team challenge some of the ideas they generated in phase two where they separated the correct tools from the tools not required (the first step of 5S – sort) and then located the correct tools on a shadow board (the second step of 5S – set).The team will challenge the need for tools and explore the opportunity to make the equipment tool-free. The team will also look for opportunities to do things concurrently and involve more than one operator in the changeover process. The team will focus on making the elimination of defects during the changeover process by mistake-proofing setup and move away from adjustments and into settings.

As described at the beginning of this chapter it is the trial and adjustment phase that takes up to 50 per cent of the changeover time. Simplifying tasks or de-skilling tasks (not a term we are too keen to use) by, for example, removing the need for an electrician to rewire by setting up 'plug and play' are other examples of this. There are many proven and yet-to-be-discovered innovative solutions that will assist in the streamlining phase as the examples in Figures 6.4 and 6.5 show.

The team will review their ideas generated from the analysis of the current-state changeover and there will be many opportunities with the simulation in terms of, for example, locating pins to position the different die plates, setting blocks that will eliminate adjustment required to the dimensions when using the standard setting templates required. In our real changeover these ideas and concepts will need to go through the PDCA cycle and verification process that we would typically use when making changes.

Figure 6.4: Mechanical methods for streamlining internal steps

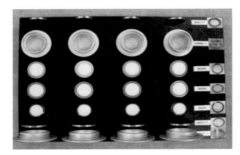
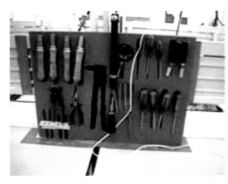

Figure 6.5: Four examples of streamlining external steps

This verification process will effectively cover the check-point questions below:
■ Have we proven the device (or improvement change) in the workshop and in the actual working environment for its intended use?
■ Does this proposed change introduce any risk to the process?
■ Have we devised and calibrated a process to maintain the functionality to the standard required?
■ Have we informed and involved all participants and stakeholders of the change in the process?

- Have we updated the standard work to reflect the change in the process using any new devices and built this into our process?
- Where relevant, have we removed previous now-obsolete components/methods to prevent us from reverting back to the previous process (as in 5S Step 1)?

A further consideration in the streamlining phase is to consider the opportunity for combining tasks being carried out concurrently by more than one operator (the C of combine as in our ECRS challenge process). The analogy here is the Formula 1 pit stop techniques where the team of operators have a specific set of tasks to do and the process has been continually improved to constantly try to remove waste and make it slicker (see Figure 6.6).

Like the F1 experience, the optimum number of operators will be determined by trial and error, as the team will discover. We have been involved in a number of improvements where the ideal changeover requires, say, three operators where previously the labour loading for the changeover was only one operator. The plant manager's response is "I don't have the labour available", but if the changeover has previously taken say 30 minutes and yet can be reduced to five minutes with three operators, the shorter changeover period can easily be coordinated by a production team worth their salt.

The important point on the new changeover method is to document, through trial and error, the new standard operating procedure in terms of who does what and when, which is similar to standard work with cycle times and sequences for each step. There may be a number of versions based on available resources and priority. For example, two-operator changeover versus three-operator changeover. In our simulation the future-state changeover becomes in most instances a two person changeover as the three operator version often leaves idle time for the third operator, plus the physical space for three operators to work is a constraint. Again, as with phases two and three, at phase four the team will calculate the saving to be made from each improvement and therefore estimate the changeover time for the future-state process based on the ideas generated.

Activity 3: Trialling improvements and embedding as standard work

The creation of standard work as a series of standard operating procedures for the new future-state changeover is a key element in attaining an improved process and this has to be devised by the people carrying out the changeover with the assistance of support functions to ensure that the process is validated, controlled and documented accordingly.

From our experience the practical application of this new process can vary from being a challenge in highly regulated environments to relatively simple in less bureaucratic industries. The key to the success comes back to the naming of this as precision changeovers as the new process we are striving to help create will result in significantly less scrap, fewer defects, and improved quality and yield. In our simulation the team are normally able to perform the new changeover in under three minutes – a significant reduction from the 90-minute initial changeover.

In summary, this simulation approach is the progressive application of the 'learning by doing' process, where classroom learning is then taken to the on-the-floor reality by applying the process and tools deployed in the learning phase. The analysis of the current-state process includes the roles of video and observing the process, filling out the changeover study flow chart, timing for each work element and the spaghetti diagram for each operator involved. The changeover is highly likely to already involve multiple operators rather than a single operator and there will be elements of concurrency, meaning that the planning and the analysis will need to be meticulous.

Figure 6.6: Formula 1 multiple-operator changeover

One further key learning point is illustrated in Figure 6.7, which suggests that any process has at least three versions:

- What you think it is
- What is actually is
- What it should be.

The good news is we can avoid the 'What you think it is' version by first observing and scripting the actual changeover routine as the basis for our current-state scenario which we 'value stream map' during the PCO training event. That encourages the ECRS mind-set challenge to eliminate or combine steps. And if we can do neither of these two, then can we replace it with something smarter? Or at least simplify it?

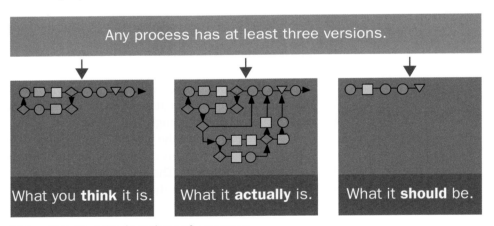

Figure 6.7: Perceived versions of a process

Activity 4: Sustaining the gains through four levels of changeover maturity

Following a changeover-focused improvement drive and implementation to reduce times via maximising value-adding effort, we often hear and witness over time a gradual erosion of the gains made.

In recognition of this fact we have developed a simple but effective audit process which is linked to four maturity levels over time as illustrated in Figure 6.8.

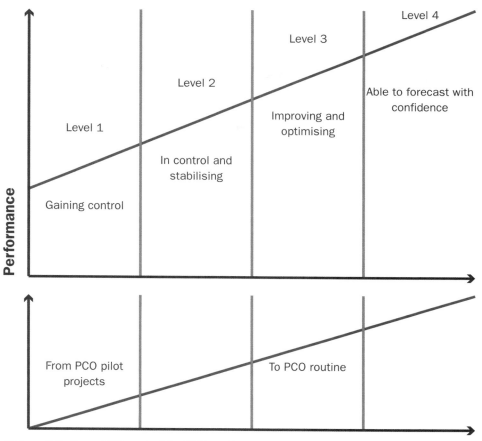

Figure 6.8: From PCO project to PCO routine

Level 1 – Gaining control

- Minimum involvement from operators in the definition of best practice routines for changeovers
- No structured workplace organisation: 5S Step 1 completed and Step 2 started
- Work procedures disorganised and preparation of setup/changeover/ adjustment time varies widely and randomly
- Little or no attempt to define best practice or standardisation
- Plan and carry out initial training for definition of 'current state' using value stream mapping
- Subject each step and activity to the **e**liminate, **c**ombine, **r**eplace, **s**implify (ECRS) test
- Define opportunities for future-state improvements (also embracing the six-step SMED methodology).

Level 2 – In control and stabilizing

- Work procedures organised (for example, internal/external distinguished)
- Future state opportunities identified and implementation started
- Preparation, setup , changeover and adjustment times improved
- Further opportunities for improvement are identified and trialled
- Variability being reduced and stabilised
- Steps 1, 2 & 3 of 5S/WPO in place.

Level 3 – Improving and optimising

- Internal activities and operations moved into external time and reduced
- Adjustment mechanisms identified and well-understood
- Trialling best practice, including Step 4 of 5S/WPO
- Error-proofing introduced.

Level 4 – Able to forecast with confidence

- Best practice optimum conditions defined as standard work
- Variability eliminated
- Steps 4 and 5 of 5S/WPO implemented
- Continuous review process in place with embedded ECRS mindset.

In Appendix 6.1 we show the four levels as audit criteria questions – each level having 10 checkpoints (hence 40 in total across the four maturity levels). The appendix shows that each check point delivery is the responsibility of a specific pillar champion as illustrated in Table 6.2 and also shown on the left hand side of Figure 6.9.

Table 6.2 Typical PCO pillar champions to drive the PCO gains

PCO Gains	Champions	Initials used in Audit Levels 1 to 4
PCO KPIs & Delivery	Production Manager	PM
PCO Planning	Planning & Scheduling Manager	P&SM
Skill Development and Follow BPR	Section Leaders	SL
PCO Process Standardisation	Prod Eng & QA Representatives	PE & QA
PCO Coordinator	CI Engineers/TPM facilitator	CI
Project Manager	Production Manager	PM
Project Sponsor	Production Director	PD

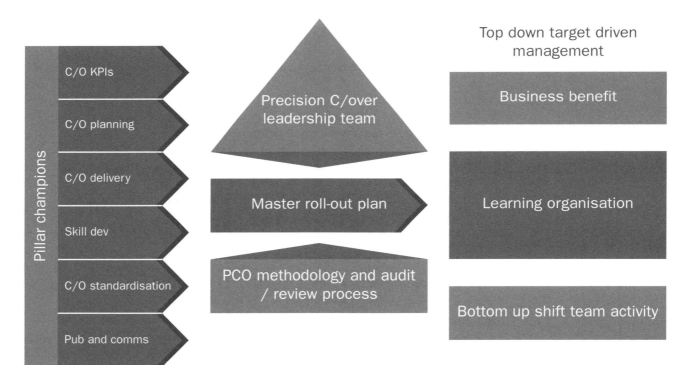

Figure 6.9: PCO governance to sustain the gains

6.5 **Centre-lining**

The art of 'centre-lining' is something that many people have heard of, but there has been very little written about it.

6.5.1 **Definition and purpose**

Centre-lining is the establishment of set points, indicators and settings within a production process that are clearly defined; this makes it possible to identify 'drift' from these settings that ultimately indicates variation in the process that needs attention and correction to be brought back to standard. Failure to bring these parameters back to standard will lead to an unplanned event or, as we have discussed throughout this book, one of the six equipment-based losses. Centre-lining is needed mainly in the process of setup during changeover, and as we can see from Table 6.1, as much as 60 per cent of total time activity for a changeover is attributed to centring, comprising dimensioning (10%) and trial processing & adjustment (50%), which typically manifest as start-up losses. Centre-lining can also help identify machine or component wear. If identified early enough and remedied, this will avoid minor stops and ultimately breakdowns (Figure 6.10).

So we can see that centre-lining is a useful method for reducing product and process variability and increasing machine efficiency in manufacturing and other industrial processes.

The two objectives of centre-lining are
1   to determine the best settings for a production process and
2   to ensure those best settings are always used during production.

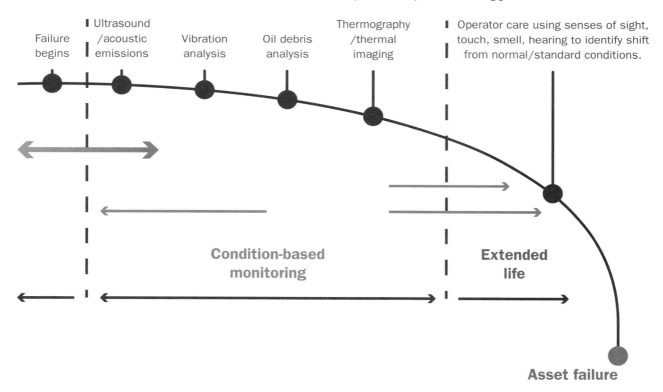

Figure 6.10: Centre-lining to capture process 'drift' early

It is ultimately a form of visible, physical, statistical process control in a production process. Consistent product quality is important because customers want to know what they can expect from the products they purchase.

One way to ensure consistency is to inspect every product after it is made and either reject or accept it. However, this is rarely an efficient quality assurance method because of the variety, complexity, and/or volume of products being made. A better way to achieve consistency is to ensure that the manufacturing process is fit for purpose and runs the same way all the time by controlling, minimising or eliminating the reasons for variation ('drift'). This is where the focus of centre-lining can help.We can break centre-lining down into two main categories:

■ Fixed – mainly used during start-up and changeover and is a precise setting with a fixed value (Figure 6.11)
■ Variable – used to monitor key settings that can be variables within a process within lower and upper control limits (Figure 6.12).

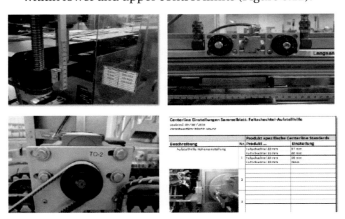

Figure 6.11: Fixed centre-lining examples

Figure 6.12: Variable centre-lining examples

6.5.2 **Four key steps to creating centre-lines**

Step 1 – Identify the critical process factors or variables to deliver safety, quality and performance

There are several tools and techniques that can help to establish these critical process factors. One method is to create a process map for the chosen asset with a cross-functional team of operatives, maintainers and support staff using structured 'Go look and see' and extensive data collection, similar to performing a Process Failure Mode Effect Analysis (PFMEA) of the asset and processing line mapping (see Figure 6.13). The application of PFMEA allows us to evaluate each key value-adding stage in a production process (i.e. where the form, fit or function of the product is changed) and assess the potential failure modes (things that can go wrong) for each element and the causes of these failure modes. These are assessed for severity, likelihood and detection and an initial RPN (Risk Priority Number) is determined for each. The severity of a failure mode can never change (if we are hit by a bus today, it will be just as bad as being hit by a bus tomorrow!) What we can do through continuous improvement ideas is reduce the likelihood of the failure mode occurring and improve the level of detection, so we can take corrective action to prevent the realisation of the failure mode. We can slow the bus down, introduce safe pedestrian crossings and introduce better visual controls to alert pedestrians that the bus is approaching. The impact of reducing likelihood and improving detection will ultimately reduce the risk of the failure mode occurring (RPN). Centre-lining is a tool that will help improve detection and/or reduce likelihood.

The use of PFMEA to determine what needs to be done must be selective, as the aim here is not to have as many centre-lines as is possible but to have them where the risk is judged significant (RPN greater than 100). Overuse and abuse of visual control will reduce the effectiveness and the importance of what is trying to be achieved – a selective approach to arrive at the vital few as opposed to the trivial many.

Step 2 – Determine the best settings and ranges for all important variables

These will ultimately be done through design of experiments (DOE) and determining the process capability (CPK) values for these variables through statistical process control techniques (SPC). In simple terms, we need to determine our ideal parameters through upper and lower control limits. Beyond these limits our process is likely to suffer from an unplanned event in terms of one of the six equipment-based losses.

Step 3 – Determine how these variables affect the process and product

This enables us to identify the red, amber and green (RAG) values in terms of the required action limits on the visual indicators that we implement through our centre-lining activity. This only applies to variable centre-lines as for fixed centre-lines there are effectively no ranges – there is only one value and any drift or deviation from it needs immediate action to bring the parameter setting back to this fixed value.

Step 4 – Ensure centre-lines are always used when processing

We can achieve this through ensuring that the centre-lines are checked at various stages in the process; for example, upon start up at the beginning of each shift, during changeover and before restart after changeover. They can also be checked periodically throughout the production window through the 'pit stop'-type approach as part of the best practice standard work introduced through the FLOACS (front-line operator asset care) established by the team as part of their TPM routines (Step 8 best practice standard work). This includes leader standard work incorporating, in the Gemba (look, go, see) visits to the assets on the manufacturing floor, checking centre-lines using the single point lessons created as part of best practice standard work. To mix it up a bit the leader will select single point lessons randomly from the standard work cards and carry out process confirmation.

Table 6.3 outlines an approach to centre-lining from the selection of the asset for implementation (activity 1) through to the continuous challenge of settings to ensure ease of use and accuracy (activity 12). This follows the classic DMAIC process commonly used in Six Sigma.

Process step via asset

Process critical points? What needs to be right? Safety Quality Performance

Can this be controlled? (settings e.g. temperature, guide rail dimension – fixed/variable

Ideas to control?

How do we make visible and easy to use?

How do we deploy and maintain?

Figure 6.13: Centre-line mapping process in action

Table 6.3 Centre-lining from asset selection (1) to continuous improvement (12)

DMAIC phase	Step	Description
Define	1	Select critical pinch point asset(s)
	2	Define performance criteria & priority
	3	Set up CL core team
Measure	4	Identify and quantify all variable and fixed adjustment points on the asset
	5	Make all variable and fixed points highly visual
Analyse	6	Monitor variable ranges & understand criticality
	7	Define critical adjust settings
Improve	8	Convert unnecessary adjustments to fixed
	9	Set down SPLs and train out as best practice routines
	10	Convert to standard work process
Control	11	Implement audit and review processes
	12	Continuous improvement through setting stretch targets

6.5.3 Summarising the benefits of centre-lining

Centre-lining offers a solution for repeatable, consistent and hence predictable performance. It is based on a visible setup and is not operator dependent; in other words, it is not reliant on an operator's own tacit knowledge. Working on the principle that there is only one best way, the methodology supports standardised best practice (Step 8) and supports standardised precision changeovers (PCO). Centre-lining makes it easier to confirm optimum performance parameters. In the same way as standard work, it is an aid to problem solving – when a problem occurs, we ask, did we follow standard work? Or in this case, did we comply with the centre-line? Centre-lines can also be an aid to condition-based monitoring as early indicators of wear and tear of parts and equipment (Figure 6.10).

6.6 **Conclusion**

As stated at the start of this chapter, changeovers are important enough to the TPM System and philosophy to merit a book in their own right. However, we hope the above highlighted areas will add to the ongoing success and sustainability of your changeover journey endeavours.

APPENDIX 6.1
Precision changeover (PCO) maturity audit/review

Audit checkpoint sheets for
- Milestone 1: Gaining control
- Milestone 2: In control and stabilising
- Milestone 3: Improving and optimising
- Milestone 4: Forecast with confidence

PCO focus	Responsible pillar champion	Initials used in audit levels 1 to 4
KPIs & delivery	Production manager	PM
CO planning	Planning & scheduling manager	P&SM
Skill development & BPR adherence	Section leaders	SL
Process standardisation	Prod eng & QA representatives	PE & QA
Coordinator/facilitator	CI engineer(s)	CI
Project manager	Production manager	PM
Project sponsor	Production director	PD

Level 1 Audit Check Points Sheet

artment: _____   \sset: _____

Has the BPR eliminated unnecessary walking and other NVA'ing tasks?	3 =In use, 4 = effective, 5= track record of CI SL +CI Eng	
Are we recording every & all changeover performance information on this Asset?	3 = recorded, 5 = improvement Production Manager (PM)	
Is Production Planning and Scheduling fully aware of Customer Reqs v. Best Changeover Sequence v. trade-offs?	3 = accepted, 5 = understood & practiced Prod Planning & SL	
	TOTAL	

Not in place with no plans to address   4. Well defined, executed and understood

Weak/deficient   5. Well defined with a track record of Continuous Improvement

Able to meet departmental/plant goals with plans to improve

Level 2 Audit Check Points Sheet

estone: 2: In Control & Stabilising   Level: 2 Audit Check Points

Review Point	Score	ence
Is there a visual record of PCO changeover performance improvement on this asset?		fined, 4=in place, 5= under ovement SL & PM,
Is there a defined and complete set of SPL's for PCO key parameters, Set up, adjustments, safety, visual inspection?		cumented, provisional standar ill standard, 5 = improved PED d Eng,
Do the Production Managers & Section Leaders make effective use of the spare capacity generated from PCO reduction on this Asset?		fined , 4=in place, 5 –track re PM & SL,
Does the Section Leader & Ops Team hold regular reviews with Planning (weekly) and (monthly) with QA and PED?		i use, 4= improved, elf directed SL + PP + QA + PEI gs
Are production targets met for this Asset as planned (>95% OTIF)		ontent identified, riory training complete ills / training matrix PM + PP
	TOTAL	

1. Not in place with no plans to address   Well defined, executed and understood
2. Weak/deficient   Well defined with a track record of Continuc Improvement
3. Able to meet departmental/plant goals with plans to improve

Level 3 Audit Check Points Sheet

artment: _____   \sset: _____

Review Point		nce
Are 'next batch' start-up adjustments & quality defect cause / effect relationships understood & Minimised ?		& SL's nalysis / 6 Sigma
Are level 4/ 5 foolproof devices in place and working?		CI Engs ples
Are short term planning activities including PCO sequencing carried out by the front line team?		PP ans / Short Interval duling
Are Front Line Team involved in PCO features of New M/cs Specification		& SL dded in EEM
Are all possible Internal Activities moved to External time and Reduced?		/ SI/ CI Eng nce
	TOTAL	

Not in place with no plans to address   4. Well defined, executed and understood

Weak/deficient   5. Well defined with a track record of Continuous Improvement

Able to meet departmental/plant goals with plans to improve

1

partners

he power to im

Level 4 Audit Check Points Sheet

estone: 4 Forecast with Confidence   Level: 4 Audit Check Points

RED= Pillar Champion Respon:

Has variability in PCO times been eliminated?		PM /SI/PED/QA/CIE Trend graphs eviden
Are there Improved New Product Introduction lead times through Standard Work PCO Methods		PED /SL/CI Eng EEM engagement
Are Priorities set for reduced level of intervention defined ? (i.e.-Single Touch Changeovers)		PED / SL /CI Eng Examples
Is there a Defined & Developed self-managed system for PCO's?		PM / PP/ SL/QA/ CI Evidence
Do Front Line Teams manage in-bound logistics?		PM / SL / PP Evidence
Do Front Line Teams have Input to future operating strategy& have a CI Process fully Embedded with a ECRS Mindset as part of LIFE?		ALL PC's Evidence

Not in place with no plans to address   4. Well defined, executed and understood

Weak/deficient   5. Well defined with a track record of Continuous Improvement

Able to meet departmental/plant goals with | to improve

sapartners

Together, the power to improve

CHAPTER 7

TPM, people, and the Shingo Model

7.1 TPM as a core system

Many companies have attempted to implement continuous improvement programmes. Fewer than ten per cent are truly successful and result in a change to the base culture of the business. Those companies that achieve self-sustaining or 'self-propelling' cultural change do so by focusing on the business through very different lenses. Dr Russell Ackoff lamented the fact that the majority of quality initiatives were deemed a failure by most organisations. Dr Ackoff blamed this failure on a lack of joined-up systems thinking. In more recent times the focus has been on organisational culture and behaviours. Those organisations that are achieving sustainable excellence tackle culture and behaviours in a very particular way by asking a very searching question:

> If we are to achieve a level of sustainable enterprise excellence, what are the ideal behaviours we need to see expressed consistently within the various business functions and levels of this organisation?

This behavioural based approach is the foundation of the Shingo Enterprise Excellence philosophy, captured within the Shingo model and its associated ten guiding principles, as shown in Figure 7.1.

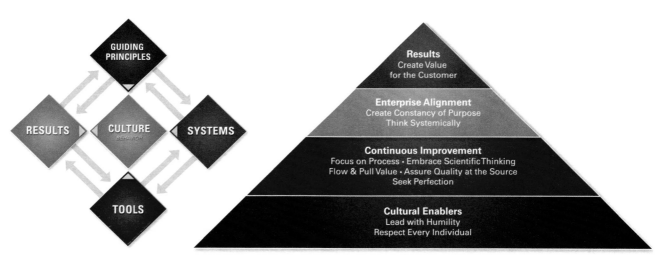

Figure 7.1: The Shingo Model (left) with its principles and dimensions

The Shingo Enterprise Excellence Philosophy also puts forward three core insights;
- Ideal results require ideal behaviour
- Purpose and systems drive behaviour
- Principles inform ideal behaviour.

If we view these insights from a TPM perspective they can have a profound effect on our approach to asset optimisation. Taking each insight in turn we can begin to align our thinking with the concept of ideal equipment-related behaviours and the processes that, viewed as a whole, combine into a complete system of asset maintenance and optimisation.

The Shingo Model and its guiding principles provides us with insights into what these ideal behaviours might be. Principles such as **focus on process**, **ensure quality at source**, **embrace scientific thinking**, **seek perfection** and the other principles within the continuous improvement dimension can easily be linked to observable behaviours associated with the maintenance and improvement of equipment performance. Such observable behaviours might include watching a team work at and test ideas where they gather data to either fix a problem (permanently) or improve the process. The principle focus on process might come into our mind as we watch and listen to a team review and discuss a piece of standard work in detail to ensure that the procedure actually reflects and highlights the critical control or checking specific areas of the equipment.

In an organisation that is achieving consistent levels of improvement in machine output and quality, we would observe ideal behaviours in relation to how familiar the operator was with their equipment and the process itself: their 'equipment and process consciousness'. We could observe the operator actively engaged in problem-solving activity and process improvement as 'part of the way we do things here'.

With the dimension of cultural enablers, we would observe mutually respectful conversations between operators and technical engineering groups who appreciate the value of the operator's day-to-day experience of the equipment. Equipment maintainers and engineers would have a real and expressed appreciation for the value this knowledge brings to problem resolution, process improvement and improvements in maintenance and reliability.

Over time, as the process continues to stabilize and improve, the key questions with the weekly 'look back' are increasingly about what new insights on the process have we come across this week that will drive innovation and improvement tomorrow? Rather than, what were our biggest issues this week? This focus on the relentless improvement on results and performance would align with the principle of Customer Value.

It may be important here to remind ourselves of some fundamental thinking around true employee engagement. Herzberg[1] makes it clear that the things that we often believe are important such as salary, bonus structures, healthcare, nice canteen, Friday bun sales, and company magazines are in effect hygiene factors and do not form the basis of employee engagement and thereby organisation excellence (the authors' inference here). True motivators are those that enable personal growth, and feeling of advancement. The contribution to meaningful work, being and feeling part of a team. These elements reach deep into the core of what makes us human. They also make the tragedy of withering humanity mentioned earlier in this book all the more tragic.

- Hygiene factors
    - Work conditions
    - Salary/bonus
    - Social events
    - Life skills programme
    - Security
    - Relationship with supervisor
- Intrinsic motivators
    - Growth
    - Advancement
    - Responsibility
    - Work itself
    - Recognition
    - Achievement

1 Herzberg, F. (2003) 'One more time: how do you motivate employees?', *Harvard Business Review*, 81(1), pp. 87-96.

TPM is a complete system to deliver asset optimisation which is also aligned to other core systems within the business. As such, it provides leaders with a framework to enable the intrinsic motivational factors which are essential to sustain a culture of operational excellence.

In sections 7.4 and 7.5 of this chapter and their associated appendices, we have evaluated and aligned Shingo's ten guiding principles against our perception of TPM as a core system within an asset-dependent business. The alignment, not unexpectedly, approaches 80 per cent.

7.1.1 Systems and ideal behaviours

Now contrast the environment above with behaviours that we commonly observe. Operators read a procedure once maybe, but they are shown how 'to get the work done' by another 'more experienced' operator. The relationship between operator and maintenance technician is fraught and often tense. Both are overworked and stressed.

Typically, the maintenance technician is being pulled from pillar to post in a constant firefighting mode while trying to keep up with maintenance schedules and corrective actions to meet deadlines. The engineers responsible for the manufacturing line decide how the manufacturing process can be improved and implement changes without any input or engagement from the maintainers or operators. Measures used to monitor performance are neither accurate nor relevant (a fact known to the team), yet they are still asked to contribute to production cell meetings or improvement activities to improve the metrics.

If we can distinguish between those behaviours that are ideal and those that are not, how do the systems in your business either enable or disable those ideal behaviours? Do your systems in fact drive bad behaviours?

A common example of a system driving bad behaviours can be observed (and measured) within many learning and development systems. One manifestation of this is when new employees are required to read, review, and sign off multiple procedures within too short a time. They may even be required to pass an online test of competence.

Faced with an almost impossible task the employee signs off procedures they have, at best, glanced at or, at worst, not read at all. But what about the online test? Many online tests are simply foiled by multiple attempts at answers until the right one is achieved. So, what is the real or subliminal, behavioural learning here?

Compliance is more important than knowledge? My signature has no real value? The key thing is to get the job done, no matter what it takes to get it done.

We regularly see maintenance teams driven to achieve maintenance task close-out rates for tasks that have no real value and should be eliminated. In carrying out these non-value-adding maintenance tasks skilled maintenance teams waste valuable time that would be better served investigating and eliminating problems or improving overall equipment performance. The focus is not only on solving problems but also on preventing re-occurrence of that same problem with the '100-year fix'.

7.1.2 An integrated system of asset lifecycle management through TPM

There can often be some confusion over what is a system and a process and how these divide into tools and tasks. To keep it simple we consider a system as the large end-to-end way core things are done in a business. For example, think of a business's 'people lifecycle management system'. By this we mean a *system* that enables the right people to be hired, developed, performance managed and retired. Such a system would be made up of many *processes*, such as how people are hired, how they undergo their annual review, how they contribute to their personal development, and how they are trained. All can be regarded as separate but connected processes within an overall system. A *tool* within the hiring process might be the interview application form, the performance review mechanism, the online training system. Whereas a *task* might be how employees update their training matrix or contribute to their personal development plan.

What about a system of asset maintenance and performance? Here we need to consider the process of asset acquisition, maintenance and performance monitoring and improvement and final decommissioning and disposal.

The fifth founding principle of TPM referred to as early equipment management (EEM) is explored in detail in Chapter 8. We want to emphasise here that TPM in its true form is a holistic system of total asset lifecycle management. As a system it needs to be fully integrated with other key systems. Examples include but are not limited to

- Strategy deployment system
- Core management system (preferably made up of tier boards based on principles of visual management)
- System of improvement
- System of training and development
- Financial systems and product costing
- Planning and order management system
- System of quality management and compliance.

In Chapter 4 we describe how our TPM model, through a focus on Purpose Process and People, enables the critical overlapping elements of engagement, alignment and improvement.

Figure 7.2: A holistic view of the overlapping elements within any organisation

In Peter Hines and Chris Butterworth's *The Essence of Excellence* they refer (p.8) to Figure 7.3 below and say:

> The Shingo Institute (2014) suggest that the secret of creating sustainable Enterprise Excellence lies in developing a principle-led approach and deploying this into the enterprise. In this sense, they propose that a principle is a foundational rule that has an inevitable consequence. It is universal and timeless, self-evident and governs the consequences of whether or not it is followed.
>
> This provides the 'know why'. Without this knowledge, we find that organisational change does not have sufficiently robust buy-in at any level of the organisation.

Hence this principle-led approach helps develop an appropriate culture in which we embed classic Lean approaches.

TPM is a prime example of a system of work where we in effect reverse the traditional order from the What?(Tools) How?(Systems) and Why?(Culture) to align with the Shingo Model's intended delivery through Leaders (Culture), Managers (Systems) and Associates (Tools).

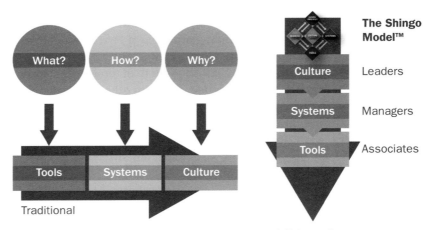

Figure 7.3: Changing the system: traditional and Shingo views

By viewing TPM as a core system in your business you can identify the ideal behaviours which you need the system to support. Such ideal observable behaviours might include

- safety awareness & management
- follow/improve/enforce standards
- team work, respect humility
- equipment consciousness, ownership, pride
- willingness to learn new skills
- seeking and using data
- problem solving root cause/ideas for problem elimination/problem prevention
- improvement suggestion
- experiment, testing to enable improvement
- listening to and acting on ideas
- customer awareness
- fastidious cleanliness, workplace organisation
- eagerness to challenge current state performance.

Clearly defining core systems and their constituent processes is a fundamental step in achieving sustainable enterprise excellence. How can we drive improvement if we do not have a way to tell the team how they are truly performing? If we do not have a process to identify – and provide the team with – the appropriate skills to understand and improve the process? How can we expect them to engage in continuous improvement activity if we do not have an environment that encourages good value-adding ideas and behaviours and communicates them to the wider business? How can the organisation hope to change its culture if the basic tools to allow teams to do their day's work are not reliable, are broken or missing? Where firefighting is praised and time to fix things and develop standards is just not available?

Recognizing the link between systems and behaviours is all well and good. But if leaders do not have the sensitivity, awareness and ability to enable and coach appropriate behaviours, or the courage and resilience to deal with inappropriate behaviours when they arise, then all the efforts to link systems to ideal behaviours will be to no effect.

7.1.3 **Self evaluation**

The section 'Measuring people's perceptions and feelings' at Chapter 4.5 provides a current-state self-assessment to help you judge where your organisation is between these two ends of the scale. When you do this assessment be honest, open and realistic. Go to the shop floor and ask questions like:

- What does a hassle-free shift look like here?
- When was the last time an improvement was made to this process?
- What happens if you have an idea to improve things?
- How were you trained to do this work?
- What happens if there is a problem with this equipment?

We encourage you to look beyond the answers and reflect on the core business systems that should be supporting appropriate behaviours – systems such as the system of improvement, the learning and development system, the system of measurement and management.

7.1.4 **The role of leader standard work with TPM**

As we both build and sustain the necessary culture around greater equipment consciousness and equipment performance, leader standard work done well acts as the 'sustaining cement'. By 'done well' we mean the LSW is carried out by leaders equipped with effective coaching skills who support the agreed behavioural norms necessary to sustain this culture. For examples of observable ideal behaviours we refer you to Section 7.1.5 and Figure 7.4.

In *The Essence of Excellence*, Peter Hines and Chris Butterworth describe the elements of leader standard work.

Leader standard work

Leader standard work is a system that ensures that leaders develop the right culture by undertaking the right activity in the right style by

- understanding the roles and responsibilities of leaders at all levels
- checking that activity is taking place to ensure business success
- recognising people's contribution to success
- identifying coaching and development opportunities so that
- the whole organisation engages its people with the members taking initiative.

As teams begin to develop consciousness and skills around equipment performance and improvement, the measurement and visualisation of performance trends becomes integrated into daily and weekly visual performance management boards. As equipment is returned to its ideal state with clear indicators for standard running conditions and surrounding workplace organisation, we truly enable the 'visual factory' which can 'speak to us' through simple visual cues. All leaders in a business that is reliant on the consistent high performance of its assets must understand how to 'read' the visual factory and 'listen' to the voice of the process.

An HR director, for example, during a formal Gemba walk or just an opportunistic visit to the manufacturing floor, can easily determine if a gauge with red and green indicators is in the red or the green. If it is in the red, then there is a duty on the leader to enquire as to why this is the case, and where necessary probe to check that the answer is plausible, and that action is underway to address the issue. This effective enquiry might go so far as to confirming that the issue has been logged on the daily and weekly management board. Such behaviour by the HR director cannot be seen as an intrusion in the operational world. If it is, something is wrong: the leadership team needs to take a step back and recalibrate their combined attitude to TPM and its associated ideal behaviours.

Where there is a divergence from an agreed standard, it must be addressed immediately with effective and thoughtful enquiry which both allows the situation to be returned to the agreed standard and is followed up by full enquiry as to the root cause of the divergence. This investigation must be immediate and cannot wait to go through the various channels before the obvious questions are asked.

The consequences of a leadership team's insensitivity to obvious and intentional signalling systems from the process are fatal to the sustainability of the desired cultural change.

If the HR director fails to make the observation when he/she is in a situation to make it, it sends many bad signals to the work team such as:

- I always knew our leadership team don't really get this!
- After all the effort the team put in to creating this visual factory our leaders are not really tuned into it despite all the noise that was made about it!

Or maybe the HR director makes a light enquiry without making the link to process performance visual management boards and problem solving. Again, the true value of the system we have worked long and hard to create is undermined.

By no means are we picking on HR directors here! On the contrary, we have observed during our coaching practice both operational and engineering leaders miss obvious visual signals that were right in front of their noses. Our point is that all senior leaders need to be in tune with the value of a systematic approach which TPM can bring in enabling and supporting necessary ideal behaviours.

To help avoid this situation a thorough TPM programme will make critical check points clearly visible around the equipment which make it simple to understand the ideal condition of the equipment at that point. An equipment diagram and guide map close to the visual management board can be used to locate these critical control points. In this way, during a Gemba or shop floor visit the leader will know what to check and where, and can therefore clearly understand what the ideal condition should be. Ideally these checks form part of daily and weekly supervisor leader standard work and can be included in senior leader's standard work as they carry out their regular Gemba walks.

The times when things are difficult or where there is a 'fire' are when leaders are most tested. In these situations leaders must be seen to uphold and observe agreed process standards and standards of behaviour. It is at these times that true leadership comes forward and fake leadership is exposed. It is often at these times that senior leaders are chastened and humbled by the leadership shown by front line teams who are committed to the maintenance of the standards and ways of working that they have developed, and they know are right. It is one of the great rewards of consultancy practice to observe leadership from the bottom up in action!

To emphasise the need to sustain the force of leader standard work and TPM we have extracted some of the Mylan Rottapharm case study material here, which is covered in detail in Chapter 10, as follows:

> The parallel improvement of the use of Leader Standard Work (LSW) and visual management has resulted in everyone within the plant having a clear understanding of what the expectations are on a daily basis in terms of process adherence and process performance. This focus has led to plant wide improvements in performance. People are more focused in getting things done on time and in recognizing when process trends require action. Every team has a visual management board with laminated sheets that are updated daily. A number of meetings take place at these boards. The first meeting is held when work starts at 07:00 in the production areas and at 08:00 in the support areas, these meetings are known as the pulse meetings and are carried out with the team and immediate supervisor or middle manager. At 09:00 the middle managers from operations, engineering, quality assurance and control, the warehouse and logistics meet at the plant operations board and review any issues that have been raised and have required escalation by the various teams. A member of the Senior Leadership team (SLT) also attends this meeting on a weekly

rotational basis. Appropriate actions are discussed and decided at the meeting. If an issue cannot be resolved and requires support from the SLT, then this item will be escalated to the Senior team meeting at 10:00 with appropriate actions decided and communicated back to the middle management team…

…The visual management boards have a standard layout that follows a 1-3-10 second rule. In 1 second you can tell if a team is winning or losing, (orange laminate) via hourly outputs that are recorded and marked with a red or green indicator to show if on target for that hour or not. In 3 seconds you can tell how the KPI charts are trending (blue laminate). In 10 seconds you can tell what the team is doing about those areas where they are losing or trending below their target (green laminate). The board also includes pictures of the team members, a safety cross for each day of the month with a tracker for appropriate safety actions and a thank you sheet to enable people to thank whom they wish for helping each other out during their work activities…

Equally important to the above extracts is the need to extend the concept of LSW in the TPM context beyond visual boards to see how TPM enables the workplace to 'speak to us as leaders'. As a Leader, the clear visual indicators enable us to ask the question and engage in effective enquirer and coaching conversations. In addition standard walk around routes for equipment with clear visual standards and point of use instructions enable effective system review as part of LSW. Is the asset management system actually working as we expect? Is it driving focused improvement and can I see evidence of this? Are we maintaining standards? Are we enabling teamwork? In response to these challenges the Mylan Rottapharm LSW case study experience goes on to highlight:

…The SLT meet with a production and a support team once a week and review the team's visual management board. Performance metrics and areas that the teams need support are discussed. Each team meets with the SLT at least once a quarter. Both the SLT and middle managers also meet with the people in the company in what are called Gemba Walks. The SLT and middle managers split into small teams and go out and ask people how they are getting on, from both a work and general perspective aimed at engaging with the people in the organisation. These Gemba walks have proven successful in allowing opportunities for improvement to be identified and in some cases explaining why certain policies or procedures are in place. This has helped to create an open and honest culture with people that are also engaged and focused on operational efficiency…

7.1.5 Ten coaching questions

'If you do not know how to ask the right question you discover nothing' Dr Edward Deeming.

Figure 7.4 lists ten coaching questions with explanatory notes which you, the leader, should be asking to help form the basis of generating the right behaviours. The behaviours link into the regular review processes using visual management boards as the point of focus (see also Chapter 3 section 3.1).

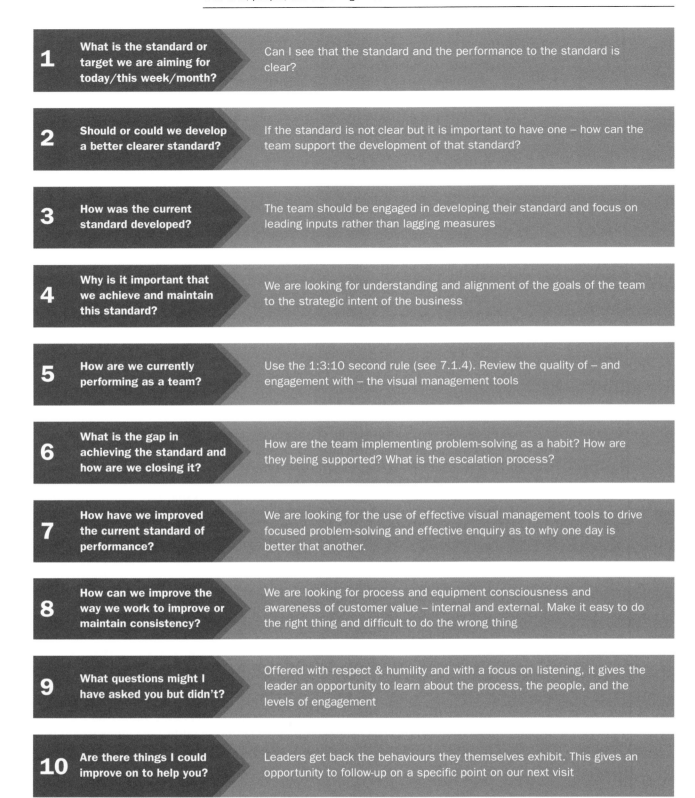

1 What is the standard or target we are aiming for today/this week/month? — Can I see that the standard and the performance to the standard is clear?

2 Should or could we develop a better clearer standard? — If the standard is not clear but it is important to have one – how can the team support the development of that standard?

3 How was the current standard developed? — The team should be engaged in developing their standard and focus on leading inputs rather than lagging measures

4 Why is it important that we achieve and maintain this standard? — We are looking for understanding and alignment of the goals of the team to the strategic intent of the business

5 How are we currently performing as a team? — Use the 1:3:10 second rule (see 7.1.4). Review the quality of – and engagement with – the visual management tools

6 What is the gap in achieving the standard and how are we closing it? — How are the team implementing problem-solving as a habit? How are they being supported? What is the escalation process?

7 How have we improved the current standard of performance? — We are looking for the use of effective visual management tools to drive focused problem-solving and effective enquiry as to why one day is better that another.

8 How can we improve the way we work to improve or maintain consistency? — We are looking for process and equipment consciousness and awareness of customer value – internal and external. Make it easy to do the right thing and difficult to do the wrong thing

9 What questions might I have asked you but didn't? — Offered with respect & humility and with a focus on listening, it gives the leader an opportunity to learn about the process, the people, and the levels of engagement

10 Are there things I could improve on to help you? — Leaders get back the behaviours they themselves exhibit. This gives an opportunity to follow-up on a specific point on our next visit

Figure 7.4: Ten coaching questions for leaders to explore

7.2 **TPM Infrastructure & governance model**

Figure 7.5 shows the site master rollout plan being driven by pillar champions (on the left) supported by the top-down site leadership governance team (the triangle), with bottom-up shift team activity around the 11-step TPM process and 5S workplace organisation. The TPM journey or 'maturity' progress is determined by both top-down and bottom-up regular and evidence-based audit processes shown on the right side of the figure.

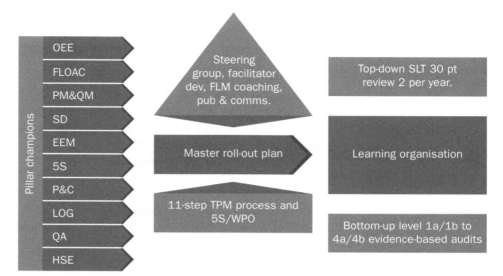

Figure 7.5: TPM infrastructure and governance model

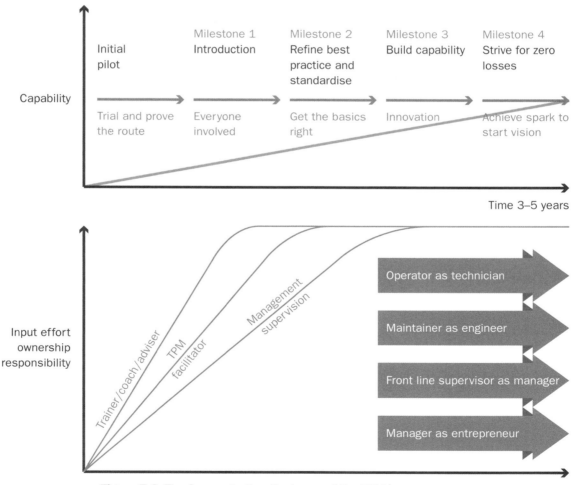

Figure 7.6: The four maturity milestones of the TPM journey

Ultimately the success and sustainability of the TPM process will depend on the degree and extent of management commitment and their visible, proactive support. The rollout plan builds on experience gained during the initial TPM pilot process application to ensure that the four maturity milestones of MS1 Introduction, MS 2 Refine Best Practice and Standardise, MS3 Build Capability and

MS4 Strive for Zero losses, becomes a reality. As such, TPM becomes a 'way of life' through self-managed teams as illustrated in Figure 7.6.

7.3 **The role of pillar champions and policy deployment**

In TPM, the pillar champion's role is to establish and then implement a relevant and robust policy to support the adoption of the founding principles of TPM.

Ultimately the policy is about problem-solving and prevention. It centres on intentions, choices and expectations.

These intentions and expectations provide a fluid set of ground rules rather than a detailed prescription for action.

These intentions are expressed through four linked phases or maturity milestones contained within the master rollout plan. Each builds on capability developed during the previous milestone programme.

Table 7.1 shows typical pillar champions for

- overall equipment effectiveness
- front line operator asset care (sometimes referred to as autonomous maintenance)
- planned maintenance and the quality of maintenance
- skills development (generic) as in team working, problem solving & IT skills
- skills development (technical) as in hand /operational equipment specific skills
- 5S-workplace organisation to create flow
- early equipment management & capital projects
- publicity and communications

… together with three site-wide support subject matter experts in logistics, quality, and health, safety and environment.

The core purpose and role of a pillar champion can be summarized as

- to understand what is required as a specific champion in order to drive continuous improvement using the TPM 'enabling' tool
- to then develop the policy for your pillar and ensuring its consistent deployment.

Table 7.1 Typical pillar champions

Pillar champion	Typical job holder
OEE	Value stream managers (+fin manager)
FLOAC	Production manager (shift supervisors)
PM & Q of M	Maintenance manager
Skill development (generic)	Human resources manager
Skill development (technical)	Production manager
5S – workplace organisation	Shift supervisors (production manager)
EEM/major projects	Manufacturing engineering manager
Publicity and communications	TPM facilitator
(Logistics)	Planning manager
(Quality)	Quality manager
(HSE)	HSE manager

7.4 **Top-down 30-statement review process**

Progress is assessed against the intentions and outcomes contained in the master rollout plan using a top-down 30-statement review audit. This is carried out every six months by the pillar champion team. Each of the 30 statements are audit check points, each of which is aligned to a specific pillar champion, so there is clear accountability and hence no escape.

In Table 7.2 are the seven headline lead-in criteria and attributes that we are looking for when the pillar champions carry out the biannual top-down 30-point review.

Table 7.2 Lead-in criteria & attributes for 6-monthly top-down review by pillar champions

	Support for characteristics of operational excellence
Business management strategy	Customer value focus
	Seen to reduce lead times (customer expectations, operations response, new product introduction)
	Align production cycle with demand profile
Infrastructure and technology	Process based organisation rather than functional
	Control variation then reduce it through equipment & process capability. Stabilise then optimise (attack sporadic then chronic losses)
Systems in place and working	Simple , effective, engaged visual systems: short interval scheduling or control by shift
	Easy to do right and difficult to do wrong
	Condition based and prevention focus to deliver process optimisation via pull logistics
Objective feedback	Shared objectives, single agenda for change
	Shop floor evidence based recognition
Training and skill development	Formalise and standardise best practice
	Simplify and fool proof
	Capture lessons learned & build capability to give flexibility towards versatility
Cultural indicators	Continuous improvement as part of 'the way we do things here': management 'trust to delegate' to give true bottom-up 'ownership'
Motivation	100% involvement – let operators have the first chance to solve problems

Figure 7.7 shows the basic matrix of the top-down audit with the extent of management encouragement compared with the degree of employee involvement.

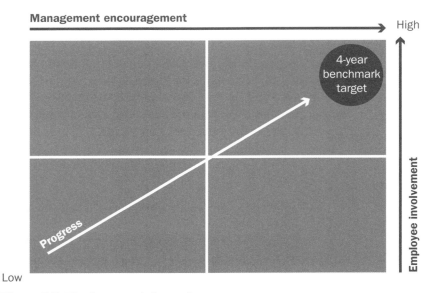

Management encouragement High

Low

Figure 7.7: The framework for audit

In Figure 7.8 we use a grid to illustrate how the top-down 30-point statement is a journey which is articulated as a strategic intention (bottom left corner) and is progressively delivered over three to four years (towards the top right hand corner).

This will result in a position on the overall grid as illustrated in Figure 7.9. Figure 7.10 shows an example of progress over three years of an exemplar and Shingo Silver Medallion award winning company. Mylan Rottapharm has followed, and used to full effect, the 11-step TPM enabling tool (the full case study is described in Chapter 10).

Optimise value creation processes, set new market agendas

Align business model with customer priorities. Formalise current value creation processes. Define core specialist competencies

Establish/identify basic systems & then secure reliable processes & equipment standards

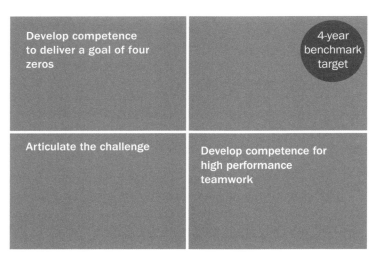

Deliver excellent recognition and motivation to continuously improve

Establish foundations for empowerment & team based roles

Provide visible information to engage workforce, build trust to overcome limiting behaviours

Figure 7.8: From strategic intention to actual delivery

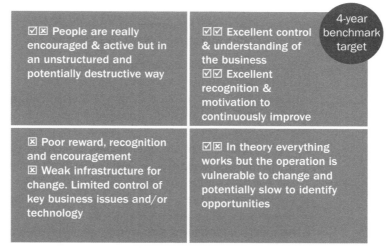

Figure 7.9: How to interpret the result

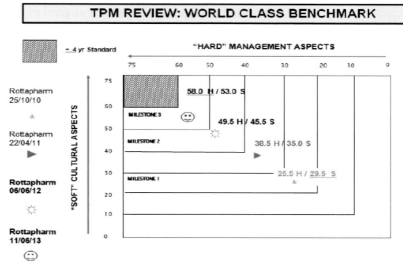

Figure 7.10: Example of progress over three years at Shingo winner Mylan Rottapharm

Further details of the 30-point top-down review process are shown in Appendix 7.1. It details the 30 vision statements, categorised into the seven headings in Table 7.2 together with a rating system.

Alignment of top-down audit with Shingo model

Within the Shingo Model there are ten guiding principles which can also be described as behavioural attributes under the focuses as listed here.

Cultural enablers focus
- Respect every individual
- Lead with humility

Continuous improvement focus
- Flow and pull value
- Assure quality at the source
- Seek perfection
- Focus on process
- Embrace scientific thinking

Enterprise alignment & results focus

- Think systematically
- Create constancy of purpose
- Create value for the customer

These behavioural attributes can be described in the sense of positive work styles and attitudes including team working and effective communication.

It is recognised within the Shingo Model that employees practicing the following three insights are more likely to deliver a sustainable business strategy through systems of work such as TPM.

- **Ideal results require ideal behaviours** To achieve ideal results, leaders should do the hard work of creating a culture where ideal behaviours are expected and are evident in every employee.
- **Purpose and systems drive behaviour** Systems have a profound effect on behaviour – and maintenance is a system of work.
- **Principles inform ideal behaviours** Principles are foundational rules that govern the consequences of behaviours. The more deeply people understand principles, the more they understand ideal behaviour, and the better they can design systems which will help drive that behaviour to achieve ideal results.

The TPM system of work can be readily aligned to the Shingo Model's ten behavioural attributes. This is set out by demonstrating the ideal behaviours for TPM to help deliver each of the ten attributes over the four 'maturity' milestones of the TPM journey. This is positioned from the three perspectives of leaders, managers and associates/front-line employees.

Each relevant statement is aligned to one or more review questions, as detailed in Appendix 7.1, through alphanumeric identifers (for example, A3 refers to question 3 in section A). Table 7.3 shows one example of the ten attributes (in this case respect every individual) and Table 7.4 shows a summary of the applicable 30-vision statements' alignment at the three job levels across all ten attributes within the three insights of operational excellence.

Table 7.3 Respect every individual

Because we believe: If we enable people they will find their own ways of doing things better

Job level	Specific '30-point vision' statements which apply	Number
Leaders create a safe and productive work environment, where the safety of all people is the highest priority.	A2, D1, E1 & E2	4
Managers regularly review the skills and competencies required of all associates and work with each one to provide appropriate opportunities for all to gain new insights.	E1 through to E6	6
Associates take full responsibility to make the most out of development opportunities provided by the organisation.	D2, D3, E1, E2 & E6, F1 to F4, G1 to G3	12

Table 7.4 Relevant '30-point vision' statements for each job level

3 focuses, 10 guiding principles	Leader	Manager	Associate
Cultural enablers			
Respect every individual	4	6	12
Lead with humility	9	11	16
Continuous improvement			
Flow and pull value	4	3	11
Assure quality at the source	5	4	8
Seek perfection	2	7	5
Focus on process	7	10	11
Embrace scientific thinking	7	5	4
Enterprise alignment & results focus			

Think systematically	8	3	10
Create constancy of purpose	7	7	5
Create value for the customer	3	3	6
No. of relevant check point statements occasions	**56**	**59**	**88**

7.5 Bottom-up, evidence-based, maturity audit process

As shown in Figures 7.5 and 7.6, the bottom-up evidence-based activity audits measure progress across the four maturity milestones of TPM to support the implementation of the master roll-out plan. The audit establishes a foundation for developing and then sharing best practice. It also provides data to support problem-solving tools and techniques and the motivation to improve.

Pillar champions direct and encourage how this is done by the way they set expectations, support delivery, set priorities and give recognition.

Co-ordinating the progress of front-line associate teams through the bottom-up audit steps provides the mechanism to implement and refine company policy and promote organisational learning.

The senior leadership team (often as pillar champions) will need to change some of their ways of working in order to create the right environment for TPM to become a *sustainable* system. This will include:

- Refocusing organisational goals to reflect the new environment
- Changes in information focus (both bottom-up and top-down) of measures to enhance understanding and share knowledge to improve management decision-making.
- Reviewing management decision processes to focus on systematic thinking.
- Ensuring reward and recognition systems align activities with top-level objectives.
- Significant emphasis on pull-through improvements – rather than push-down initiatives – where employees have the opportunity to create positive results rather than react to circumstances.
- Enhancing supplier/customer relationships both internally and externally.

The four maturity milestones of the TPM journey have checkpoints in the bottom-up evidence-based four-level audits that continue to raise standards and track progress.

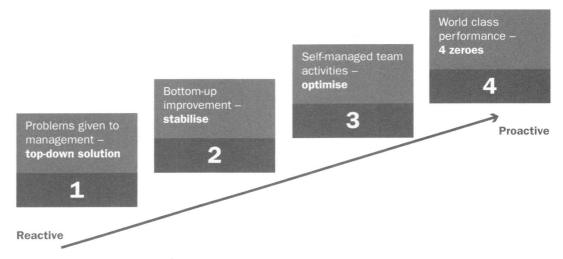

Figure 7.11: The four maturity milestones of TPM

Figure 7.11 shows what TPM sets out to do: to minimise process variability, by gaining control at milestone 1 (MS1) and then moving to stabilised conditions (MS 2) and then to optimised conditions (MS3) and then onwards towards the four zeros of zero accidents, zero defects, zero interventions and zero breakdowns (MS4).

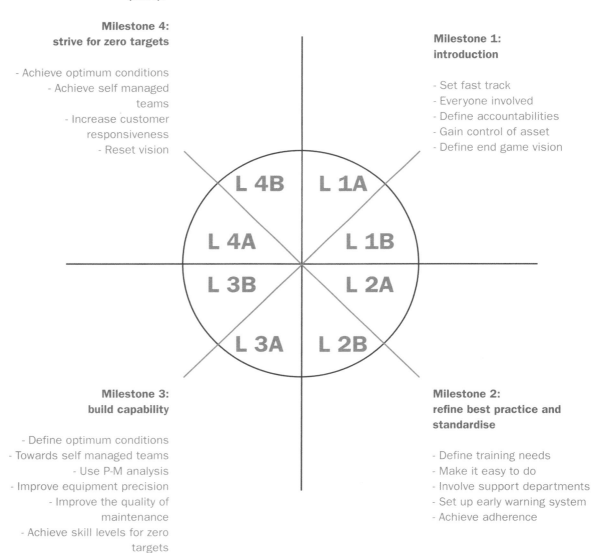

Figure 7.12: The TPM 'learning by doing' journey

In the cultural/behavioural sense, we are in parallel moving from top-down control (MS1) to bottom-up improvement via engagement (MS2) and then towards self-managed teams (MS3) and then striving towards the four zeros (MS4).

In Figure 7.12 each of the four levels of the bottom-up evidence-based audits have 20 specific check points (10 at level 1A and a further 10 at Level 1B and so on, through to the final 10 check points at level 4B, making a total of 80 across the four milestones).

Broadly speaking ,we can categorise each of the 80 check point audit criteria under one or other of these four main groupings shown in Table 7.5. Audit check points type A and B are both 'Hard & Physical Equipment related', whilst audit check point types C and D are 'Soft, Cultural & hence Behavioural related'.

- A: Asset performance improvement metrics
- B: Equipment reliability & predictability through targeting the six classic equipment losses
- C: Building hand/operational skills capability, including the progressive transfer of tasks from maintenance technicians to operators
- D: Individual and collective behavioural development toward minimising door-to-door management losses and hence towards self managed teams

Table 7.5 Primary focus of audit checkpoints

Grouping	Level 1A 1B	Level 2A 2B	Level 3A 3B	Level 4A 4B
A: Asset performance improvement metrics	4	7	-	2
B: Equipment reliability & predictability	11	9	7	6
C: Building hand/operational skills capability	3	3	6	-
D: Individual and collective behavioural development	2	1	7	12
Audit checkpoint total	**20**	**20**	**20**	**20**

If for example, we wanted to know which audit check points at which specific milestone addresses category C grouping around building hand/operational skills capability including transfer of tasks from maintenance technicians to operators, then the typical (but not exhaustive) examples of the specific check point audit statement at each milestone that address the above C group characteristics are shown in Table 7.6.

Table 7.6 Category C grouping around building hand/operational skills capability

Milestone (MS)	Strapline	Audit checkpoint	Statement/question
1	Introduction	Level 1b-CP 7	Are there **SPLs** for correct operation, key parameters, setup, interlocks, safety, visual inspection?
1		Level 1b-CP10	**Evidence of training in basic maintenance techniques** (e.g. lubrication, hydraulics, bolt tightening)
2	Refine best practice & standardise	Level 2a-CP 2	Are equipment operating and **TPM standards established** for all equipment? (See standards list)
2		Level 2a-CP 3	Is there a **systematic training process in place** for all operating and TPM standards?
2		Level 2a-CP 5	Is there a **standard** for equipment condition (to reduce accelerated deterioration)?
2		Level 2b-CP 3	Are all routine **activities** standardised and **routinely improved**?
2		Level 2b-CP 9	Are **routine maintenance** activities **simplified** for completion by suitably **trained operators**?
3	Building capability	Level 3a-CP 2	Are **task transfer priorities (M to O) identified**?
3		Level 3a-CP 3	Are **routine service activities transferred to operators**? (thermometer? injection needle?)

Table 7.6 Category C grouping around building hand/operational skills capability

Milestone (MS)	Strapline	Audit checkpoint	Statement/question
3		Level 3a-CP 6	Are **parameters for sustaining optimum conditions identified and actions to deliver** them in place?
3		Level 3a-CP 7	Is **basic maintenance training for non-operating personnel** in place?
3		Level 3a-CP 9	Have **specialist engineering/skills been used to optimise process/quality capability**?
3		Level 3a CP 10	Has **precision of testing** been **defined** to support assessment of **optimum conditions**?
3		Level 3b-CP 5	Are all **routine activities transferred** to front line teams?
3		Level 3b-CP10	Has the **workplace been refined to support task transfer & team autonomy**?
4	Towards zero targets	Level 4a-CP 7	Is there a **process** in place to support **team self-management**?
4		Level 4a-CP 9	Do shift teams **manage their own skill analysis**?
4		Level 4b-CP 1	Are shift teams involved in **setting their own budgets/KPIs**?
4		Level 4b-CP 6	Defect levels **minimised & stabilised** – with plans to increase precision-CPK capability
4		Level 4b-CP 7	Shift teams **set & manage their own training plan**

The above example also helps to explain the TPM 'maturity' journey in terms of progressive capability, being delivered by people – especially maintainers and front line operators – equipped with the skills and mindsets to do so.

These bottom-up evidence-based audit processes need to be placed in the context of the complementary top-down 30-point audit review process completed by pillar champions twice a year as described in Sections 7.2, 7.3 and 7.4.

The full details of the four maturity milestone bottom-up evidence-based audit review processes, including their alignment to help deliver the Shingo Model, are shown in Appendices 7.2 and 7.3. Appendix 7.2 shows each of the eight audit sheet lay-outs, each with 10 audit criteria statements and a scoring system from milestone level 1A to milestone level 4B. Appendix 7.3 illustrates a live example of a level 2a/2b completed audit sheet, together with the TPM team's celebration sheet to be posted line-side on their TPM activity board.

The TPM system of work can deliver each of the ten Shingo Model behavioural attributes over the four maturity milestones of the TPM journey. This is given from the perspective of the bottom-up evidence-based audit process aligned to four typical statements for each of the ten Shingo behavioural attributes.

Table 7.7 Seek perfection

Behaviour	Potential impact of TPM*	At what milestone onwards
We document our work processes and make them visible so everyone can see how work flows.	3	MS1
My organisation looks at the process as the primary cause of error, as opposed to blaming people first.	2 to 3	MS1
We always focus on improving the process rather than just creating temporary workarounds.	2 to 3	MS3
All parts, materials, information, etc. are ready when they are needed to keep the work moving.	2	MS1
% Significance	**83%**	

Impact: 0 = zero impact, 1 = some impact, 2 = significant impact, 3 = major impact

Table 7.7 illustrates one of the ten guiding principles (in this case 'Seek perfection') and shows an 83% 'significance' of TPM's potential ability to deliver that specific Shingo attribute/guiding principle. The percentage significance is arrived at by adding up the four ratings, which in this example is 10 out of a possible 12 maximum, which as a percentage is 83%.

Table 7.8 shows the summary picture of TPM's impact on all 10 Shingo guiding principles with a potential significance score of 76%.

Table 7.8 TPM impact on Shingo guiding principles

Principle	% Significance
1. Respect every individual	71%
2. Lead with humility	79%
3. Flow and pull value	79%
4. Assure quality at the source	67%
5. Seek perfection	83%
6. Focus on process	100%
7. Embrace scientific thinking	67%
8. Think systematically	71%
9. Create constancy of purpose	71%
10. Create value to the customer	75%
Total significance	**76%**

It is important to note that these assessments and judgements have been made with the help of two exemplar TPM practitioner companies one of which, Mylan Rottapharm, was awarded the Shingo Prize.

7.6 Emphasizing teamwork between operators and maintainers

One way of describing the TPM journey and the way in which both the maintenance technicians' and operators' use of time and skill sets are progressively developed more productively is to review Figure 7.13 (we used this same figure and profile in Chapter 3.2).

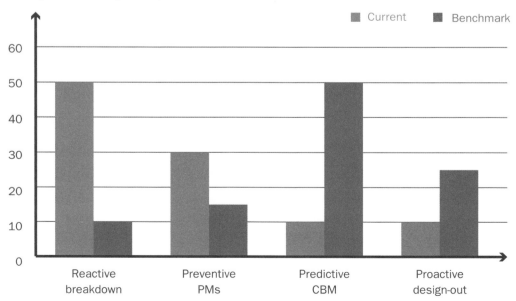

Figure 7.13: Maintenance time allocation: current vs three-year benchmark

Without repeating the detail here, it is worth stressing two key points:

- The whole philosophy around TPM centres on teamwork between the operator and the maintenance technician in sharing responsibility for the health and reliability of their equipment assets. So we need to view and consider both roles together in order to define who does what – and hence the why, when and how. We encourage the analogy that healthy equipment is just like a healthy body. In this scenario the operator is the nurse of the asset (the patient) and the maintenance technician is the doctor (and occasionally the surgeon in an emergency).
- There are three factors to be mindful of when explaining 'autonomous maintenance' or, as we prefer to call it, front line operator asset care checks (FLOACs).
  - These health checks probably don't get done by anyone at the moment (so it's not a hidden agenda to get the operator (the nurse) to do the maintenance technician's job (the doctor)
  - Those front line checks do not involve using any spanners, screwdrivers – far less voltmeters
  - They are developed with both the operator *and* the maintenance technician – who also helps train the operators to carry them out via single point lessons and standard work. This is the focus of Step 8 of the 11-step TPM process.

So it can be stated with some conviction that adopting the TPM philosophy enhances – rather than dilutes – the skill sets of both the operator and maintainer.

7.7 **The four milestones and seven steps of AM**

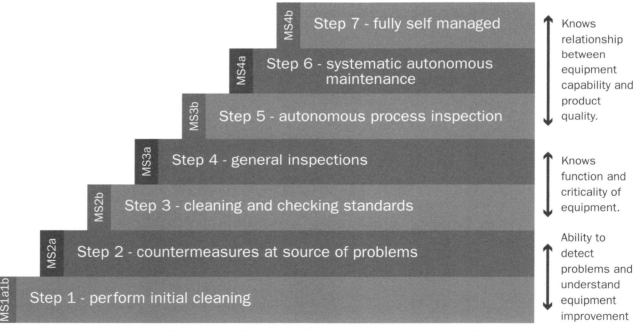

Figure 7.14: Alignment of four maturity milestones with the seven steps of autonomous maintenance

The Japanese evolved the concept of TPM during the 60s, 70s, 80s and beyond through work by various luminaries and experts such as Seiichi Nakajima's *Introduction to Total Productive Maintenance* (1988, Productivity Press, Cambridge, MA) and subsequent numerous publications through the Japan Institute of Plant Maintenance where the principle of the seven steps of autonomous maintenance were clearly defined as being central to the TPM philosophy. As authors and practitioners of TPM we are indebted to these early and brilliant insights.

The seven steps of autonomous maintenance are strongly aligned with the four milestones of our TPM model. As discussed in some detail in Section 7.5, there are evidence-based audit criteria for each milestone, each comprising ten check points at each level – a total of 80 check points over the TPM journey towards self-managed teams.

Figure 7.14 illustrates that alignment with the seven steps of autonomous maintenance. Within each of the milestones there are audit criteria which relate specifically either to hardware/equipment performance goals or to people-development goals. These people-development criteria relate to both hand/operational equipment-specific skills as well as to the generic, softer skills of, for example, team working, problem solving and IT. Each audit criterion must be judged on evidence – both visual and written – and not on hearsay or opinions. Similarly the numeric key performance indicators within the audit checkpoint criteria must not only be relevant to the business but also designed to drive the right behaviours, as described earlier in this chapter.

7.8 **TPM programme governance**

In order to provide an effective TPM programme governance system it is very important to position TPM as **an addition** to what we are already doing on our operational excellence programme rather than setting up a separate **instead of** governance infrastructure.

The example at Figure 7.15 illustrates this integration issue with a company that already has a significant track record of continuous improvement and where TPM has been integrated within the existing operational excellence programme governance.

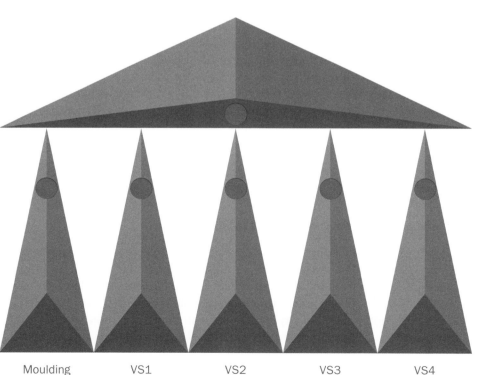

OpEx group level 1
Chair: site lead
VSMs + moulding manager
+ eng manager
(+ logistics + HSE + QA
PCs as required)
Site CI/TPM coordinator
(+ publicity and
communications)

Monitoring group - level 2
VSMs + moulding manager
Site CI/TPM coordinator
Local TPM facilitators and
team leaders
Shift-based TPM-CI team +
area 5S activity
Team leaders + operators
+ maintainers

Moulding   VS1   VS2   VS3   VS4

Figure 7.15: TPM organisation and governance

Figure 7.15 refers to a full time site CI/TPM co-ordinator (or facilitator) who is the essential link between the site-wide and local value stream or production supply level TPM activity.

As well as this structure, it is equally important to spell out the terms of reference for the TPM element of the company's CI activities at both the site and local value stream or production department level as described here.

7.8.1 Terms of reference for site CI/TPM governance group Level 1

- To provide the CI TPM governance group with a monthly TPM progress update
- To communicate and co-ordinate the CI TPM activity across the company site
- To ensure that any roadblocks to progress are escalated, addressed, action agreed, and resolved
- To establish the level of resource and infrastructure to support the TPM activity site-wide and agree the key success and risk assessment factors
- To establish the TPM policy and procedures and their consistent deployment for the site operations via the pillar champions
- To set up the necessary TPM audit, review and measurement process for the four implementation milestones (both top-down 30-point bi-annual review, plus bottom-up level 1a to 4b evidence-based audit processes)
- To establish common TPM training programmes, materials, procedure and completion criteria for TPM (from pilots to roll out to continuous improvement).

7.8.2 Terms of reference for the TPM monitoring group

This group, at the local value stream/production unit Level 2, meets monthly just ahead of the CI/TPM governance steering group:

- To review regular and detailed updates of the TPM pilot projects progress within the manufacturing value streams and any common feeder production supply areas
- To monitor and conduct the TPM audit & review and measurement process for the four implementation milestones (bottom-up Level 1a to 4b) plus regular waste/5S/asset care Gemba-focused walks and morning meeting reviews
- To confirm TPM pilot meeting dates set by the facilitators, to ensure these meetings take place, and that equipment is released for any essential planned refurbishment, planned maintenance and asset care activities
- To ensure examples of best practice are being fully exploited, including temporary secondment of staff to generate standard operating procedures
- To ensure that any local roadblocks to TPM progress are addressed, action agreed and resolved and if not, are escalated to the Level 1 CI /TPM governance group.

7.9 Some further considerations

The word Lean has some sad connotations and meanings to the uninitiated. Most people think being lean is doing the same with less and unless you enlighten them straight away you won't get much support, far less sustainability. It needs to be spelt out at the outset, without any jargon, that lean thinking is about maximizing value added through the elimination of waste in all its guises – and we can all buy into that.

Yes, it can be apparently complex, so we find it useful to divide the sustainability issues into two main categories – the mechanics (hard, management issues) and the culture (soft, behavioural issues).

The mechanics part is relatively easy to define and comprises the three main elements of

- Infrastructure and governance, which has clear leadership, definition and direction, with steering groups and pillar champions
- Selecting and using the right mix of the well-proven lean tools and techniques
- Measuring progress against well-defined milestones which have robust audit and review exit points that can be pinned back to specific pillar champions.

This leaves the more difficult part of generating the right behaviours and a culture where all of your staff – from the CEO to the operating floor – want to continuously challenge and change 'the way we do things here'. This is easy to state, more difficult to deliver as a sustainable belief. This is why we have stressed in this chapter the need for robust audit and review processes that align with the leadership and cultural challenges implicit and embedded in the Shingo Model.

However, bear in mind that as an employee – whatever my 'rank' – I will do something different on four conditions:

- First, you actually seek and ask my opinion about the best way of doing this task.
- Secondly, subject to safety and conformity, you actually embody that opinion in our future ways of working.
- Third, you tell me the result, and ...
- Fourth, you give me the training and time to do something about that result.

Conversely, if you impose your solution on me through your fancy new system – sure, I'll tick a few boxes for you but I will not actually take responsibility or ownership of the result. In fact I'll tick the boxes at the start of my shift. Why is this the case? Because I have no 'ownership' of the new system. I do, however, have a mind of gold if you can tap into it.

At the end of the day all I want is a hassle-free shift. It's not because I'm lazy – it's because I really want to work smarter and be an effective part of the team.

It is worth remembering that the traditional team leader's job has changed dramatically over the last few years. Nowadays he or she has three main responsibilities. With the proviso that it has the <u>proactive support</u> of their 'process owner' or manager they have to

- manage and deliver the shift manufacturing processes – on time, in full – for that specific shift
- progressively manage and develop their team members – both individually and collectively
- 'facilitate' some form of target-driven continuous improvement.

The first two are usually both a 'given' and accepted. If the third one is ever regarded as optional it will **not** happen.

All of the above requires a major change in leadership behaviour based on

- **Standards** which are consistently applied (both metrics and behaviours)
- **Responsiveness & pace** when deviations occur (through clear accountability)
- **Continuous improvement** by stretching those standards
- **Striving for perfection** so we continue to make progress
- **Specified value streams** throughout the organisation (not just manufacturing)
- **Respect** for our customer and employees, plus our products and the above standards
- **Autonomy** ultimately putting our people first.

The common denominator in all this is that it is your people who will make the difference. And remember that managers tend to get back the behaviours that they themselves exhibit.

Michelangelo is quoted as saying, around the year 1450,

The greatest danger for most of us is not that our aim is too high and we miss it, but that it is too low and we reach it.

We can interpret this powerful and profound message 570 years later by suggesting:

If we strive for perfection through the four zeros (accidents, defects, breakdowns and unplanned interventions) we may not achieve it, but at least we will be making progress.

The sustainability issues surrounding any continuous improvement programme are considerable, but we hope the above gives you some useful guidance to minimise the risks.

If one strips back everything to the fundamentals then the concept of operational excellence will be difficult to achieve without operational **basics** in place.

This requires an initial and fundamental focus on:

- standard (and safe) operating procedures,
- best-practice workplace organisation/5S
- basic manufacturing process control
- a disciplined, self-determined, TPM-driven asset care regime
- reliable data collection and interpretation
- continuous development and training of your people.

The people part of the three Ps we have explored (purpose, process and people) can be illustrated as in Figure 7.16.

A **sustainable** continuous improvement environment demands:

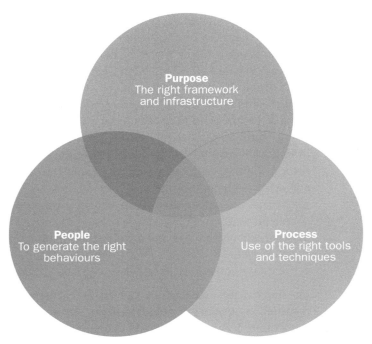

Figure 7.16: The three dependencies

It's your people that will make the difference – but only if they get the right support and encouragement. **This starts and finishes with effective and consistent leadership and direction**.

APPENDIX 7.1
Master TPM top-down 30-point audit document

How the audit sheets' 30 points are laid out under the seven categories of 'A' through to 'G'

Category	Description	No. of Statements
Hard management aspects		
A	Business management strategy	3
B	Infrastructure and technology	4
C	Systems in place and working	7
D1	Objective feedback communication	1
Sub total		*15*
Soft cultural aspects		
D2	Objective feedback communication	2
E	Training and skill development	6
F	Cultural indicators	4
G	Motivation	3
Sub total		*15*
(Check total)		(30)

Category	Vision statement	Assessment		Action
		Score	Comments	
SCORE KEY: 1=Poor, none, zero, 2=Fair, some, little, 3=Adequate, still much scope, 4=Very good, almost there, 5=Excellent, achieved world class.				
A Business management strategy	1 Management understands the value of hidden costs and the 6x major equipment losses			
	2 Management know what TPM adds to their strategy and how to use the benefits of increased capacity, reliability and flexibility to support the achievement of world class performance by striving for zero targets.			
	3 Equipment management is a co-ordinated function from initial design concepts through the complete equipment life cycle.			
	Total A			

Category			Vision statement	Assessment		Action
				Score	Comments	
SCORE KEY: 1=Poor, none, zero, 2=Fair, some, little, 3=Adequate, still much scope, 4=Very good, almost there, 5=Excellent, achieved world class.						
B	Infrastructure and technology	1	Technology issues are understood and under control.			
		2	There are clearly defined equipment management roles and responsibilities.			
		3	All departments play a positive role in improving equipment effectiveness.			
		4	TPM is integrated into the normal fabric of operations management.			
			Total B			
C	Systems in place and working	1	Routine TPM carried out by self-directed teams of operators and maintainers			
		2	Lifetime mainenance systems are in place for all equipment			
		3	Lifetime cost information is available and accurate			
		4	Visual management in use on the equipment, for performance trends, training aids and to support flawless operation.			
		5	Effective problem solving and equipment early warning feedback to design technologists and engineers are in place			
		6	Standard procedures used widely recognising the principles of 5S including the use of shadow boards and lineside stores.			
		7	Appropriate condition monitoring in place.			
			Total C			

Category			Vision statement	Assessment		Action
				Score	**Comments**	
SCORE KEY: 1=Poor, none, zero, 2=Fair, some, little, 3=Adequate, still much scope, 4=Very good, almost there, 5=Excellent, achieved world class.						
D	Objective feedback communication (Hard)	1	Clear priorities are set by management and translated from the management vision into departmental goals in support of maintaining zero targets and world class OEE levels.	☐	☐	☐
			Total D1	☐	☐	Total 'Hard' score (of 75 max)
	Objective feedback communication (Soft)	2	Dedicated 'TPM time' is planned and facilitated to support the application of TPM concepts such as routine maintenance and solving problems for good.	☐	☐	☐
		3	The TPM promotional activities are effectively integrated within the organisation structure so that company values such as customer service drive bottom-up team activities.	☐	☐	☐
			Total D2–3	☐		
E	Training & skill development	1	Personnel are encouraged to enhance skills and improve ability to support the use of TPM concepts.	☐	☐	☐
		2	TPM is understood at every level of the organisation.	☐	☐	☐
		3	TPM training and education is appropriate in terms of scope and depth to the job level in the organisation.	☐	☐	☐
		4	The effectiveness of the TPM training & education is measured in terms of self-assessment and regular feedback. This can include external recognition and accreditation.	☐	☐	☐
		5	Skills training needs analysis has been carried out and matched to the individuals and the tasks/jobs.	☐	☐	☐
		6	Individuals' skills and competence levels are regularly monitored and progressively enhanced.	☐	☐	☐
			Total E	☐		

Category			Vision statement	Assessment		Action
				Score	Comments	
SCORE KEY: 1=Poor, none, zero, 2=Fair, some, little, 3=Adequate, still much scope, 4=Very good, almost there, 5=Excellent, achieved world class.						
F	Cultural indicators	1	Cross-departmental small group problem solving activities are autonomous and self-directed and resourced.			
		2	The small group activities are goal and target driven which are self-monitored at regular and lively group meetings.			
		3	Interest in finding out more is stimulated by simple models and sketches. Maintainers treat breakdowns as an opportunity to train operators.			
		4	There is a clean, bright working environment. Up to date TPM boards and visual methods are used effectively and everywhere to communicate goals and performance results.			
			Total F			
G	Motivation	1	There is a positive response to new ideas and high equipment ownership at all levels throughout the organisation.			
		2	There is an active 'Idea Deployment' system in place with regular and frequent reviews, implementation and appropriate team-based recognition.			
		3	Shop floor teams are encouraged to give presentations of their TPM activities to visitors and also to outside public conferences and seminars.			
			Total G			Total 'Soft' score (of 75 max)
Action summary						

There is a supporting document describing which pillar champion is responsible for each of the specific 30-point vision statements. It includes guidance on the evidence to look for, the tasks to deliver the evidence and the process for getting there, in order to make a realistic judgement.

APPENDIX 7.2
Audit sheet layout

Eight bottom-up audit sheets: checkpoints and scoring criteria.

Level 1A Audit Criteria Sheet

Milestone: Introduction   Level: 1A

Department: Asset :

Auditors: Date:

	Review Point	Assessment	Evidence Indicators
1	Is there a TPM Activity board in place for this improvement Asset		3 = up to date 4 = improved
2	Are Safety Procedures defined		3 = used 5 = improved
3	Workplace initial clear and clean (5S Step 1)		5S Audit Results
4	Equipment initial clean		4 = maintained 5 = improved
5	Cross Shift Supervisor prioritisation		3 = agreed 4 = effective
6	Identification of frequent problems (6 Losses) and root causes fishbone		3 = recorded 5 = improvement
7	PLC/Computer Software Back Up		3 = available 4 = effective 5 = improved
8	Equipment description (Sketch, critical areas, parameters, process flow chart)		3 = acceptable 5 = understood
9	Checkpoints (e.g. pressure, temperature, RPM) and preventive maintenance schedule		3 = available 4 = effective
10	Problem register in place recording equipment history including identification of accelerated deterioration		3 = recording up to date 5 = reduction in stoppages
		TOTAL	

Minimum score 30 = Pass level 1A (With no 1's or 2's)   40 =Proceed to level 1B (With no 3's)

Rating based on procedures/systems which are:

1. Not in place with no plans to address
2. Weak/deficient
3. Able to meet departmental/plant goals with plans to improve
4. Well defined, executed and understood
5. Well defined with a track record of Continuous Improvement

Level 1B Audit Criteria Sheet

Milestone: Introduction   Level: 1B

Department: Asset:

Auditors: Date:

	Review Point	Assessment	Evidence Indicators
1	Workplace neat and tidy (5S Step 2)		Audit Results
2	Have sources of contamination been identified and dealt with		3 = identified, 4 = contained, 5 = eliminated
3	Are cleaning methods and standards set/applied (includes difficult to access areas on equipment identified and addressed)		4 = cleaning time reduced, 5 = significant continuous improvement trend
4	Are equipment operating and TPM standards established for critical equipment (see standards list)		2 = documented, provisional standard, 3 = full standard, 5 = improved
5	Condition appraisal and refurbishment of critical items		3 = completed, 5 = long term prevention
6	Refurbishment plan to raise equipment condition		3 = planned, 4 = completed
7	SPL for correct operation, key parameters, Set up, interlocks, safety, visual inspection		2 = training started, 3 = in use, 5 = improved
8	Use of visual indicators for detecting abnormalities		3 = in use, 4 = improved
9	Joint operator & maintainer improvement actions		2 = started, 3 = examples, 5 = history of success
10	Training in basic maintenance techniques (e.g. lubrication, hydraulics, bolt lightening)		2 = content identified, 3 = priory training complete
		TOTAL	

Minimum score 30 = Pass level 1B (with no 1's or 2's)   40 =Proceed to level 2A (with no 3's)

Rating based on procedures/systems which are:-

1. Not in place with no plans to address
2. Weak/deficient
3. Able to meet departmental/plant goals with plans to improve
4. Well defined, executed and understood
5. Well defined with a track record of Continuous Improvement

Level 2A Audit Criteria Sheet

Milestone: Refine BPR and Standardise   Level: 2A

Department: Asset:

Auditors: Date:

	Review Point	Assessment	Evidence Indicators
1	Are production and maintainer workplace easy to keep clean, and maintain order (5S Step 3)		5S Audit results
2	Are equipment operating and TPM standards established for all equipment (See standards list)		3 = in place, 5 = improved SPL's
3	Is there a systematic training process for all operating and TPM standards		3 = in place, 5 = improved SPL's
4	Are methods of inspection formalised covering moving parts, hydraulic and pneumatic, electrical, nuts & bolts		Supported by SPL's & training matrix
5	Is there a standard for equipment condition (to reduce accelerated deterioration)		3 = maintained, 5 = improved
6	Are sources of contamination eliminated		Including human error
7	Are countermeasures to losses such as breakdowns recorded and their effectiveness confirmed		3 = recorded, 5 = improved MTBF improving
8	Are there defined short term priorities to improve the quality of maintenance (rapid response and feedback)		3 = in place, 4 = reduction in number of stoppages, 5 = no sporadic losses MTTR reducing
9	Are there defined short term action plans to extend component life		As 8 above
10	Are there defined action plans to address specific loss areas (e.g. minor stops, reduced speed losses etc.)		As 8 &9 above
		TOTAL	

Minimum score 30 = Pass level 2A (with no 1's or 2's)   40 =Proceed to level 2B (with no 3's)

Rating based on procedures/systems which are:

1. Not in place with no plans to address
2. Weak/deficient
3. Able to meet departmental/plant goals with plans to improve
4. Well defined, executed and understood
5. Well defined with a track record of Continuous Improvement

Level 2B Audit Criteria Sheet

Milestone: Refine BPR and Standardise   Level: 2B

Department: Asset:

Auditors: Date:

	Review Point	Assessment	Evidence Indicators
1	Is 80% or more of maintenance time spent on planned activities		Profile & Trends of Maint Activity (+ MTBF & MTTR&R)
2	Is 80% of spares policy based on effective condition monitoring by operators & maintainer +PM's		Categories & Trends of usage
3	Are all routine activities standardised and routinely improved		Standard Work as BPR's & SPL's
4	Are all locations clearly labelled (where, what and how many)		4 = floor, shelf, bench and cupboards, 5 = improved
5	Has the initial best of best performance targets been achieved		3 = achieved, 5 = outstanding history of improvement
6	Are unit costs reducing		Confirmation from Finance
7	Are production targets met as planned (95% OTIF)		Manuf promise date v. Customer promise dates
8	Are difficult to maintain components/tasks identified and addressed		Planned, implemented & achieved
9	Are routine maintenance activities simplified for completion by suitably trained operators		Planned, implemented and achieved
10	Does documentation make effective use of sketches and diagrams supported by visual indicators		Encourage hand drawn as well as SPL's
		TOTAL	

Minimum score 30 = Pass level 2B (with no 1's or 2's)   40 =Proceed to level 3A (with no 3's)

Rating based on procedures/systems which are:

1. Not in place with no plans to address
2. Weak/deficient
3. Able to meet departmental/plant goals with plans to improve
4. Well defined, executed and understood
5. Well defined with a track record of Continuous Improvement

Level 3A Audit Criteria Sheet

Milestone: Build Capability   Level: 3A

Department: _____   Asset: _____

Auditors: _____   Date: _____

	Review Point	Assessment	Evidence Indicators
1	Are D2D supply chain losses and non-value added activities identified, understood & tackled?		Reflected in TL & Shift Supervisor Job Descriptions + Level 4 WPO / 5S
2	Are task transfer priorities (M to O) identified?		Incl Set Ups / CO's Involvement
3	Are routine service activities transferred to Operators (thermometer? injection needle?)		CBM Training / Intermed & Basic Skills Matrix
4	Is accelerated wear / contamination under control?		Extended MTBF / Reduced Lub Issues
5	Is critical component life stabilised?		Reduced Spares Usage
6	Are parameters for sustaining optimum conditions identified and actions to deliver them in place?		P-M Analysis / 6 Sigma
7	Is basic maintenance training for non-operating personnel in place?		i.e. TL's / Superv's / QA
8	Are areas of human error / safety risk defined and improved?		Level 4 / 5 Error Proofing / Innovations
9	Have Specialist engineering / skills been used to Optimise Process/ Quality capability?		Involvement of Design, Manufact, Process, Tooling Engineers (& OEM?)
10	Has precision of testing been defined to support assessment of optimum conditions?		QA checks / oil D / Thermog / Vba
	TOTAL		

Minimum score 30 = Pass level 3A,(with no 1's or 2's)   40 =Proceed to level 3B (with no 3's)

Rating based on procedures/systems which are:

1. Not in place with no plans to address
2. Weak/deficient
3. Able to meet departmental/plant goals with plans to improve
4. Well defined, executed and understood
5. Well defined with a track record of Continuous Improvement

6

Level 3B Audit Criteria Sheet

Milestone: Build Capability   Level: 3B

Department: _____   Asset: _____

Auditors: _____   Date: _____

	Review Point	Assessment	Evidence Indicators
1	Are external lead times reduced & OTIF Improved for customer?		Charts / Graphs
2	Are short term planning activities carried out by the front line team?		Kanbans / Short Interval Scheduling
3	Is the level of routine intervention reduced?		MS Down /MTBF Extended
4	Are priorities (zero targets) for quality defect reduction identified?		Projects Completed / In Hand
5	Are all routine activities transferred to front line teams?		Basic to Intermediate to Advanced Skills
6	Are opportunities for low cost automation identified / under implementation?		Examples + C/B justification
7	Are quality defect cause / effect relationships understood?		P-M Analysis / 6 Sigma
8	Are level 4/ 5 foolproof devices in place and working?		Examples
9	Has quality of maintenance been maintained?		Projects defined / Executed
10	Has work place been refined to support task transfer / team autonomy?		5S - Level 5
	TOTAL		

Minimum score 30 = Pass level 3B,(with no 1's & 2's)   40 =Proceed to level 4A (with no 3's)

Rating based on procedures/systems which are:

1. Not in place with no plans to address
2. Weak/deficient
3. Able to meet departmental/plant goals with plans to improve
4. Well defined, executed and understood
5. Well defined with a track record of Continuous Improvement

7

Level 4A Audit Criteria Sheet

Milestone: 4 - Strive for Zero Targets   Level: 4A

Department: _____   Asset: _____

Auditors: _____   Date: _____

	Review Point	Assessment	Evidence Indicators
1	Shop Floor (SF) Teams have regular contact with New Suppliers & Customers		Invite to 'Come See'
2	Plan to transfer management routine to Self Directed Teams		Push horizon beyond Shift / Daily SIC towards Weekly /Monthly/Qrtly
3	Improved New Product Introduction lead times		Evidence through Involvement of EEM
4	Critical component life extended		Q of M + P-M analysis, DMAIC / A3 & CPk
5	Priorities for reduced level of intervention defined-No Touch Ops		PCO levels 3 &4
6	Development of self-managed system		See CP2 + Agree with VSM the objectives parameters, frequency and content
7	Process to support team self-management		Set up and monitor CP2 & CP 6
8	SF Teams manage in-bound logistics		SC Logistics-RMat/Kits + Prod. scheduling-SIC
9	SF Teams manage skill analysis		Generic skills v. Hand operational skills-collective and Individual + gap analysis and plan to close
10	Improved measurement of defect levels		P-M analysis, Q of M impact, Process capability. Catch at source
	TOTAL		

Minimum score 30 = Pass level 4A (with no 1's or 2's)   40 =Proceed to level 4B (with no 3's)

Rating based on procedures/systems which are:

1. Not in place with no plans to address
2. Weak/deficient
3. Able to meet departmental/plant goals with plans to improve
4. Well defined, executed and understood
5. Well defined with a track record of Continuous Improvement

8

Level 4B Audit Criteria Sheet

Milestone: Strive for Zero Targets   Level: 4B

Department: _____   Asset: _____

Auditors: _____   Date: _____

	Review Point	Assessment	Evidence Indicators
1	Shop Floor (SF) Teams involved in setting budgets / KPI's		Shifts Patterns & Skill mix, KPI's on unit costs, maintenance costs, energy and labour costs
2	SF Teams Input to future operating strategy		MORSE standards-EEM Project participation, Process Flow Layouts, End to End SC
3	Extend time between intervention		MTBF extending & MTTR&R reducing
4	Predict equipment life (Cradle to Grave)		EEM Involvement
5	Clear support for Zero A's ,D's , MS's & BD's		KPI's for all four Zero's & GAP Boards
6	Defect levels stabilised – plans in progress to increase precision towards optimal		Q of M evidence 6 sigma / Cpk capability
7	SF Teams set & manage own training plan		Including Skills Capability Matrix Internal & external courses
8	SF Teams manage out-bound logistics		Involvement in planning / scheduling routines & warehousing plans
9	Future technology specification standards refined		Inputs of knowledge base to EEM projects-MORSE check lists
10	Regular contact with new customers		Guided tours of their local plant area, Story board presentations-Supply chain visits to customer plants / facilities
	TOTAL		

Minimum score 30 = Pass level 4B, (with no 1's & 2's)   40 = Full TPM Accreditation-Reset the TPM Vision (with no 3's)

Rating based on procedures/systems which are:-

1. Not in place with no plans to address
2. Weak/deficient
3. Able to meet departmental/plant goals with plans to improve
4. Well defined, executed and understood
5. Well defined with a track record of Continuous Improvement

9

APPENDIX 7.3
Audit example

An example of a completed Milestone 2 bottom-up Level 2a/2b evidence-based audit result, together with the TPM team's recognition of success celebration notice.

Milestone: Refine BPR and Standardise
Asset : B2
Auditors: TPM Team Lead and Team+PW

Level: 2A
Zone: VS1
Date: 13th June 2017

	Review Point	Score	Comments
1	Are production and maintainer **workplace easy to keep clean**, and maintain order (5S Step 3)	4 to 5	Very high level because of step 4 standardised routines
2	Are equipment operating and TPM **standards established** for all equipment (See standards list)	4 to 5	8 off examples C/overs down from 3 x hrs to 1 x hr
3	Is there a **systematic training process** for all operating and TPM standards	4 to 5	Yes –and all relevant
4	Are methods of **inspection formalised** covering moving parts, hydraulic and pneumatic, electrical, nuts and bolts	4 to 5	Some good examples re sensors
5	Is there a **standard** for equipment condition (to reduce accelerated deterioration)	5	Exemplary high standards-5 hrs saved per week via operator driven relevant checks
6	Are sources of contamination **eliminated**	5	As above supported by 2 x examples
7	Are **countermeasures to losses** such as breakdowns recorded and their **effectiveness confirmed**	4	4 x solid examples
8	Are there defined short term priorities to improve the **quality of maintenance** (rapid response and feedback)	3 to 4	This meets needs but general need across all cell assets to raise understanding of QofM
9	Are there defined short term **improvement plans to reduce accelerated deterioration**. (Extend component life)	5	8 x excellent actions delivered
10	Are there **defined action plans** to address specific loss areas (eg minor stops, reduced speed losses etc)	5	4 x clear actions supported by 3 x evidence charts

TOTAL SCORE 45.5 Minimum score 30 = Pass level 2A, 40 =Proceed to level 2B
(Proceed subject to cp 8 becoming a 4)

Milestone: Refine BPR and Standardise
Asset : B2
Auditors: TPM Team Lead and Team+PW

Level: 2B
Zone: VS 1
Date: 13th June 2017

	Review Point	Score	Comments
1	Is **80%** or more of **maintenance** time spent on **planned activities**	3 to 4	Answer is YES- but Evidence needs bolstering via MTBF & MTTR&R Evidence
2	Is **80%** of **spares policy** based on effective **condition monitoring** by operators/maintainer	4	All spares ordering now triggered by pull system
3	Are all routine **activities** standardised and **routinely improved**	5	8 x Examples given
4	Are **all locations** clearly **labelled** (where, what and how many)	5	Evidenced by many excellent examples
5	Has the initial **best of best performance targets** been **achieved**	5	45% April 2013- Now 91% =100% improvement in Productive capacity = Choices!!
6	Are **unit costs reducing**	5	1.3 mill 2,400 hrs v.1.3 mill 1,800 hrs = 600 hrs = €29k benefit
7	Are **production targets met** as planned (95% OTIF)	5	Cust Req Date 14% & Manuf Promise Date 10% = 4% positive convergence
8	Are **difficult** to maintain components/tasks **identified** and **addressed**	4	Yes as far as limited opportunity allows
9	Are **routine maintenance** activities **simplified** for completion by suitably trained operators	4	3 x v.good examples given
10	Does **documentation** make effective use of **sketches and diagrams** supported by **visual indicators**	4	4 x high level examples shown

TOTAL SCORE 44.5 Proceed to <u>level 3A</u> subject to CP 1 becoming a solid

Figure 7.17: B2 team's audit results and comments

The TPM team were formally Audited and Assessed on Tuesday 13th June 2017 and passed with the following scores:

Level 2a 45.5 out of 50 – Brilliant !!

Level 2b 44.5 out of 50 – Also Brilliant !!

We can now move on with confidence towards Level 3a/3b

Peter Willmott our external TPM Coach commented...

'The M/c B2 team have done an outstanding job. There is a real sense of achievement around the team – and so there should be!!

This is evidenced by a 100% increase in productive capacity during the last 15 months. Which means the Value Stream can make more choices of flexibility to quickly respond to market challenges – a choice they didn't enjoy 15 months ago.

The B2 team can move on towards 3a/3b with a great deal of confidence.

CHAPTER 8
Early equipment management (EEM)

In this chapter the fifth founding pillar of TPM, early equipment management, is reviewed. Abbreviated to EEM, it is also occasionally referred to as 'TPM for design' to highlight the fact that it is about involving your existing operators and maintainers at the very start of a capital equipment investment – at the concept and definition stage.

Table 8.1 below illustrates the EEM alignment to the four maturity milestones (MS1–MS4), and shows how this alignment between all five foundation pillars moves towards the goal of striving for the four zeros of zero accidents, zero defects, zero breakdowns and zero operator interventions.

Table 8.1 EEM alignment to the four TPM maturity milestones (MS1 – MS4)

5X foundation pillars of TPM	Ms1 introduction	Ms2 refine BP and standardise	Ms3 build capability	Ms4 towards 4 zeroes
Increase OEE	Formalise & gain control	Standardise & in control	Transform & improve	Optimise & able to forecast
FLOAC (AM)	Define	Awareness & training	Practice with support	Self directed
Planned maint & Q of M	Restore	Simplify	Stabilise	Extend
Skill development	Standardise	Improve	Transfer skills	Systemise
Early equipment management	Define	Design	Refine	Improve

8.1 The principles of early equipment management

EEM is a systematic and structured way of using common sense. Namely, if you are going to design or buy a new machine, then make sure you involve the existing operators and maintainers in the vital investment decisions by tapping into their existing practical knowledge at the earliest possible opportunity.

It is generally accepted that a manufacturing organisation's commercial and financial people need to work with their design engineering colleagues at the design concept stage to set the customer expectations and the financial and performance guidelines that a new machine or process has to work within. EEM suggests there is a fourth and vital member of this partnership, and that is 'operations'. The aim here is to acquire a machine or process that is both easy to operate and easy to maintain by considering the views of the existing front-line operators and maintainers at the design concept stage, not when it is too late and/or expensive to change things at the commissioning and ramp-up stage. This knowledge has been acquired through practical experience and exposure to running and maintaining their existing physical assets over the last several months/years.

8.2 Four major considerations embedded in the EEM philosophy

8.2.1 The essential partners in EEM

Behind the plant and equipment used in any operations process there are three functional groups that are the essential partners for new product and equipment introduction, namely:

- Commercial (sales, marketing & finance)
- Engineering (design, product, tooling, equipment, process & procurement)
- Operations (operators & maintainers)

EEM philosophy recognises that these activities must be coordinated and focused on the TPM objectives as a shared responsibility. The partnership requires a sustained drive towards improving project and design management performance through the early identification and elimination of hidden losses such as poor maintainability, operability, reliability, safety and environment (easily remembered as MORSE), as depicted in Figure 8.1. These losses should be picked up, addressed and eliminated early in the equipment design/acquisition process, and not when the equipment arrives on the manufacturing floor for start-up production. The goal might be described as 'flawless operation from day one'. Without EEM the typical result is illustrated in Figure 8.2.

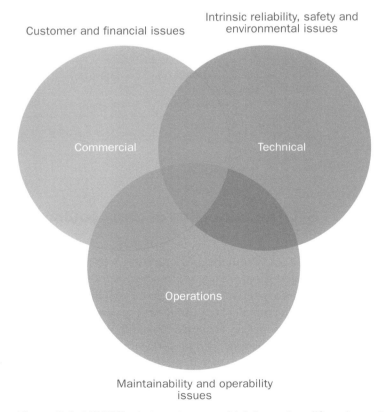

Figure 8.1: MORSE: six target areas which impact on lifecycle costs

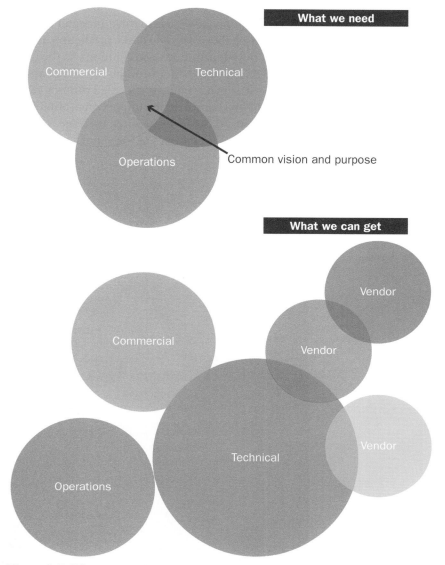

Figure 8.2: What we tend to get without EEM

Typical benefits of adopting the EEM approach are illustrated by these three cameo examples:

- Dry packing: $150k annualised benefits from early management capital project
- Chemical process line: $300k additional annualised benefits from capital project
- Machining centre: new capital investment ramped up to 75% OEE in three weeks against a historical background of circa 45%.

Further, more detailed, case studies are in Section 8.4.

8.2.2 The hidden costs of investment decisions

Like the iceberg shown in Figure 8.3 the true costs of investment decisions are mostly hidden. It is easy to measure the capital expenditure cost when we buy a new machine or process, but the costs of owning the equipment over its lifetime (named here as total lifecycle costs – TLCC) will include

- the cost of ongoing spares
- how much we spend on maintenance
- how much the equipment costs to operate
- the hidden lost-opportunity costs of ineffective performance, and hence low OEE.

An item of equipment costing less than another at the time of purchase may well cost significantly more to run and repair over its useful working life. Only by estimating those ongoing costs, predicting their impact, and comparing the different potential options and solutions 'at the front end' can we understand the added value and hence profitability of that asset over the long term. If the equipment does not meet its specified running rate, and causes safety and/or environmental concerns, the impact on profitability can be significantly greater than the initial differences in purchase price. The EEM process might not resolve all these issues, but it forces us – and our suppliers – to plan, predict and secure better outcomes.

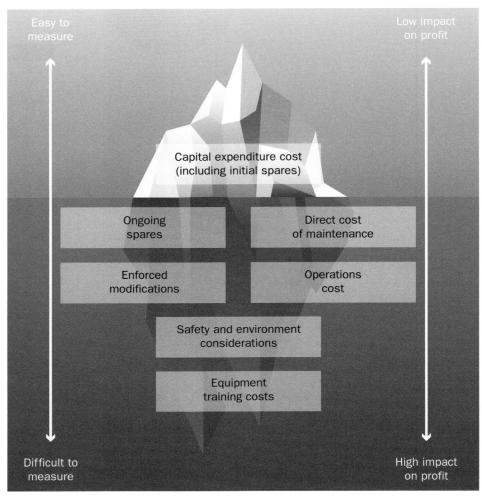

Figure 8.3: The true cost of investment decisions

8.2.3 **Tackling the 'urgency addiction' dilemma**

A dilemma facing many companies is what we might call 'urgency addiction', where project timetables and unrealistic customer 'promises' conspire against getting the appropriate people involved at the right time – at the front-end. Urgent design deadlines mean that ideas are defined and selected and the project moves on to the next phase without sufficient thought, challenge, discussion and debate. The reality – and the accepted wisdom – is that as much as two thirds of total life cycle costs are determined but not yet spent in the early design concept and high-level design specification: hence the need for EEM to be embedded in the TPM system to ensure the early involvement of all parties at this critical stage.

It is important to note here the strong links that EEM provides in the case of new product development (NPD) that demands a rapid response and turnaround time to market. This is especially true in FMCG markets where daily innovation is the life-blood for survival. Tapping into the existing operator and maintainer knowledge base helps get new or major equipment upgrades right at the concept, equipment planning and design-for-manufacture stages. However, having stated the obvious, there may well be huge implications for closing any gaps via continuous skills development where there is, for example, a clear shift away from traditional mechanical linkages towards digital drives and software controls.

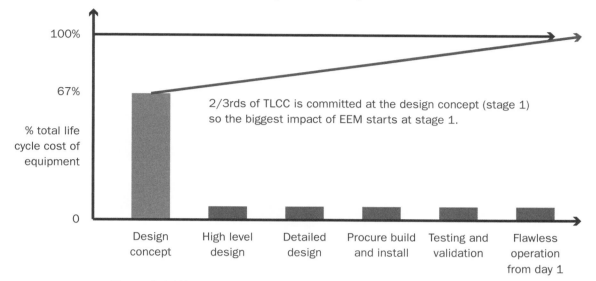

Figure 8.4: Where the costs are committed

In Figure 8.4 six main phases within the 'concept to delivery' cycle are proposed:
- design concept
- high level design
- detailed design
- procure, build and install
- testing and validation
- flawless operation from day one.

Figure 8.5 illustrates how the phases of an asset's life cycle may be managed from an operations and maintenance viewpoint by the four TPM milestone management levels described as define, design, refine and improve, where:

At milestone MS1, Define	=	Concept to delivery.
At milestone MS2, Design	=	High level and detailed design.
At milestone MS3, Refine	=	Fabrication, procurement and build.
At milestone MS4, Improve	=	Testing, commissioning & operations.

The typical management focus and delivery characteristics are shown as outputs on the right-hand side of the figure. The four levels have clear alignment to the four TPM maturity milestones, which are complementary and integral to the five TPM founding principles shown in Table 8.1, EEM alignment to the four TPM maturity milestones.

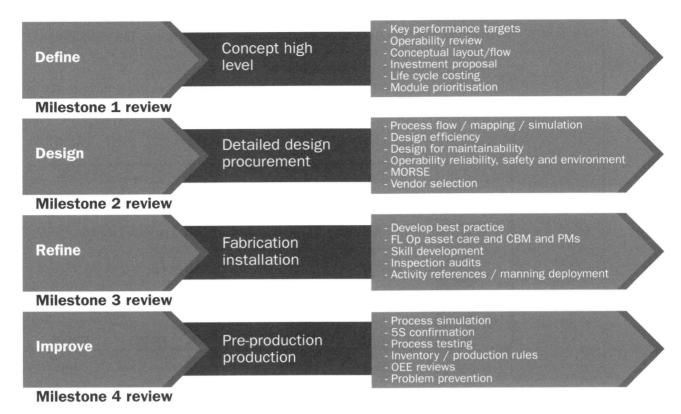

Figure 8.5: The EEM route to vertical start-up from day one

8.2.4 What enhancements can EEM bring to the business?

In order to identify what 'additionality' EEM can bring to a company's existing new product development, and hence new equipment processes, we need to highlight the rationale as follows:

There are three main 'TPM for design' techniques used via EEM:

- objective testing
- knowledge-base management
- milestone management

and these are illustrated in Table 8.2 as the potential contribution which EEM delivers by focusing on maintenance prevention, and the operator's contribution and impact.

Table 8.2 Potential contribution of EEM

Technique	Design for manufacture	Operational weakness	Alternative technology process options
Objective testing of new ideas	✔	✔	✔ ✔ ✔
Tapping into existing knowledge	✔ ✔ ✔	✔ ✔ ✔	✔ ✔
Milestone management	✔	✔ ✔ ✔	✔

Where ✔ = some contribution, ✔ ✔ = significant contribution,
✔ ✔ ✔ = major contribution

We need to be specific about what we mean by the technique 'tapping into existing knowledge' used in Table 8.2. One of the best ways of doing this, as far as TPM is concerned, is to remind ourselves of what the TPM teams of operators and their maintenance colleagues experience when they work through the eight equipment steps on their TPM pilot projects on existing equipment assets. This means they can bring this knowledge – based on 'learning by doing' – to the next generation of equipment and hence to the EEM party.

This learning experience can be illustrated as shown in Table 8.3, by tapping into the operator's and maintainer's knowledge base.

Table 8.3 Tapping into the operator's and maintainer's knowledge

TPM step	Description	Design concept	High level design	Detailed design	Procure, build & install	Test and validate	Implement and use
1	Sources of info & history			✓	✓	✓	✓
2	OEE performance	Set targets	Assess trade-offs	✓	✓	✓	✓
3	Six loss assessment	Setting zero targets				✓	✓
4	Criticality assessment	Optimum conditions	✓	✓			Support training
5a	Condition appraisal	Feed back current weaknesses	✓	Feed back current experience	Set operation and maintenance standards	✓	✓
5b	Refurbishment programme	Assessment of lifetime costs	✓	✓			
6	Future total asset care			Define	✓	✓	Support training
7	Problem solving: RCA/ FMEA/DMAIC/ A3	Target setting		Build in current experience	✓	✓	✓
8	Best practice routines, standard work			✓	✓	Flawless operation on day 1	Support training

Where: RCA   = Root cause analysis
        FMEA   = Failure modes and effects analysis
        DMAIC   = Define, Measure, Analyse, Improve, Control

8.3 Potential benefits of adopting the EEM approach

What can EEM give us that we are not already getting?

EEM is a proven management system by which front-line manufacturing personnel may participate in the early project phases of concept and design in order to develop equipment that

■ is easier and safer to operate, and is environmentally friendly
■ requires less maintenance, and is more easily maintained when maintenance is required.

This front-end involvement also allows us to define training and skill development needs for maximising the new equipment's performance potential from day one of operations/production.

EEM also recognises that opportunities exist in the concept, high level, design phases to effect change with more leverage than would be possible when compared to a reactive action caused by 'urgency addiction'. This leverage is supported by

- the finance function having a commercial input to verify that such changes meet and improve the goals of total life cycle costing, as opposed to capital acquisition cost only
- the engineering function, having developed feedback procedures to avoid repeating similar problems on other future projects.

Early equipment management has been shown to provide benefits in three main areas of the equipment, the people and the business process, as follows:

Equipment benefits

- Setting a front-end vision to strive for flawless operation from day one production start-up.
- Improved reliability, product quality and productivity.
- Established standard work and best practice procedures before start up, including focusing on the MORSE checklists.

People benefits

- Structured feedback ensures all opinions are considered and respected.
- Prior knowledge and experience is captured and embodied.
- Early involvement builds trust, ownership and realistic expectations.

Business benefits

- Reduction in life cycle costs as a measurable route to increased profitability.
- Milestone sign-offs prompt a regular, structured and precise business review.
- Production ramp-up is faster with key performance indicators agreed and in place before start up.
- In the case of new product development involving new equipment or major upgrades EEM will reduce response time to market.

8.4 **EEM case studies**

The following four case studies taken from different industries show what it is possible to achieve through the diligent application of the EEM principles.

Case study: Food manufacturer

Background

The company wanted to improve profitability of jam- and cream-filled sandwich cakes. It was considering investing capital in automation to reduce labour costs and improve process flexibility.

Case study: Food manufacturer

Opportunity

A cross-functional team of production operators, engineering and technical personnel undertook a design review of the end-to-end process to identify the effectiveness of the design and potential for automation.

The team used an EEM operability review and desktop simulation of the automation concept. They also developed a lifecycle cost model to compare options of full and partial automation with improvement ideas on existing production line assets.

The review identified that although the proposed capital expenditure would improve profitability there were other low-cost solutions which could achieve a similar and more rapid gain. The review also found that improving the precision of an upstream process would create significant savings in materials at the jam/cream filling stage.

Likewise the use of the MORSE checklists prompted questioning and highlighted that pick and place robot suction pads were erratic in terms of repeatability and precision. Further investigation showed that the root cause was mechanical 'backlash' accelerated wear in the location arm mechanism. Initial refurbishment followed by retaining control of this critical physical phenomena through regular and relevant condition monitoring led to dramatically improved material yield performance and also improved visible product quality appearance – all for relatively low cost solutions.

Benefits

The automation project was shelved and the lower cost improvement options implemented. These reduced lifecycle costs by £1.8m over 10 years.

Case study: Aerospace press design and installation

Background

The company was expanding capacity to improve responsiveness and flexibility in line with a company goal of reducing manufacturing lead times. This also formed part of the development of the company's in-house production system for a total equipment management module.

Opportunity

The programme involved a two-day early equipment management workshop with representatives from commercial, engineering and operations to review capital investment plans and specifications. This was followed by a four-week action plan to support the installation of new plant. The EEM workshop idenified current asset design effectiveness and developed specification improvements for future assets. The workshop outputs included installation and commissioning checklists based on the MORSE approach, tailored to their requirements for a new press due to be installed within the following 10 weeks.

Benefits

Lifecycle (10-year) cost savings of £10.5m were found by addressing nine areas of design weakness to improve ease of operation and maintainability. The programme also identified retrospective improvements to current presses to increase capacity by 25 per cent. This included extending time between major maintenance cycles by 50 per cent by reducing reasons for accelerated wear through relevant and proactive condition monitoring. This was made possible by tapping into the knowledge and experience of the front line operators and their maintenance technician colleagues. Sharing this knowledge in a structured way with the design and project engineers resulted in improved understanding of both equipment criticality and failure modes & effects analysis (FM&EAs) and hence better-informed decisions.

Case study: Offshore oil extraction facility

Background
Requirement to develop new techniques to extract oil and gas from fields 500 metres beneath the North Atlantic via production system design, construction and operation for a floating production storage and offload (FPSO) vessel. This involved the conversion of an existing vessel.

The hostile conditions which the FPSO vessel had to operate under added to the importance of trapping problems early and dealing with them before production operations started.

Opportunity
Project teams were created to collate knowledge and translate into design standards for application in this new environment.

The programme involved personnel from three major stakeholders including the vessel constructor, the vessel operator and the field asset owner.

The project challenge demanded open communication across stakeholder boundaries to be able to fully use the knowledge and expertise of each organisation.

This collaborative approach enabled the early equipment management workshops to collate tacit knowledge and translate it into design standards.

These sessions were also used to capture working assumptions and develop checklists for use at future reviews. These reviews focused on working practices and implementation of commissioning activities to trap problems early and assure flawless operation from production day one.

Benefits
The converted FPSO vessel operated as planned. It started up with no significant problems.

The asset-owner manager estimated that the EEM approach had saved four years compared to traditional ways of working. Less than two years after the vessel completed conversion and trial operations, they set a daily production record for the field of 132,000 barrels of oil per day.

Typical of the practical benefit through the early involvement of existing maintenance engineers and equipment operators was the design assimilation and options of essential mezzanine stairs, walkways and floors. Their collective knowledge and experience ensured optimum and safe access to essential prime motors, pumps and generators which would otherwise have been potentially compromised.

The vessel operator also chose to use 16 diesel generators running in high pressure gas for the 50Mw of power generation – the generators were designed to be easily maintained by the marine crew on the ship. In year two, the OEE of 93 per cent for the vessel was best in class for the operator. A sister FPSO (not designed to take account of EEM struggled to achieve an OEE of 55 per cent in the early years of production and was scrapped after 15 years of operation – to be replaced by a new FPSO with a field development cost of £3 billion. The EEM approach FPSO continues to operate successfully and is now in its 22nd year of operation.

Case study: Nuclear fuel waste retrieval butterfly skip handler

Background
Capital investment was being considered to address a bottleneck in the processing of historic waste.

A cross-functional team of production, maintenance and design engineering reviewed the current process to develop a specification for the purchase of improved process and asset hardware.

Case study: Nuclear fuel waste retrieval butterfly skip handler

Opportunity　　　　　　An EEM team carried out a detailed review of the existing assets and processes. This included the retrospective application of the MORSE checklists to ensure safety, environmental, operational and maintainability issues were fully understood and to pin-point conditions and reasons for the current low levels of effectiveness.

　　　　　　　　　　　　As a result of this MORSE-led 'challenge' process, the team were able to identify and implement low cost solutions to the existing physical asset via refurbishment underpinned by a more relevant and enlightened future asset care regime, thus avoiding the need for a new hardware asset.

Benefits　　　　　　　　£1.3m saving in capital avoidance.

8.5 **Benefits that EEM can provide to the business**

Figure 8.6 is a useful way of illustrating the 'before and after' of using EEM. The green line illustrates how the EEM system captures significant total life cycle cost (TLCC) impact changes as improvement opportunities early in the development cycle. This is as opposed to the red line where changes are forced upon the team as expensive retrofit necessities.

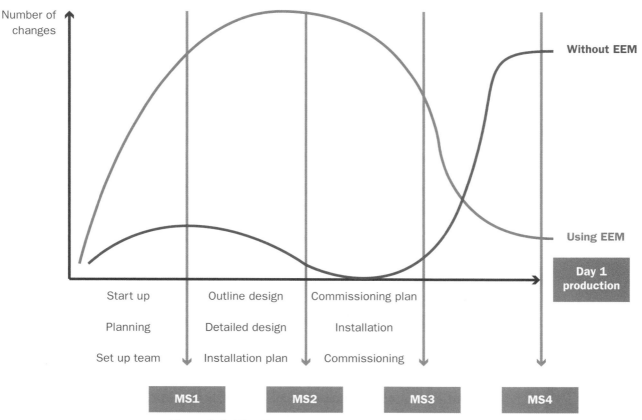

Figure 8.6: Why EEM makes sense

8.6 **Getting started with EEM**

Inevitably there is a lot more detail behind these principles and techniques described above. This section will also refer to four appendices attached to this chapter and referenced as:

- **Appendix 8.1** A typical agenda for a two-day EEM practitioner's workshop.
- **Appendix 8.2** EEM honesty check, as a 10-point exercise.
- **Appendix 8.3** An EEM project data checklist: 16 challenging questions to ask ahead of the start/mobilisation of a new capital project.
- **Appendix 8.4** Shows an example of MORSE checklists (being maintainability, operability, reliability, safety and environment considerations). These illustrate the practical potential of adopting the EEM philosophy as a series of 'what if' questions/checkpoints to ask retrospectively on a recently commissioned and installed capital project, to highlight what would have been done differently if we had used this MORSE checklist tool at the high level design stage.

8.7 **Initial front-end planning**

Typically, an EEM planning day would set out to agree the following:
- Identification of potential upcoming live project(s) in which to trial the EEM philosophy and system.
- The project team structure, its members and their roles & responsibilities.
- The perceived enhancements that the EEM process might bring to the project, taking into account the necessary alignment tailoring to the company's existing new production development (NPD) and new asset systems and processes (as set out and described in the User Requirement Specification (URS)).
- How EEM will enhance (rather than replace) an existing project management tracking processes.
- How knowledge gained through applying the TPM system to existing assets can be transferred and how this will benefit a forthcoming new project involving significant capital expenditure.
- Changes to and expansion of the MORSE checklists to reflect a specific organisation's product technology, vocabulary and resultant asset characteristics.
- The two-day EEM practitioners workshop: attendees, purpose, content, outcomes and timing.

8.8 **EEM practitioners workshop context**

(See also Appendix 8.1 for a typical two-day EEM Practitioner's workshop agenda)

The purpose of the two-day practitioner's workshop is to address, by doing and application, how these activities need to be co-ordinated and focused on business and manufacturing imperatives in order to maximise their potential. This requires a sustained drive towards improving project and design management performance. It also requires that the EEM process is effective as early as possible through eliminating potential hidden losses which arise from poor or inadequate MORSE issues.

In the example given in Appendix 8.1, the intention is to use an upcoming 'XYZ' project to see where EEM could enhance the company's existing and well-proven new production development (NPD) processes. The intention is to use and embed any learning arising from the two-day practical EEM workshop by building on to the existing and well-proven processes as part of their embedded culture of continuous improvement towards operational excellence.

8.9 **Summary**

In this chapter, we have set out to describe how adopting the EEM philosophy within the TPM System can potentially bring significant and measurable benefits to the business. As always it is not a 'one size fits all' solution.

However, the underlying principle of tapping into your existing knowledge base is at the heart of not only classic TPM as applied to the existing asset base, but also for future asset acquisitions.

There is no rocket science involved here. It is the diligent application of common sense by embracing the 'company team' in determining a profitable future.

The huge impact of our emerging technologies within Industry 4.0, both now and in the future, discussed in Chapter 2, means that the EEM philosophy as the fifth founding pillar of TPM has a renewed opportunity to bring the well-proven principles of EEM into clearer reality. We for our part will need to be agile and adapt those principles to the emerging realities.

APPENDIX 8.1
Two-day EEM practitioners workshop

The workshop content; a typical agenda based on a 'live' case study

Workshop Day 1

08.30 Introductions

08.45 Why EEM? – appropriate site leadership member.

09.00 Ice breaker ('world class' sports analogy exercise).

09.15 Our XYZ project & discussion – project leader.

09.40 EEM overview – slide show of what EEM is, and equally what it is not.

10.15 (See Appendix 8.2, attached) EEM honesty check – a ten point exercise in pairs, plus discussion of the results.

10.45 Refreshment break.

11.00 First review – divide delegates into two syndicate teams and carry out an initial review of:

- Current company documentation (this will include the existing eight-step project, tool design and process automation processes; current user requirement specification –URS and project plan Gantt)
- EEM documents. This will include the 16-point EEM project data check-list given in Appendix 8.3, plus the project roles and responsibilities briefing document, and the design process review documents.

12.00 Briefing for manufacturing floor visit for same two teams to conduct a high-level criticality assessment and a retrospective MORSE evaluation (see Appendix 8.4 attached) on two recent (about twelve months old) and hence recently-commissioned equipment assets.

12.30–13.15 Lunch break.

13.15 Go, see, and conduct a) high level criticality evaluation and b) MORSE evaluation.

14.00 Complete the exercise back in the training room and share the results and key learning, plus applying these enhancement tools to the new XYZ project.

15.00 Refreshment break.

15.15 The briefing for tomorrow's second in-depth review of the company's existing eight-gate process and EEM five elements. Review the milestone process, designed as an exercise to map the current state as a brown paper mapping exercise and subject each step to an ECRS challenge which can be described as

- Which of these steps can we eliminate or combine? Or replace or simplify? And then
- Standardise the outputs of this challenge in order to define a future state best practice model to be applied to the XYZ project.

16.00 Discussion of today's key learning points and tomorrow's agenda.

16.30 Close.

Workshop Day 2

08.00 Recap today's intention, split into the same two teams and independently carry out the process mapping exercise on brown paper. Subject the outcome to the above ECRS challenge.

09.30 Start to develop the Future State options.

10.30 Refreshment break.

10.45 Each team will feed back to each other and start to collectively agree a joint best practice future model to be used on the XYZ project as a final version for trialling.

12.30–13.15 Lunch break

13.15 Carry out an exercise in the same two syndicate teams to address the following three questions to assess what has been learned and experienced over the previous day and a half.

- What enhancements can the EEM philosophy bring to our existing company's NPI processes and their associated capital expenditure processes?
- What will stop these enhancements taking hold?
- What countermeasures need to be carried out to minimise the risks?

14.00 Decide an action plan regarding the way forward in terms of the what, how, when, and who, using the roles & responsibilities document and a monthly project review governance forum using the design process review five milestones format.

15.00 Feed back to the site leadership team the key learning points and propose the way forward for the XYZ project.

15.45 Workshop evaluation & close.

APPENDIX 8.2

Where are you now with your EEM practices?

In order to position where you are now in your EEM practices it will be a useful exercise to complete the following 10-point evaluation as a joint activity with, say, two representatives each from the financial, engineering and operations teams: namely the key influencers on any capital equipment total life cycle costs. Set the scene by reading this script.

While we have developed structured, detailed and apparently cost effective approaches to our capital project programmes here at our plant, we still suffer from significant over-runs and resultant unacceptable equipment performance, risks, losses and costs. Why is this the case? Maybe the following ten statements can give us an insight. From your own experience, based here at your own plant/facilities/operations, please rank each of these ten statements below as follows:

Very True/ Strongly Agree	Score 3
True/ Agree	Score 2
Partially True/ Partially Agree	Score 1
False/ Disagree	Score 0

1. Our existing plant, machines and equipment may not be fit for our current and future process/production demands.

2. The equipment specification defined by the design and engineering processes often conflicts with the experience of the people who will actually operate & maintain the equipment (i.e. operations).

3. Our operations staff were not involved in the concept or high-level design specification. So they have little ownership at the commissioning & ramp-up stage.

4. Our operations staff were also not involved in the detailed design, so their 'front-line 'experience is not included, and problems only become apparent at installation & commissioning.

5. Instead of measuring the total lifecycle cost (from concept to grave) we only measure the direct cost of acquisition. In other words, we are pre-occupied with front-end costs rather than total life asset ('effectiveness') costs.

6. We know that plant and equipment reliability is affected by ease of maintenance and the way in which it is operated. However, maintainers and operators are not encouraged or involved in the asset acquisition process by 'design engineering' other than simply as 'a necessary evil' or if we've got the time.

7. Operations/production demands and load conditions continually change, but further design engineering involvement does not happen because our people are not encouraged, or given the time to review & update the practices.

8. The link between our plant and equipment's condition and its performance effectiveness is not reviewed regularly for significant refurbishment and/or up-grade opportunities.

9. From my perspective, commercial (i.e. finance, procurement and marketing), operations and engineering seem to have different objectives and priorities and, as a result, these often conflict.

10. The ease or difficulty of carrying out the maintenance is not looked at, so tasks that are difficult and take a lot of time are sometimes not done or left to run to failure.

Total score out of 30 maximum

This list of 10 check points was prepared as the result of running a series of EEM practitioner's workshops for the offshore oil & gas industry, aero engines, food & drink, packaging, electrical/electronic and life sciences manufacturers, where focusing on new product/new equipment is paramount in the total life cycle delivery.

The point is that the EEM systematic approach addresses each one of these ten fundamental reasons for the gaps in our existing new product introduction and capital project spend practices. It also recognises that it is the person carrying out the front line day-to-day tasks on that new capital asset who is the key, and the way in which they are supported is vital to achieve true cost effectiveness.

So what is your Benchmark Score out of 30?

Score range	Significance
21 to 30	We have a major opportunity for improvement
12 to 20	We have significant scope for improvement
5 to 11	We are doing well, but can still gain some benefits
1 to 4	We are almost world class
0	We are the world's best!!!

From experience, many companies initially fall into the top two ranges if they conduct the exercise with honesty and healthy debate with both the commercial and engineering representatives, and including their internal customer colleagues representing production/operations. Solid evidence has been accumulated showing that revisiting the same exercise two to three years down the road of pursuing a robust and relevant TPM programme, including EEM principles, means that their scores drop into the 5 to 11 range and even one or two into the 1 to 4 range.

APPENDIX 8.3
16 EEM scoping questions for a capital project

Rate each point below on a scale of 1 = Poor, 2 = Fair, 3 = Adequate, 4 = Very Good, 5 = Excellent. Get commercial, engineering and operations teams to separately rate each question and share the results. Use the points of variation (especially 1s, 2s and 3s) to discuss the whys and the actions needed to make them solid 4s and 5s.

Do we have a site layout plan of the future installation including services?	☐
What are current/proposed key performance levels, for example service levels, productivity, quality, cost delivery?	☐
What are the project goals, timescale and projected expenditure (lifecycle cost basis, if possible)? What are success factors on which the project will be judged? What are the commercial, engineering and operations drivers/problems that this project will address? What new opportunities will it provide?	☐
How many employees will be involved in the project throughout its life? What are the working arrangements of the project team and proposed organisation? How will any transition be managed?	☐
What is the project organisation, roles and responsibility (commercial, engineering and operations)? How will this change at each project stage? How does this relate to the customer's organisation and/or the proposed organisation for future operation? How will the handover be organised?	☐
Do we have a flow-chart of the main process including details of bottlenecks, inputs and outputs, critical components and those with known weaknesses/potential problems to be overcome?	☐
What is the capital approval/monitoring process and commercial relationship between the company and the vendors? How close is this to a win/win relationship? How much autonomy does the team have to amend/refine the project terms of reference?	☐
What are the ideal project team skills/competencies? How closely does the project team match those skills? How will the development needs of the project team members be met?	☐
What systems are used to co-ordinate and control progress? Include the philosophy and aims of meetings, the reporting hierarchy, the result of progress against plan, the knowledge base update. Include examples of records of problems found, overcome, and outstanding.	☐
What problem-solving/solution development methodologies have been or are planned to be used (with examples if available)?	☐
What is the historic performance against the goal of flawless operation from day one production; for both the customer and the organisations/functions involved in the project?	☐
What communication methods/processes have been or are planned to be used to explain and build ownership within the existing/new operations?	☐
What continuous improvement goals precede the new operation and follow day one production?	☐
What is the production and maintenance strategy/philosophy, including operability and maintainability?	☐
What is the technical engineering philosophy (including reliability, safety, constructability)?	☐
What is the commercial philosophy (including the lifecycle cost model structure and definition of customer needs)?	☐

APPENDIX 8.4
The EEM MORSE checklists

The MORSE checklists are a powerful series of 60 prompt questions that are asked under the headings of

- **M**aintenance   -15
- **O**perations   -18
- **R**eliability   -11
- **S**afety& **E**nvironment -16

Before using this standard list, it is important to review each statement as part of the EEM planning day and, where necessary, to amend it using the appropriate terminology and/or vocabulary for your particular business and industry.

During the two-day EEM practitioners' workshop as described in Appendix 8.1, two multi-disciplined teams with members from commercial, engineering and operations will apply the methodology in order to understand the potential of EEM via the MORSE checklist as a retrospective exercise carried out on recently commissioned equipment, by asking the question:

If operators and maintainers had been involved right from the concept stage, would we have done things differently?

Against each of the 60 check points the teams use a rating system on a scale from 1 to 5, where:

1   Poor (unacceptable – needs urgent attention now)
2   Fair (identify improvement options to gain a 4 or 5 rating)
3   Adequate (but can it be further improved to a 4?)
4   Very good (what would make it excellent?)
5   Excellent (this represents best practice)

Illustrated here is an example of the Maintainability 15 Check Points template (similar templates exist for the operability, reliability, safety and environment check points).

	Description	Applicable Yes	No	Score	Comments
1	Have any visual aids been developed to assist routine maintenance tasks?				
2	Are all spare parts details known; has replacement, access been improved/simulated?				
3	Are correct tools available as required to perform all activities listed in 2 above?				
4	Are MTTR and MTBF details documented for all replacement parts?				
5	Are all condition monitoring test points identified and footprint details documented?				
6	Are difficult to access areas known with plans to improve?				

Description	Applicable		Score	Comments
	Yes	No		
7	Are all limit switches/solenoids etc. labelled to show what they control, and how identified?				
8	Are all pressure gauges at eye level with colour limits where possible/relevant?				
9	How long is the equipment cover, setup and adjustment time?				
10	How frequently does the equipment need adjusting or calibrating once in production?				
11	Can we extend any maintenance intervals or take out unnecessary tasks?				
12	Can we move fixed internal PMs to be done based on condition checks?				
13	Can we use effective condition monitoring checks to catch deterioration?				
14	Are all junction boxes at eye level?				
15	Are critical mounting bolts and nuts marked to show any loosening?				
Totals				
% score				

The checkpoint templates are followed below by Table 8.4 which show the outputs of two multidiscipline teams using the MORSE checklists on two recently acquired assets, where they have applied the 'mind-set' of: *If operators and maintainers had been involved from the concept stage, would we have done things differently?*

Table 8.4 Results of using MORSE checkpoints for two teams

Team A summary scores			
Maintainability	30/75	40%	
Operability	29/70	41%	
Reliability	28/50	56%	
Safety & environment	36/60	60%	
Spiroflo totals	*123/255*	*48%*	
Checkpoints with rating of 1: poor	17	34%	
Checkpoints with rating of 2: fair	9	18%	52% score 1 or 2
Checkpoints with rating of 3: adequate	14	28%	80% score 1, 2 or 3
Checkpoints with rating of 4: very good	10		
Checkpoints with rating of 5: excellent	1		
Total Team A applicable checkpoints	*51*		
Team B summary scores			
Maintainability	30/65	46%	
Operability	37/85	44%	
Reliability	41/55	75%	
Safety & environment	44/70	63%	
Team B totals	*152/275*	*55%*	
Checkpoints with rating of 1: poor	15	27%	
Checkpoints with rating of 2: fair	10	18%	45% score 1 or 2
Checkpoints with rating of 3: adequate	11	20%	65% score 1, 2 or 3
Checkpoints with rating of 4: very good	11	20%	
Checkpoints with rating of 5: excellent	8	15%	
Total Team B applicable checkpoints	*51*		

The first team found that 80 per cent of their ratings scored a 1, 2 or 3

The second team's score was 65per cent within 1, 2 or 3.

In both cases the results are striking in the sense of illustrating the potential power of addressing approximately sixty very practical and relevant MORSE checklist questions at the front-end design stage and not, as here, in hindsight.

CHAPTER 9
Total productive administration: TPM in support functions

9.1 Overview

Figure 9.1 illustrates where both TPM and TPA are key enablers to achieve a totally productive operation across the end-to-end value stream from suppliers to manufacturing plant to customers – where the common goal is to maximise added value by eliminating waste in all that we do.

Ultimately there is little merit in increasing site-wide OEE on our equipment assets if our key manufacturing support functions then become 'pinch-points' in our endeavours to achieve operational excellence because of administrative ineffectiveness – whatever that might mean in reality.

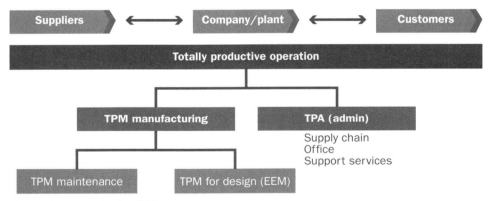

Figure 9.1: Positioning TPA

So let's first consider three observations about administrative ineffectiveness.

9.1.1 The potential for TPA

Recent surveys reveal that typically 35–60 per cent of administration time is spent on non-value-adding activities due to
- excessive information retrieval time
- multiple channels of communication
- duplicated and/or fragmented processes.

All of the above are non-productive and usually result in significant hidden losses. It is also very difficult to perceive this level of waste when wrapped up in the day-to-day activity itself.

9.1.2 **The misuse of technology**

Those same surveys suggest that over 50 per cent of systems implementations fail to deliver their true potential. And, typically, only around 25 per cent of system functionality is used (think about your phone or your iPad and your domestic equipment at home).

In our experience, poor understanding and data input inaccuracy are the main reasons for low system usage. The TPA system approach and philosophy described here provides the bridge between the users and the technology they need.

9.1.3 **Why TPA can be the solution**

The biggest pitfall of implementing administrative improvement activities is underestimating the cultural and behavioural changes that are needed.

The technology part is usually the easier component because, generally speaking, it is robust and probably well-proven. However,

- most companies believe that they should look only for a technology solution
- they neglect to take account of the changes in people's mindset and the new methods of working that are required
- TPA addresses both of these issues through the involvement of all stakeholders.

9.2 **Leadership behaviours as prerequisites for TPA success**

Managers and supervisors will need to be prepared to change their behaviours and to consider future ways of working. This will include the need to

- understand the purpose of the system and manage the organisation as a system with trust & delegation
- design the system against demand and deal with demand variety
- derive measures from the work – not set arbitrary targets
- modify traditional management thinking of set, measure & monitor resources to one where it is necessary to recognise that
- the role of management is to set the standards, then delegate and trust staff to act on the system with pace and responsiveness when deviations occur.

9.3 **Application areas for TPA**

Typical application areas for TPA are
- Management information systems
- Finance & financial services
- Design & engineering
- Research & development
- Project management
- Purchasing & procurement
- Production planning & scheduling
- Stores & warehousing
- Despatch and delivery
- After sales customer support
- Change control processes
- Sales order processing
- New product introduction
- HR & training

- Quality assurance
- Administration offices

We illustrate this support dependency in Figure 9.2.

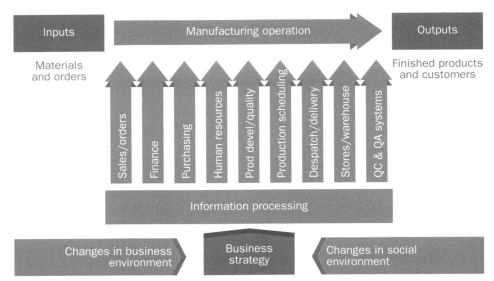

Figure 9.2: Information processing to support the manufacturing operation

9.4 **The purpose of TPA**

The TPA philosophy is a continuous improvement process combining value stream current- and future-state mapping, together with office 5S within critical manufacturing support systems.

The description below sets out how to introduce the TPA principles, philosophy and practicalities into an organisation in a structured, sustainable, common-sense, step-by-step approach. This is called the TPA implementation journey or purpose and is illustrated in Figure 9.3.

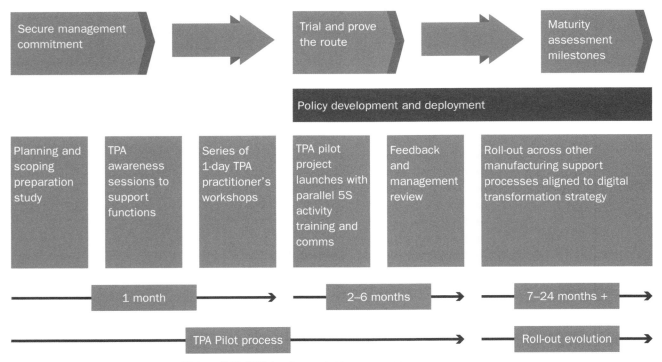

Figure 9.3: TPA implementation purpose

It is a journey which comprises:

- Securing senior management commitment at the front end via a planning and preparation scoping study
- TPA awareness sessions to explain the TPA philosophy and help engage the hearts and minds of the manufacturing support personnel. The sessions include their selection of the preferred TPA pilot application system
- Training up a critical mass of TPA 'practitioners' through a hands-on one-day practitioner's workshop. Here the focus is on a value stream mapping exercise, producing a current-state map of the existing system step-by-step process which is then challenged by the participants to produce a 'first cut' future state map
- Trialling and proving the TPA enabling tool (the process) as part of the policy development through a series of TPA pilot projects. This is the key phase for moving from strategic intent to making it happen.
- Deployment of that policy through maturity assessment milestones, based on driving change through a rollout sequence that is aligned to the operation's digitalisation transformation strategy (as referenced in Industry 4.0, Chapter 2), which in turn is linked to the essential people development journey.

Typical timescales will of course vary according to the size of the operation, a current-state health check to establish where they are on their operational excellence/TPM/CI journey to date, the amount of people, money and time committed, and hence the pace at which change can be initiated and absorbed.

All these key aspects plus a first-cut cost/benefit appraisal are addressed within the front end scoping study or 'planning the plan' phase.

Thorough planning, and buy-in of that plan from the site leadership team, are essential forerunners of a successful and sustainable TPA implementation journey.

9.4.1 Front-end planning and scoping preparation

A key part of the preparation to achieve the above is planning the plan – a structured scoping study (Figure 9.4) which will include
- creating the future vision of where we want to be
- establishing where we are today and how well we do it via a 10-point honesty check (see Appendix 9.1)
- understanding what people really think
- deciding on the candidate TPA pilot application areas (see below)
- defining both the internal and external customer requirements.

This includes the initial scope definition and potential financial benefits, culminating in a site leadership buy-in session just ahead of running a series of-one day TPA practitioner's training workshops. The purpose of these activities is to raise managers' and employees' understanding of what TPA is and, equally important, what it is not. It is also to define what TPA can add to current initiatives and how it will support delivery of the business drivers and priorities towards operational excellence.

Provided the scoping study is well planned with a scheduled agenda it can typically be completed over two or three days.

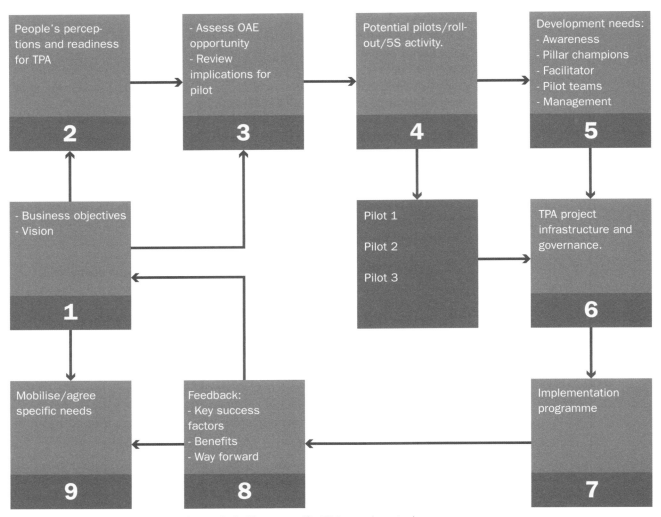

Figure 9.4: Plant-specific TPA scoping study

The objective of the plant-specific scoping study is to address each of the above nine elements in order to validate where the specific plant is on its continuous improvement journey, evaluating its business drivers, future vision, plans and intentions to create a 'maturity assessment'.

- Assess perceptions and readiness for the TPA programme among those involved and affected. This will include one-to-one interviews using the 28 perceptions prompt explained via an example in 9.4.2
- Identify TPA pilot opportunities and priorities within the manufacturing support services and systems, together with a first-cut cost/benefit appraisal for the preferred first application systems
- Identify the critical success & risk factors plus countermeasures to minimise risk
- Develop a first cut TPA site-wide rollout approach
- Specify full implementation, training and coaching plans to cover
  - potential TPA pilot(s) with the likely benefits from those pilots
  - pilot project team size and membership
  - key contact membership and roles
  - logistics and resource implications plus their associated costs
  - initial awareness, communication and training plan plus its timing
  - facilitator support requirements plus their personal development training
  - TPA programme governance and steering group membership and terms of reference.

9.4.2 **Measuring people's perceptions and feelings**

A key part of the scoping study phase is to gauge people's readiness for the TPA-enabling tool. We do this by interviewing a small but representative number of employees who we group into three clusters as support staff, internal customers and managers.

The one-to-one interview asks the individual to rank 28 statements. Fourteen of these statements relate to how involved the individual employee feels about workplace decisions that affect them. The other 14 statements (under the ME column) provide a measure of that person's perception of how far managers encourage a climate to enable that employee's proactive involvement.

Some important points to note:

- The statements are not handed out for completion before the interview
- Only the person's job title is noted – to respect the spirit of anonymity
- The interview is conducted across the table privately, using the 28 statements as a structured focus to promote open and honest discussion that can be subsequently analysed by response, strength of feeling, and job role
- This also allows the interviewer to encourage clarification of a specific response or rating and hence gain useful insights as to why the interviewee feels that way
- The interviewer asks a final question of the interviewee: "If you were a member of the site leadership team, what would you try most to change or influence over the next say two years?" The responses to this question are often very enlightening.

Each response is then analysed and fed back as per the example below of a four-element schematic (Figure 9.5) and Tables 9.1–9.3.

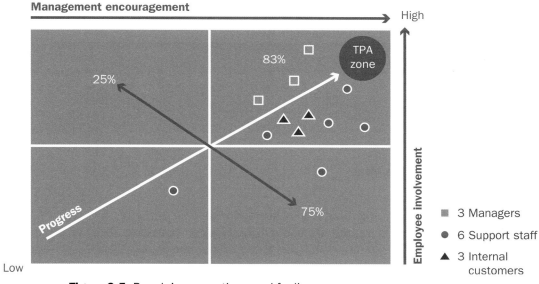

Figure 9.5: People's perceptions and feelings

Table 9.1 What hinders progress? Top eight statement scores
Lower scores better. Over 50% supporting statement **shown in bold**

		Support staff	Internal customers	Managers	Total
1	We have a 'you support us we bring in the money' mentality	**89%**	**67%**	**62%**	**77%**
6	Support staff and direct earners seem to pull in opposite directions	**67%**	47%	33%	**54%**
20	We don't spend enough time developing our internal 'customer relationships'	**60%**	**67%**	22%	**52%**
24	Back-up procedures are not as good as they should be	25%	**67%**	43%	40%

Table 9.1 What hinders progress? Top eight statement scores
Lower scores better. Over 50% supporting statement **shown in bold**

		Support staff	Internal customers	Managers	Total
4	Groups do not get together to work on common problems	25%	47%	43%	44%
8	Skills are picked rather than learnt systematically	44%	33%	43%	40%
26	Problems regarding our organisation & effectiveness are not faced up to	33%	27%	**53%**	40%
11	Lessons learnt do not get transferred within the business	33%	**53%**	33%	40%

Table 9.2 What helps progress? Top eight statement scores
Higher scores better. Under 80% supporting statement **shown in bold**

		Support staff	Internal customers	Managers	Total
22	We should introduce a CI/quality of service approach	100%	100%	100%	100%
28	Standard methods are seen as important	100%	100%	100%	100%
5	People are not reluctant to say what they really think	85%	100%	100%	93%
9	The company operates on new ideas	80%	87%	100%	87%
15	People would welcome more challenge in their job	80%	87%	93%	85%
2	Lines of responsibility & accountability are clear to me	**70%**	87%	95%	81%
7	I am asked my opinion by my boss about the job I do	**78%**	**73%**	90%	80%
27	The link between the business vision and what my dept does is clear to me	**67%**	86%	100%	80%

Table 9.3 How I feel ...
Lower scores better. Scores over 30% **shown in bold**

	Support staff	Internal customers	Managers	Total
... I am treated	**46%**	24%	11%	**32%**
... The team works	**54%**	**36%**	**36%**	**45%**
... The management works	**35%**	28%	11%	27%
... The company works	**30%**	16%	22%	25%
Staff involvement	**37%**	**31%**	**32%**	**33%**
Progressive management	28%	20%	20%	24%

In this analysis, the lower the score the better. Anything above 30 per cent represents an opportunity for improvement. The TPA process will definitely address the high scores on how the team works.

9.4.3 **Overall interpretation of the perceptions result**

- The summary matrix Figure 9.5 shows 83 per cent of the sample (12 employees) feel both encouraged and involved
- However 75 per cent of the sample (below the diagonal line) feel that the encouragement is not always delivered strongly enough through actual involvement
- The TPA philosophy and its reality will address each of the top eight perceived 'hinders'
- The perceived top eight 'helpers' will be strengthened and underpinned by the TPA process
- The biggest potential reward from learning how people feel will come from improved teamwork and the involvement of the support staff, their internal customers and managers as a single team

- A significant number of those interviewed – irrespective of their job function – freely volunteered the observation that the work environment has definitely improved over the last two years or so, and that the company-wide approach to continuous improvement via TPA with more regular reviews will make it a better place to work and underpin the gains achieved by their internal customers through TPM
- However, there is also a strong sense of frustration that 'across the fence' communications can be greatly improved
- 'Understanding of each other's problems' has some way to go
- Most expect change to continue, although some may still resist it because they feel they already have too much to cope with.

9.4.4 What makes a good TPA pilot project process/system candidate?

A good approach to answer this question is to run a series of two-to-three-hour interactive TPA awareness sessions. Representatives should typically be drawn from job functions represented by the key contacts and potential future TPA core team members shown in Figure 9.6 below.

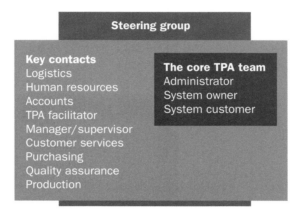

Figure 9.6: The TPA core team and their key contacts

A typical agenda for this initial three-hour awareness session would be:
- Introductions, expectations and purpose of session
- Present slide deck of TPA principles and a relevant case study
- Conduct a TPA self-assessment exercise in groups of two to four based on a 10-point honesty check (see Appendix 9.1 for details) and share the results to provoke group discussion
- Present an explanation of the TPA 9-step improvement process (see Figure 9.8)
- Facilitate an open forum discussion to list and agree potential TPA pilot project candidate(s) (see selection criteria below)
- Share key learning points
- Agree way forward with the who, what, where & when spelt out.

9.4.5 Selection criteria for potential TPA pilot projects

Candidate projects are typically
- relatively complex procedure(s)
- frequent-demand 'failure modes and effects'
- interdependencies with other systems and/or functions involving more than one person
- relatively high volume of transactions, typically several times per day or week (compared to less frequent once a month type of processes).

Candidate examples might be, for example,

- Finance expense control
- QC-failure investigation in lab
- Customer shipping approval procedure
- QA-supplier defects process.

Each candidate process will need to be rated on a scale of one to five where one is a simple process that rarely goes wrong, and which is easily corrected, and five is a relatively complex process, which frequently goes wrong and is difficult to correct when it does.

In order to fully test the TPA methodology it is usual to select between two and four initial pilot 'proving' projects from different support functions.

9.5 **TPA pilot project process**

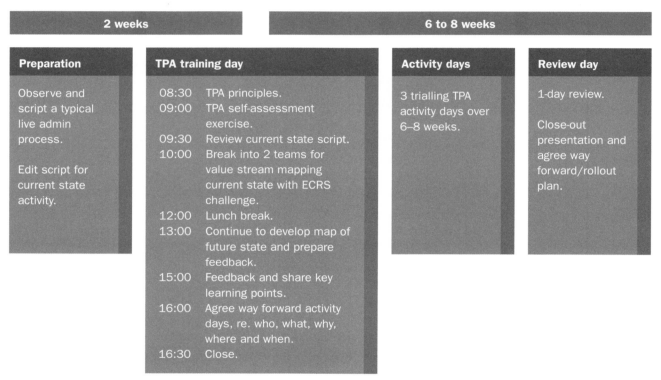

Figure 9.7: The TPA pilot programme process

Following the TPA awareness session and pilot application selections, a one-day TPA practitioner's event is organised as shown in Figure 9.7 which illustrates the TPA pilot project process that is followed.

The key elements of the pilot project process are

- A current-state time-lined detailed script is produced as a result of observing the pilot-specific system application. This essential step is based on the reality that any system or process has at least three versions:
  – What you think it is
  – What it actually is
  – What it should be.
  The good news is we can avoid the 'what you think it is' version by first observing and scripting the actual system routine in all its detail as the basis for our current-state scenario, which we 'value stream map' during the TPA practitioner's training day.
- This script is then verified and edited ahead of running the TPA training day. Delegates typically include members of the system administration and their key

contacts (as in Figure 9.6 above), plus the local manager and project sponsor and a TPA facilitator/CI engineer.

■ During the workshop, the delegates map the current state and scrutinise each step or activity by using the **ECRS** challenge: can we **eliminate** this step? And if not, can we **combine** with another step upstream or downstream? And if not, can we **replace** it with something smarter or at least **simplify** it?

9.6 **Some notes on value stream process mapping**

■ To visually map out the A to Z as a step-by-step timeline of a specific system routine previously observed and scripted, and referred to as the 'current state map'.
■ To critically assess every current state step/event/activity in the system process by using the ECRS challenge.
■ To act as a focus route-map for discussion/agreement to minimise waste by
   ■ eliminating non-value adding activities and steps in all its forms
   ■ avoiding duplications (overlap/excess copies)
   ■ identifying and streamlining dependencies (both core and indirect)
   ■ defining inputs/outputs and links to other procedures & routines
   ■ identifying all gaps and omissions.
■ As a result of the above, to then define and populate the resultant 'future state system' for subsequent trialling and refining.
■ This leads to defining the best practice routines as standard work in order to maximise the value added.

9.7 **Three-cycle nine-step TPA improvement plan**

At the heart of the TPA philosophy is a three-cycle, nine-step TPA improvement plan as shown in Figure 9.8. It comprises measurement, process mapping and problem prevention cycles.

Measurement cycle

■ **Step 1** TPA awareness session and pilot selection as described in Section 9.4
■ **Step 2** Define the overall administration effectiveness (OAE) and other relevant KPIs (as described in Section 9.8 and the supporting Figure 9.9)
■ **Step 3** Collect essential system information to form the basis of the current state map.

Process mapping cycle

■ **Step 4** Selection of critical system activity (developed from Step 1 awareness session)
■ **Steps 5**, **6** and **7** are carried out during the TPA practitioner's one-day workshop.

Problem prevention cycle

■ **Steps 8** and **9** Progressive development of best practice as standard work based on realising the future-state map specified during the TPA practitioner's workshop and subsequently proven by implementing the ECRS opportunities.

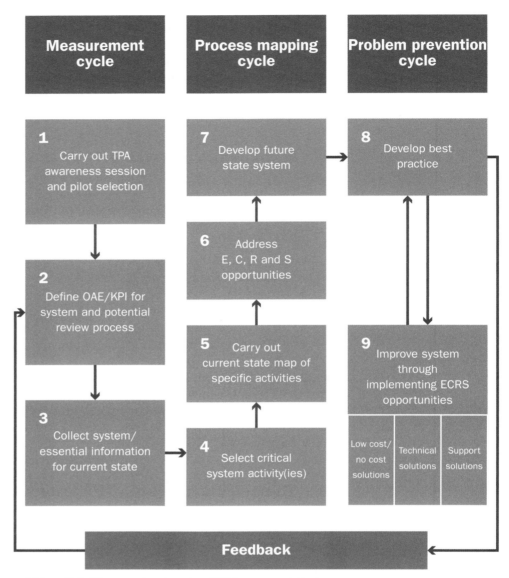

Figure 9.8: Three-cycle nine-step TPA improvement plan

9.8 **How to measure the improvement potential**

Many of us will be familiar with the application of 5S in the office, which is about creating an office environment that is safe and fit for purpose. This is both worthwhile and a great help in creating physical flow, with everything in its place and a right place for everything.

But what about the opportunity for integrating that philosophy of creating information flows in the office with a focus on challenging whether those information flows are indeed the right ones and just how effective they are?

We know about the OEE of our equipment-based assets from previous chapters. This included a review and focus on the 'management losses' which we called door-to-door losses in order to differentiate them from the OEE floor-to-floor losses.

So let's extend this OEE logic to one of overall administration effectiveness (OAE) in the manufacturing support functions where we want to continue with the TPM mindset – minimising waste of human effort by maximising added value.

To illustrate this we will take a relatively straightforward example of a production scheduling administrator whose daily routine centres around data entry into the forward manufacturing plan. Inputs are based on new received customer orders which need to be netted off via a bill of material which takes account of current stock and work in progress 'rules', plus the routing file of the load/capacity 'rules' of the physical work centre's capability in the factory.

Sounds easy enough, doesn't it? Well, maybe not so straightforward.

We can take a snapshot of a typical day for the production scheduling administrator by asking them to keep an hourly diary of 'interruptions' under three headings of events or occurrences that

- stop the task from starting such as missing information (which affects your 'availability')
- extends the time of the task because of unplanned interruptions (which affects your 'performance rate')
- affects the quality of what is being done such as incorrect or inaccurate information (which affects your 'quality rate').

All of these unplanned impacts are the result of having to respond to what we might refer to as 'failure demand'. We can also transpose that production scheduling administrator's diary into an OAE picture as shown in Figure 9.9.

In our experience an OAE of 60 per cent is fairly typical. What this is telling us is that the production scheduling administrator is only effective for the equivalent of three days out of five each week. That represents a far cry from a stress-free day at the office.

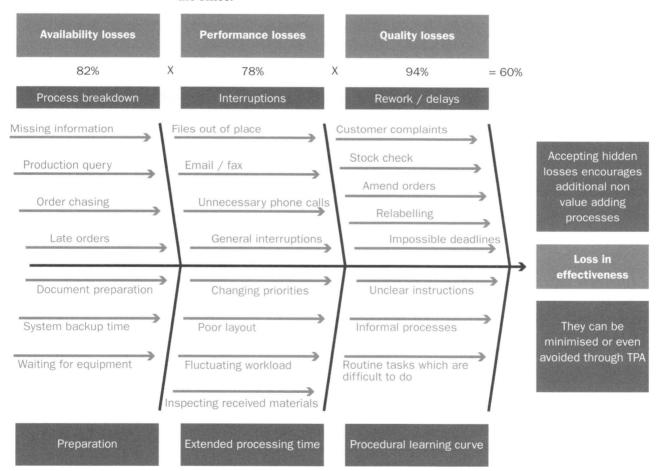

Figure 9.9: Overall administration effectiveness

Typical losses reflected in the above include

- waiting (availability) for data from other 'steps'
- checking (performance) collecting signatures
- store/stack (performance) piles of files
- over-processing (performance) searching and non-standard procedures

- movement (performance) documents or people travelling around plus illogical filing systems
- defects (quality) wrong or incomplete information
- rework (quality) excessive copying, altering.

The opposite to these losses would be to set a future vision and hence aspiration that says a world class support function delivers
- the right information
- in the right format
- at the right moment
- in the right place
- at lowest cost and effort

We all aspire to this goal. Here is how TPA can help achieve it.

9.9 A cameo case study

Shown in Table 9.4 are the result highlights for three identified pilot application areas at Mylan Rottapharm. This was achieved by scripting the current-state process and then running a TPA practitioner's training day following the process described in sections 9.5 to 9.7 above. The company went on to secure and embed these benefits before rolling out the TPA philosophy to other appropriate manufacturing support functions across the site.

Table 9.4 Three TPA pilot applications in a pharmaceutical company

TPA application	A: current events/ steps	B: future events/ steps	A–B difference	Current state time	Future state time
FG batch approval	55	44	−11	4.2 hrs	2.0 hrs
Supplier deviation	44	18	−26	37.5 mins	16.0 mins
QC-non-test task function	133	50	−83	39.0 hrs	26.0 hrs

9.10 Benefits of TPA

The benefits of TPA fall into three categories.

9.10.1 Business benefits

- Improvement in OAE as a measurable route to increased value and speed of response
- Improved internal customer and supplier networking and integration
- Flexibility by being able to react quickly to market, business and social changes.

9.10.2 People benefits

- Increased utilisation and acquisition of new skills through improved capability
- Increased flexibility of administration staff
- Tapping into the true potential of your people
- Practical and effective team-working and empowerment process

- Ownership of the solutions through involvement.

9.10.3 **Administrative benefits**

- Highly reliable and predictable systems/procedures
- Optimal use of administrative resources and technology
- Improved communication and functional integration towards processes (rather than existing silos)
- Provide high quality and timely information to support management and front line decision making.

Once again, the emerging world of Industry 4.0 provides huge opportunity with one major proviso – it is your staff in the back office that will make the difference through their engagement and empowerment.

APPENDIX 9.1
Systems and procedures assessment exercise

Whilst we have developed structured, detailed and apparently cost-effective approaches to our support systems and procedures here at our operations , we still suffer from significant backlogs and resultant unacceptable performance, risks, losses and costs. Why is this the case? Maybe the following ten statements can give us an insight:

From your own experience, based here at the xyz operations, please rank each of these ten statements below as Very true/strongly agree 3, True/agree 2, Partially true/partially agree 1, False/disagree 0.	Score
Our support systems and procedures may not be fit for our current and future process and business demands	
The tasks and routines defined by the specific system and procedure often conflict with the experience of the person actually carrying them out	
Our support staff were not involved in putting together these routines. So they have little ownership for the quality of the work carried out as described by the task	
Our support staff are also not involved in system and procedure upgrades either, so their 'front-line 'experience is not included and problems remain	
Instead of measuring the reason why we do the task (i.e. to support the effectiveness of the specific business processes) we only measure the direct cost of doing it. In other words, we are pre-occupied with support 'efficiency' rather than support 'effectiveness'	
In my view we, individually, do not spend enough quality time on developing our 'internal customer' relationships	
Customer demands, product profiles and factory load conditions continually change, but the support systems and procedures do not change because our people are not encouraged, or given the time to review and/or update practices.	
When it comes to different company functions (i.e. admin, QA, scheduling, HR, technical, etc.) the left hand doesn't know what the right hand is doing	
Support departments and manufacturing seem to have different objectives and priorities and, as a result, resource and/or timing issues often conflict.	
The ease of carrying out support procedures is not looked at, so tasks that are difficult and take a lot of time are sometimes not done or left until a default /procedural failure occurs.	
Total (max 30)	

Example in use

Eight employees in four pairs completed the questionnaire.

Within the maximum of 30 points, the pairs scored their support systems at 17, 16, 13, and 12.

Our benchmark scores suggest

- 21 to 30   Major opportunity for improvement
- 12 to 20   Significant scope for improvement
- 5 to 11   Doing well, but can gain some benefits
- 1 to 4   Almost world class
- 0   The World's Best!!!

All the delegate pair scores were in the range 12 to 20, 'significant scope for improvement'.

TPA addresses each of these ten fundamental reasons for the gaps in our existing systems and procedures. It recognises that it is the person carrying out the tasks who is the key, and the way in which they are supported is vital to achieve true cost effectiveness.

- 21 to 30   Major opportunity for improvement
- 12 to 20   Significant scope for improvement
- 5 to 11   Doing well, but can gain some benefits
- 1 to 4   Almost world class
- 0   The World's Best!!!

CHAPTER 10
Case studies

10.1 The ingredients for success

Before examining the case studies, it is important to remind ourselves of some of the essential requisites for success that we explored in earlier chapters.

10.1.1 The purpose of TPM (Chapter 4)

The purpose of this system and philosophy is to
- generate and maintain flow through your critical physical assets
- get the foundations – operational basics and behaviours – in place
- focus not only on asset *reliability* but also on asset *predictability*
- validate, stabilise and then optimise your operational processes
- unlock your installed productive capacity, by unlocking the full potential of your people
- engage the 'hearts & minds' of your people through proactive involvement from day one of your TPM programme.

We can achieve all this by recognising that the TPM system and philosophy is a continuous improvement process, combining well-proven operational-excellence-enabling tools described elsewhere in this book. These include, among others, value stream mapping, lean six sigma, precision changeovers (SMED), 5S workplace organisation, visual management techniques, root cause analysis, asking why five times, failure modes and effects analysis, A3 problem solving and P-M analysis, plus cost & loss deployment. These are underpinned with leader standard work and all within a continuous improvement mind-set that says 'what's good enough today will not be good enough tomorrow'.

10.1.2 The TPM process (Chapter 5)

The TPM system is a journey that comprises
- securing leadership and management commitment at the front end
- training a critical mass of TPM 'practitioners' via the 4-cycle 11-step TPM implementation process on the company's critical physical assets
- trialling and proving the TPM 11-step system as part of the policy development and then …
- deployment of that policy through four maturity milestones, based on system owners as 'Pillar champions' driving change through a roll-out sequence into logical geographic improvement zones across the plant or facility.

Typical timescales will of course vary according to the size of the operation, its relative manufacturing or utility complexity, and the amount of resource committed in terms of people, money and time. Also relevant is how far the organisation has progressed in terms of its operational excellence transformation journey to date, and thus the pace at which change can be initiated and absorbed.

All these key questions plus the cost/benefit potential are addressed within the scoping study or 'Planning the plan' phase. Thorough planning is an essential and non-optional forerunner to secure leader and management buy-in and hence ongoing successful implementation.

10.1.3 **The pitfalls to avoid (Chapters 1.9 & 7)**

In Chapter 1, Section 9, we listed six consistently recurring reasons why change programmes and continuous improvement initiatives in general – including TPM – wither on the vine and fail to deliver their full potential:

- Lack of clear, consistent leadership and direction
- Lack of thorough planning, preparation, measurement and feedback
- The change programme has no clear 'end game' vision and purpose
- Lack of a thorough risk assessment and countermeasure definition at the start of the programme
- Poor, inadequate, inconsistent and ineffective communication
- Unclear roles, responsibilities, accountabilities and expectations.

We also examine these six reasons in Chapter 7 and how each one's impact and potential risk can be minimised via a relevant and robust CI/TPM infrastructure and governance system, including top-down and bottom-up robust evidence-based audit processes.

In addition, and as stated in Section 10.1.2 above, the solution to these challenges is to start to address each of the above six issues using a front-end scoping/planning/diagnostic study, which concludes with a senior management 'buy-in' workshop.

10.1.4 **What can TPM give my business?**

The benefits are both 'hard' business benefits and 'soft' cultural benefits, achievable because the TPM system

- provides a structured and systematic approach
- is time-tabled and scheduled
- encourages wide engagement, from the bottom up
- sets clear roles, responsibilities, accountabilities and expectations
- is proven to be sustainable in the right hands
- is, above all, very practical because of its emphasis on 'learning by doing'.

10.1.5 **Case studies**

This chapter presents three detailed case studies, plus a further three brief examples to illustrate the potential power of the TPM system to deliver your operational excellence aspirations:

- Mylan Damastown – a Shingo Medallion Award-winner from the pharmaceutical industry
- Welsh Water – an award-winning public utility
- Warwick Chemicals – chemical processing industry
- Three further cameo examples from the pharmaceutical and medical devices industries.

10.2 Mylan Damastown (formerly known as Rottapharm Dublin)

By Richard Hayes, Operational Excellence Director

Company background

The facility was established in 1999 and currently employs approximately 200 people. It became part of the Mylan group of companies, which has a workforce of 35,000 people worldwide, in August 2016. The Damastown site produces finished oral solid dosage pharmaceuticals in tablet, capsule and sachet formats. Liquid drop manufacturing and packing operations also commenced in early 2016, adding new technology and complexity to the site. The site took responsibility for new products involving the production of liquid drops, even though other sites within the group had the technology and capability to produce the new products. This was in recognition of the track record of cost competitiveness, ability to deliver projects and quality products on time and was also based on an outstanding record of operational excellence over the previous ten years.

Drivers behind Damastown's operational excellence aspirations

Figure 10.1: Pat Gerrahy, Managing Director of Rottapharm, receives the Shingo Silver Medallion at the Shingo Conference April 2017

The Dublin facility has an established history of running lean operations and using tools such as Six Sigma since 2006 and Total Productive Maintenance (TPM) since 2010. A positive culture and many desired behaviours developed from the use of these tools, but the emphasis was initially on the tools and the results they provided, rather than on the culture that was being created using these tools and systems of work. In a search for a benchmark as to how the company was performing, Damastown identified the Shingo Model™ to help shape how lean tools and thinking were deployed and to develop the culture within the organisation.

In 2013 the company introduced a strategy of cultural change within the Dublin plant aimed at providing excellent sustainable results through a principle-based model. This case study provides some examples of how the site has achieved excellence through behaviours based on the guiding principles of the Shingo Model, especially over recent times. As a result, the company received the Shingo Silver Medallion for operational excellence at the Shingo International Conference in Atlanta Georgia in April 2017.

The strategy and associated activities pursued by the Damastown site over recent years and particularly over the last two to three years have been aimed at securing the long-term future for the plant. The objectives of the company are to provide the best products for customers (patients) and develop employees for the future by working in a sustainable manner for the benefit of the environment. The Shingo Model™ with its guiding principles has been used to develop the culture within the plant that allows people to thrive in their normal job and push the boundaries, enabling people to realise their full potential.

The role of TPM as an enabling tool to deliver efficiency and results

Over the past number of years, the site has focused on efficiency throughout the plant production and support functions. The introduction of Total Productive Maintenance (TPM) and development of a continuous improvement (CI) system with a focus on removal of waste have resulted in substantial improvement in terms of business results.

Against the backdrop of the business need to absorb products and equipment from Europe by unlocking their existing capacity and retaining the same overhead and employment base, Damastown is very proud of its success in using TPM as its main foundation 'enabling tool'. In 2010 the company initiated a TPM programme, which they called Total Productive Manufacturing to emphasise the implied and necessary teamwork between **production** and **maintenance**. Following an initial and thorough planning and scoping phase, the TPM journey comprised a chronological focus and sequence as highlighted here:

- Initial diagnostic/scoping study to establish the business case
- Site leadership team 'buy-in' to the TPM process to help deliver the business imperatives
- Initial four-day TPM practitioner's 'hands-on' training workshops – Go see & do, 'learning by doing'
- TPM pilot projects, roll-out planning and programme governance
- Progressive middle and senior management TPM 'pillar champion' coaching and mentoring
- Focused improvement activities such as VS mapping, 5S workplace organisation, area clearances/precision changeovers (SMED)
- Early equipment management/TPM for design
- Total Productive Administration in the manufacturing support functions
- Regular evidence-based top-down and bottom-up TPM audit and review processes
- An annual 50-point maintenance strategy review
- Integrating safety, environment and energy conservation opportunities into the day-to-day good manufacturing practice (GMP) tasks.

This step-by-step sequence and focus has helped the site to not only avoid some of the common pitfalls, but to continually remind and suggest how the business could best improve its competitiveness. This approach also ensured that other improvement activities, such as safety, environment and energy conservation opportunities, were integrated into the day-to-day GMP tasks within the plant. The business has also made significant savings by applying total productive administration (TPA) in the support departments.

A key part of the initial diagnostic/scoping study phase was to describe the manufacturing and packaging logic, sequence and interdependencies of the facility (Figure 10.2).

In parallel with, and based on the early successes of the initial TPM pilot projects, the site then set about defining the TPM roll-out plans for the ensuing four years (Figure 10.3).

A great deal of effort was also put into defining the TPM programme infrastructure and governance processes (Figure 10.4) linked to regular evidence-based top-down and bottom-up TPM audit and review processes.

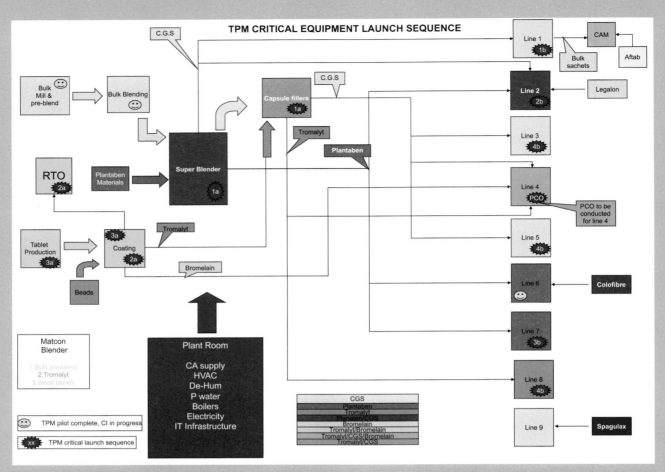

Figure 10.2: Site manufacturing and packaging process flows

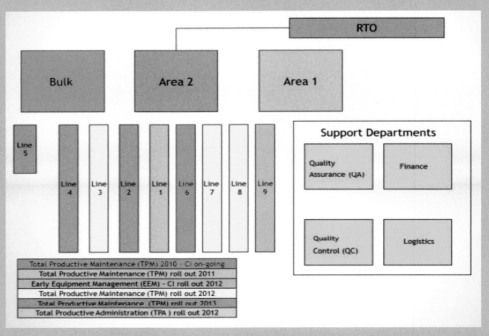

Figure 10.3: Four-year TPM roll-out plan sequence

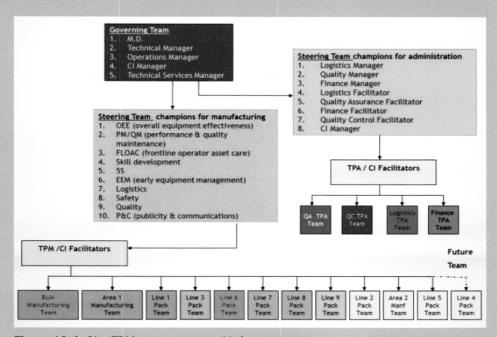

Figure 10.4: Site TPM governance and infrastructure

As an illustration of the level of improvements made possible using the TPM system, Figure 10.5 shows the results for one of the packaging lines over a nine-month period to Milestone 2 audit criteria achievement.

12 Months Average 2010		Improvement	4 wks Average by 30 Sept 2011
OEE	20.7%	x 2.5 increase	49.5%
Eq Failures	25.7%	Down by x 6	4.0%
Idle Time	38.0%	Halved	21.5%
No Data	2.1%	Eliminated	0%
Line Restraint	5.9%	Eliminated	0%
Minor Stops	7.8%	Down by 65%	2.7%
Actual v. Target (Prod Plan)	73.0%	100% OTIF	100 %

Figure 10.5: Initial TPM pilot project packing line 6 results to Milestone 2 achievement

As illustrated in Figure 10.5, TPM is designed to enhance OEE by increasing equipment availability, decreasing rework and rejects, and hence increasing productivity. It involves the integration of engineering maintenance, project engineers, production process operations personnel and the wider workforce, thereby encouraging teamwork and asset care practices. By using the 11-step model shown in Figure 10.6 TPM seeks to involve workers at all levels and departments. The resultant improvements are felt in time, money and other resources in dealing with reliability, availability, maintainability and performance issues. In many process-based industries, maintenance costs, together with energy costs, can represent the largest part of operational budgets.

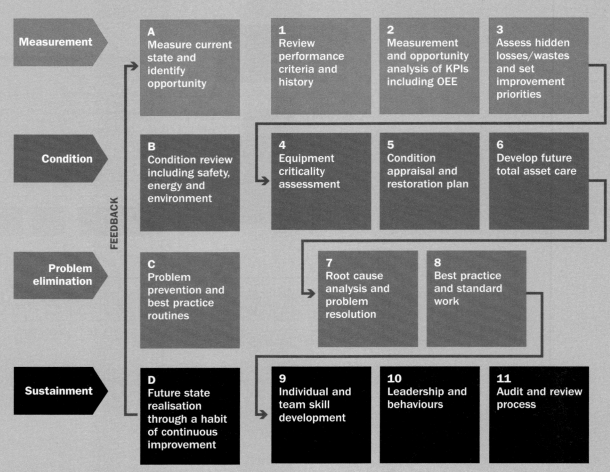

Figure 10.6: The TPM four-cycle process

Operational performance is measured using metrics commonly employed across a variety of industries. The McKinsey study of 2011 published a comparison between the pharmaceutical industry and other industries. While the report indicates that the pharmaceutical industry lags behind other industries, Damastown stands out as best in class within pharma. Through a sustained focus on OEE, the company has created value for the customer by generating year-on-year improvements and continues to show world-class levels of OEE (typically between 10% and 60% for the pharmaceutical sector, according to McKinsey). As Figure 10.7 illustrates, the OEE for Damastown, at 63% for 2016, continues in a steady upward trend as a result of the culture of operational excellence within all the teams in the company.

Batch completion time is a measure of the length of time taken to approve each batch record once a batch has been completed in production.

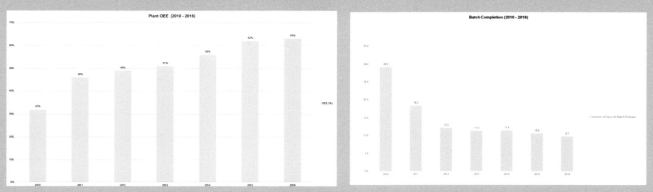

Figure 10.7: Rising OEE and falling batch completion times, 2010–2016

Figure 10.7 shows a decreasing trend in batch completion times from 2010. Over recent times this trend has continued downwards, with the current average number of days standing at 8.5 days.

Damastown has embraced scientific thinking and deployed many tools to conduct investigations into problems and eliminate recurring deviations. Solutions ranging from quick fixes on equipment to full-scale six sigma projects have been used to resolve difficult process issues. The trend on this metric has continued to decrease, with the current number of deviations reduced by 20% on the 2016 figure. The on-time delivery metric has improved over the past number of years (Figure 10.8). In June 2016 the metric was changed to Release On Time In Full delivery (OTIF). During 2017 this metric, which is harder to achieve than the previous one, had an average figure of 99% with eight of those months hitting 100%.

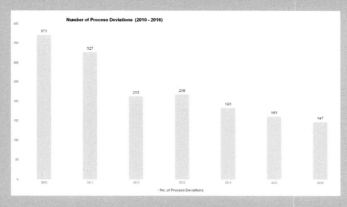 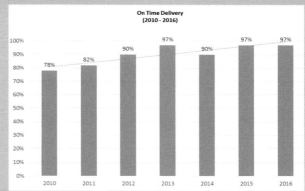

Figure 10.8: Reduction of process deviations an improvement in on-time delivery

Figure 10.9: Leader Standard Work (LSW) task sheet for the packaging line lead operator

Operational efficiency using LSW

The parallel improvement of the use of leader standard work (LSW) and visual management has resulted in everyone within the plant having a clear understanding of what the daily expectations are in terms of process adherence and process performance (see Figures 10.9 and 10.10). The focus on process performance and adherence has led to plant-wide improvements in performance. People are more focused on getting things done on time and in recognising when process trends require action. Every team has a visual management board with laminated sheets that are updated daily. A number of meetings take place at these boards. The first meeting is held when work starts at 07:00 in the production areas and at 08:00 in the support areas. These are known as the pulse meetings and are carried out with the team and immediate supervisor or middle manager. At 09:00 the middle managers from operations, engineering, quality assurance and control, the warehouse and logistics meet at the plant operations board and review any issues that have been raised and that required escalation by the various teams. A member of the senior leadership team (SLT) also attends this meeting on a weekly rotational basis. Appropriate actions are discussed and decided at the meeting. If an issue cannot be resolved and requires support from the SLT, it will be escalated to the senior team meeting at 10:00 with appropriate actions decided and communicated back to the middle management team.

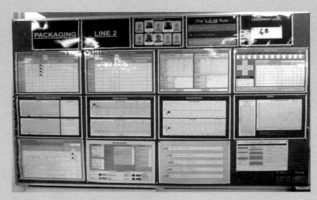

Figure 10.10: Standard visual management board to sustain focus and operational efficiency

The visual management boards have a standard layout that follows a 1-3-10-second rule. In 1 second you can tell if a team is winning or losing (orange laminate in the photo example); hourly outputs are recorded and marked with a red or green indicator to show whether or not they are on target for that hour. In 3 seconds you can tell how the KPI charts are trending (blue laminate). In 10 seconds you can tell what the team is doing about those areas where they are losing or trending below their target (green laminate). The board also includes pictures of the team members, LSW, a safety cross for each day of the month with a tracker for appropriate safety actions and a thank-you sheet to enable people to thank whom they wish for help during their work activities. The SLT meet with a production and a support team once a week and review the team's visual management board. Performance metrics and areas where the teams need support are discussed. Each team meets with the SLT at least once a quarter. Both the SLT and middle managers also meet with the people in the company during gemba walks. The SLT and middle managers split into small teams and go out and ask people how they are getting on, from both a work and general perspective, to engage with the people in the organisation. These gemba walks have proven successful in allowing opportunities for improvement to be identified and in some cases explaining why certain policies or procedures are in place. This has helped to create an open and honest culture with people who are also engaged and focused on operational efficiency.

Innovation: 3D hand scanner and printer for local spares provisioning

The emergence of Industry 4.0, combined with improvement in operational efficiency using TPM, precision changeovers and lean tools has accelerated the introduction of technology and removal of the use of paper records from the plant, which in turn has resulted in the creation of additional time for improvement activity. See Figure 10.11.

An example of this is the time provided to technicians to work on innovative and value-adding activity. Technicians and engineers have been trained on advanced design software packages such as Solid Works and applications to aid design, such as failure analysis software. The investment in both equipment and training in Solid Works and a 3D printer and scanner has empowered technicians and engineers to use the new technologies in their normal day-to-day activities.

It has resulted in users developing their ideas, designing prototypes and printing out their models for testing. If the prototypes are not suitable for the designed application, the designer can modify the design and print another test piece. This brings cost savings by not having to manufacture actual parts that may not be suitable for their intended use, before producing the actual finished working piece. Technicians have also saved on the costs of purchasing spare parts from vendors by producing spare-part designs and having them manufactured by local tooling companies, with typical savings of between 70% and 90%.

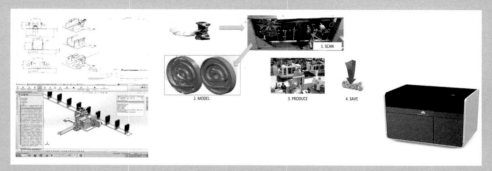

Figure 10.11: Capturing parts shapes from CAD systems or physical scanning, then outputting a replacement part on a local 3D printer

During 2016 technicians scanned and generated over 300 parts for inclusion in a virtual store. These designs can be then sent to the local supplier when needed and made available for use within 24 hours, substantially reducing typical lead times from the equipment vendors of up to three to four weeks. The aim for the engineering department is to reduce spares inventory by up to 50% over the next two to three years.

The development of the technicians in the use of these innovative tools is also particularly evident in their ability to scan worn parts in place and produce a drawing for a replacement part based on the scan, and in the use of CAD and Solid Works to reverse engineer and reproduce the required part. The associated costs for the scanner, Solid Works software and 3D printers (the original has now been replaced by a more advanced model) and training for the technicians has paid itself back multiple times over.

Raising quality standards

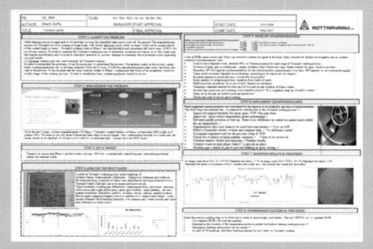

Figure 10.12: 8-step A3 methods used to solve problems

A focus on standardisation and training according to best practice for how tasks are completed has helped increase the quality of products and the operation of processes within the Damastown facility. These steps are well aligned with the Shingo principle of seeking perfection and supporting concepts of standardising processes, keeping it simple and visual, identifying and eliminating waste, and integrating improvement with work. For example, production and maintenance personnel have developed single point lessons (SPLs) that cover routine equipment operation and operator and technician maintenance tasks. The team members capture and agree the best practices and then illustrate those practices in a simple and visual way – see Figure 10.12. SPLs can be accessed from any PC in the company via the internal SharePoint site. SharePoint is also used for managing the versioning system to ensure that only up-to-date SPLs are available. In addition to the use of SPLs, training videos are also used to demonstrate the operation of computerised systems and safety systems for trainees. By allowing the users to create the standards and continually improve those standards, the level of product quality and the processes creating those products have improved. The focus on problem solving and removing root cause issues has also helped improve quality throughout the company. Problem-solving projects and continuous improvement activities have been completed in all areas of the organisation. The use of 8-Step A3 methodology and problem-solving boards, designed by the technicians and production operatives, are located throughout all the production areas and have helped reduce deviations by 20% over the last 12 months.

Summary

This case study contains a sample of activities deployed at the Mylan Damastown plant in the area of operational excellence, using TPM principles as our start point and the foundation to drive our wider but focused improvement endeavours. Key performance indicators covering cost, quality, service, safety and the environment are all extremely positive. In the period 2010 to 2017

- the number of accidents decreased by 63%
- on-time delivery increased by 24%
- the incidence of complaints decreased by 68%
- energy consumption per pack decreased by 36%
- the time for batch release post production decreased by 64%.

The site now has an international reputation for world-class operational excellence practices and regularly hosts best practice visits for companies from within Ireland and abroad. Mylan Damastown are also recognised within the Mylan group as a best practice site and this has been reinforced through the recent awarding of additional products, which will support the 2014–2024 vision of tripling production output. The future and outlook are bright for the Damastown site as a result of building a high-performance culture that provides excellent sustainable business results.

10.3 **Application of TPM at Welsh Water**

By Jackie Gray, Lean Deployment Specialist and Dan Edwards, Lean Deployment Specialist, Welsh Water

Background

In November 2015, as part of the lean programme within Dŵr Cymru Welsh Water (DCWW), two Waste Water sites were identified as pilot areas for the wider deployment of Lean using the principles of TPM. One is called Cog Moors waste water treatment works (WWTW) and the other Five Fords (WWTW). The Cog Moors site was identified because it was the most expensive site for reactive costs in the whole DCWW area. Cog Moors WWTW serves Cardiff, Barry and the other local coastal region, and has approximately 206,000 customers, a treatment flow of 2,145 litres per second and a storm flow of 4,340 litres per second.

Five Fords located in North Wales was selected as the second site for deployment because of its large size and because it is the only gas-to-grid plant in DCWW.

Both sites have significant high value capital intense physical assets with a wide age range and condition profile.

The Lean deployment programme also included other business functions such as capital delivery, water services, finance and procurement

Our Lean deployment programme was very much bespoke to fit in with the utilities industry and adapted in order that the nomenclature was not interpreted as 'this is only applicable to what factories do'.

Figure 10.13 illustrates our lean model and Figure 10.14 shows how we articulate it.

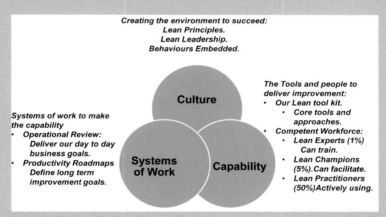

Figure 10.13: The lean model

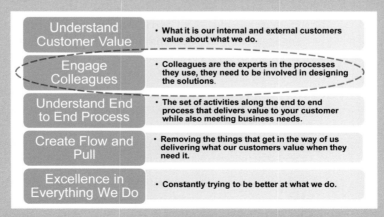

Figure 10.14: The five lean principles adapted to our needs

The third part of our improvement strategy focuses on people development intentions in order to engage colleagues (Figure 10.15).

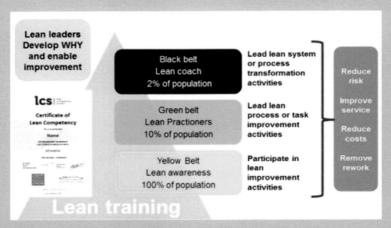

Figure 10.15: Skills development and recognition

Although in the utilities sector, a 'product' is actually being processed and there are distinct value streams. It was critical to create an ownership culture in the business – 'this is what we do'. Subtle changes in terminology, for example a different take on the five lean principles (as in Figure 10.14) could be the difference between the programme becoming accepted as part of the culture of the company or – using the analogy of organ transplant surgery – being rejected due to incompatibility that could have been avoided by more detailed planning, analysis, tailoring and testing.

Engaging colleagues is not strictly part of the original lean principles (as expressed by Womack & Jones in *Lean Thinking*) but is something we have included because it is hugely important in getting the right culture change and engagement from the team. That recognition of team members can then be expressed as 'You are the experts who know this process inside out and this is your site'. In this way the ownership of actions, improvements and successes is never in doubt. From the outset, respect for site staff at all levels was essential for a positive deployment and sustainable outcome.

An example of the importance of engagement and ownership from previous lean deployments was that when lean **reliability-centred maintenance** (RCM) had been implemented, it had a detrimental effect on the senior operators' views on lean. This was because that person spent a large amount of time on it, including assisting with constructing standard operating procedures, but saw little or no direct benefit from it.

The RCM programme had a poor reputation and at one site, the remark that 'Lean just came in and threw out all our good stuff' was made by some members of the team. RCM can be a very effective tool. However, deploying tools without proper strategy and alignment and without ensuring the leadership behaviours and engagement is in place from the beginning resulted in the initiative failing to stick in some key areas of the business.

The plan was that once stakeholder engagement had been secured, then value stream mapping (VSM) would be carried out at both sites, to identify issues, bottlenecks and opportunities for improvement in the sludge treatment value streams. It was decided that TPM would be the most appropriate tool and philosophy to address issues relating to improving asset effectiveness.

Following a period of deliberation, it was decided that the approach in both these WWT plants would be called **asset optimisation** (AO) as opposed to TPM, as the lean leadership group correctly felt that classic TPM did not fit in the utility environment. This caution was also based on the fact that the business had been running an RCM programme that had yielded a mixture of results in terms of tangible benefits, but had not delivered in terms of the 'ownership' culture change that the lean programme aspired to achieve. RCM is a tool above the waterline (Figure 10.16) and on its own, it will not be possible to sustain benefits without a clearly defined strategy and embracing the right management behaviours and leadership below the waterline, no matter how well the tool is deployed.

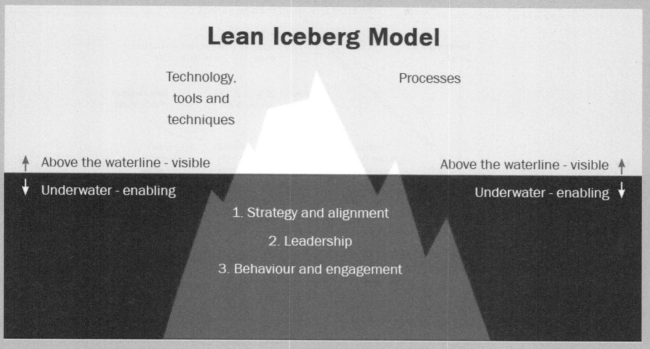

Source: P. Hines, P. Found, G. Griffiths & R. Harrison, *Staying Lean*, 2008

Figure 10.16: The lean iceberg model

The idea behind asset optimisation was to 'build on' what RCM had delivered and certainly not 'replace' the RCM programme. As it transpired, over time the asset optimisation approach was adopted across all waste water and clean water product value streams and effectively became the primary tool used in the business to improve total asset effectiveness. A plan was put in place to align the deployment strategy and build capability while also improving site performance, and then based on this positive experience, to roll out the asset optimisation tool on both sites.

Overall approach: scoping and securing commitment

In both the Cog Moors and the Five Fords waste water work streams a value stream map (VSM) exercise was undertaken by cross functional team members working in both of the WWT plants.

Before this diagnostic process could take place, it was imperative to get stakeholder buy-in so that the process and the people involved would get full support and to ensure countermeasures were put in place to secure success. Meetings took place with the geographic area manager and the head of waste water treatment services to discuss the scope, key activities, targeted benefits, critical success factors and resources. It was agreed that the initial work would be to undertake some lean awareness training sessions on both sites for all staff before undertaking a VSM process at each site to identify specific opportunities and issues, that the right resources would be available and that any potential barriers were identified.

Establishing a good relationship with the managers and site supervisors with open and honest conversations was essential to ensure that they would support the necessary culture change. Central to this was coaching and frequent and appropriate feedback to encourage all levels of site staff throughout the VSM and asset optimisation process. Taking the time to share the benefits of their experience and technical knowledge and allowing staff the freedom to try new approaches to running the process equipment proved to be extremely beneficial.

The VSM process followed the typical procedure as outlined in Figures 10.17 and 10.18.

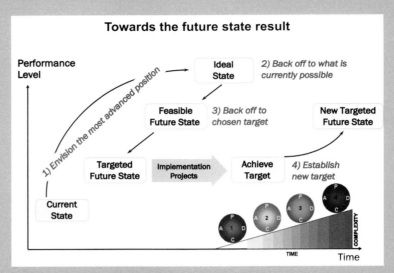

Figure 10.17: Value stream mapping

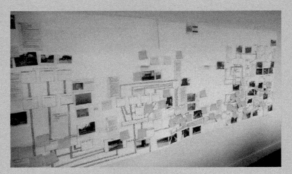

Figure 10.18: Putting value stream mapping into practice

Putting VSM into practice

Charters were put in place for asset optimisation of the gravity belt thickeners (GBTs), centrifuge, digester and the aeration lanes. An example of a charter is shown below in Figure 10.19. The projects were structured so that the supervisor would lead on the GBT with the support of the operator and then they in turn would also lead on the Centrifuge AO with another operator for support. This would develop the competency of two key staff on site as a useful operational tool. The AO projects were also deemed suitable for submission as Green belt case studies for accreditation and recognition (see Figure 10.15).

Other improvements identified were discussed and entered onto the forward-looking maintenance plan (FLCM). In addition, some straightforward issues were taken through a four-step problem-solving process to establish actions for implementation by the on-site team.

In terms of facilitation the plan was to deploy AO on the GBT with the lean coach and the mentor (a supporting SA Partners consultant). The next AO project on the centrifuge would be facilitated by the lean coach with the supervisor supporting. The plan was then for the supervisor to facilitate the roll out of AO for the digesters with the support of the lean coach. This fully aligned with the company's objective to build specialist capability within the lean team and to ensure competency on site. The first wave of AO on the GBT would consist of a team from the Cog Moors site including the supervisor, senior operators, senior craft, operators and an electrician.

Project Scope Out
Owner: Site supervisor
What is the title of your project?
Gravity Belt Thickner Optimisation
What is in scope and what is outside of scope?
In the scope are the 3 GBTs, poly usage and primary tank de-sludge optimisation. Outside the scope will be everything downstream, (digesters feed etc)
How will you measure success (Cost, Risk, Speed, Skills, Ways of Working etc)?
Reduction in Poly and breakdown costs, less manual interventions, reduction in cost/ton of sludge, better flow and consistency of thickening/dewatering improved, reduction in Belt
Who will be the project sponsor?
Catchment(Area manager)
Who will need to be involved in the project (Responsible, Accountable, Consulted, Informed)?
Operators,Maintenance,Site supervisor,instrumentation,technical services, OEM vendors,Poly supplier technical expert ,Director of waste services, Lean specialist, Consultant
What activity, risk, issue or opportunity is it trying to resolve or improve (Object & Defect)?
To produce a more consistent flow from the SDMs and across the belts with improved dewatering. Increasing the final product (%ds) to an optimum rate of 6-7.5%. Reduce the operating costs of the equipment and optimise poly usage. Improve automation and increase H&S by reducing manual interventions. Improve OEE.
Describe the current state situation - what are the customers seeing?
Inconsistent sludge to belt, with potential to back up in PSTs where thick sludge will cause scraper failure and potential tankering costs.
No structure of pre-planned maintenance on common faults regarding blockages instead it's on a as and when basis
Thick sludge feed onto the belt results in the belt running out of design spec and hinders the transfer pump getting the sludge away.
Uncontrolled poly usage often results in belt blinding hindering dewatering and increasing cost per ton.
Intermittent failure due to rag/fat build up in transfer pumps and rising mains causing discharge failures
Wash water pumps blocking due to FE quality
Transfer pumps not being controlled by VSD
Frequently wouldn't run overnight without intervention (potentially taking advantage of cheaper overnight tariffs).
Poly mixing poor on shear valves
Not confident to operate 2 belts on Primary manually, (never been done before)
Timeline
March - October 2016
Coach
Lean specialist,Consultant
Communication to stakeholders?
Regular updates to Catchment Manager and Head of Waste. Regular contribution to 5 box updates to support steering group meetings
Regular feedback to wider site team via team meetings

Figure 10.19: Asset optimisation statement of intent for Gravity Belt Thickener Optimisation

The aim of the AO was to improve sludge quality (within a consistent range of 6.5% to 7.0%) and improve reliability of the equipment which would ensure a smooth delivery to the next customer in the process; the digester. This would lead to a positive reduction impact on both the site's reactive costs as sludge 'cost per tonne' and 'cost to serve'.

The project charter (Figure 10.19) details what the objectives are, what the current state is, what success will look like, who the team and the key stakeholders are, and how we will keep the key stakeholders informed of progress or issues along the journey. It also details what parts of the site and equipment are in scope and out of scope.

A perception survey was carried out in both the WWT plants involving one to one confidential discussion with operators, maintainers (mechanical, electrical and instrumentation) and their key contacts such as supervisors and managers.

As highlighted by two examples of the perception statements in Table 10.1, while the key contacts often had differing views compared with maintainers and operators, there was one factor regarding spares provisioning where most respondents agreed that we have a major issue and hence opportunity for improvement.

This major repeating concern was that spares are not held on site for critical equipment, especially when you consider that a WWT plant is more like a power station than a waste treatment works. It generates the company substantial amounts of revenue through its renewable energy sources, such as CHP (combined heat and power) generation and bio-methane injection. Having assets unavailable, waiting for spares that cost as much as £500, could in addition be costing more than £7,000 per week in lost revenue.

Likewise there was a strong sense of feeling that our skill sets are not acquired in a structured way. Again an issue that is addressed as a key component of the AO system of work.

Table 10.1 Perceptions Analysis-two highlighted main hinders to progress

Statement	Maintainers	Operators	Key contacts	Weighted total
Our spares stock holding is not as good as it should be	100%	93%	67%	93%
Skills are picked up rather than learnt systematically	83%	73%	33%	67%

Asset optimisation (AO) initial training and pilot project launch

Referring to Figures 10.20 and Table 10.2, the purpose of the four-day AO workshop was to familiarise the AO team with the first eight equipment-based steps of the 11-step four-cycle process in order that they had the appropriate knowledge to continue working on these steps over the next three to six months to work towards Milestone 1 (see Figure 10.27). Typically the workshop would be run in a four-day consecutive block with a team of between ten and twenty attendees taken off-line. From the operational shift logistics perspective of a waste treatment works this was not a practical option. So it was decided with the team's agreement and support to run the workshop in two blocks of two consecutive day sessions. However it's interesting to note that even with this forward planning, the second two-day block had to be re-scheduled due to unplanned breakdowns on site!

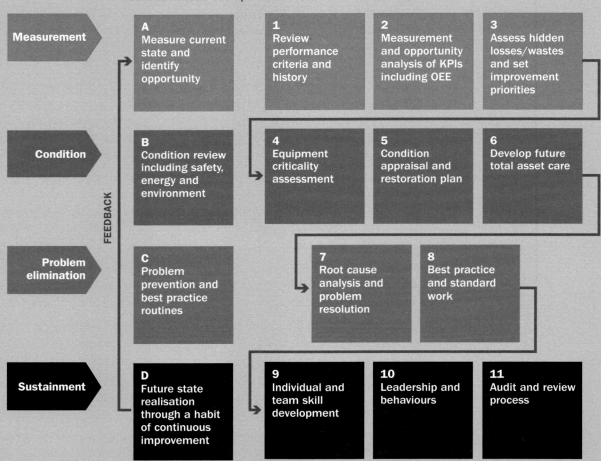

Figure 10.20: Asset optimisation – the 4-cycle 11-step process

Table 10.2 Asset optimisation 4-day hands-on 'learning by doing' training programme

Day 1	Day 2	Day 3	Day 4
Introduction to asset optimisation (AO) Maintenance Assessment Exercise • AO PRINCIPLES • Case studies • OEE Exercises.	Recap Brief Visit to Pilot and Plan the Plan Equipment Description MEASUREMENT CYCLE On-the-Job) 1) History/Records 2) OEE Measures 3) 6 loss Assessment	• Building AO Activity Boards • Consolidating Measurement and Condition Cycles • SUPPORTING TECHNIQUES • Set-up Reduction • 5S/ workplace Org CULTURAL CONSIDERATIONS	Dry Run Presentations SYNDICATE PRESENTATIONS REVIEW AND KEY LEARNING POINTS Next steps PILOTS & 4 STAGE ROLLOUT
AO TECHNIQUES AND 11 STEP IMPROVEMENT PLAN TEAMWORKING & FACILITATING BRIEFING FOR SYNDICATES On–the-Job Pilot Study	CONDITION CYCLE Exercise – Criticality assessment (On-the-Job) 4) Criticality assessment 5a) Condition appraisal 5b) Refurbishment Plan 6) Future asset care	PROBLEM PREVENTION CYCLE (On-the-Job) 7) Problem Solving 8) Best Practice Routines PREPARE AO ACTIVITY BOARD PRESENTATION	Getting Started LAUNCHING THE PILOTS Course Assessment 16.00hrs CLOSE

This experience resulted in an improved plan for the next workshops, ensuring that the supervisor would review not just staff who would be on leave, but also the standby rota as well, as callouts frequently result in unavailability (sleep time) the next day.

One of the scoping issues that was discussed prior to commencing the AO programme on the gravity belt thickeners was the need to develop their own OEE 'case study example' and hence illustrate what would be classed as 'in scope' and 'out of scope'. The team concluded that it was not only the gravity belt thickener that was in scope, but also the sludge feed pump and discharge pump (Figure 10.21). Data from these assets was also invaluable in the quest to work out an OEE both across and within this critical 'pinch-point' process flow.

Sludge Feed Pump   **Belt Thickener**   **Discharge Pump**

Figure 10.21: Micro process flow

As the AO programme developed and the competency of the coaches to deliver AO training and facilitation improved, they were able to develop the material to be more specific to the water-utility context by including real-life examples from inside the business to help with the learning experience. Some of the training exercises used within the AO playbook were also made more interactive, improving the 'learning by doing' experience.

As the teams progressed through each AO pilot asset, an AO activity board was used to track and communicate progress as shown in Figure 10.22. The process took around 20 weeks for the first three assets to reach and achieve the Milestone 1 audit and review.

Figure 10.22: The AO board for the centrifuge at Cog Moors (left) and the AO board for the thickener belts at Five Fords (right)

The continuous improvement cycle – future state realisation through the habit of continuous improvement (steps 9, 10 & 11)

Individual and team skills development – step 9

At Cog Moors as the asset optimisation process progressed with what was a relatively new team, it became obvious that there had been little or no formal training (this was also identified in the perception survey). Equipment was operated as it always had been with information handed down from one operator to another over the years. No-one on site knew what the original design specification of equipment was. The AO team decided that some extended enterprise would be appropriate in the form of external master classes run by the various suppliers of the equipment that were negotiated at no cost and were arranged at the pull of the site staff (see Figure 10.23).

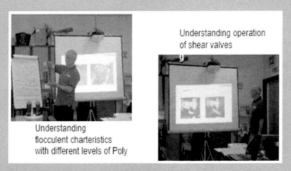

Figure 10.23: External supplier-led masterclasses

Customer-led success (CLS)

Every five years, the industry is subjected to a Water Services Regulatory Authority (OFWAT) price review which sets out the agreed spending for a five year period. These targets are always challenging and there is always an expectation to deliver more value for less cost. These cost constraints imposed on the business mean there is a constant challenge to be more efficient and effective. The strategy of becoming a lean organisation is seen as a way to meet these cost challenges and the tactical delivery mechanism for this is called the asset management plan (AMP), and is where the AO system of work is the central driver. The business strategy is based around customer led success (CLS) and AO within the lean deployment programme is viewed as the vehicle to deliver CLS. Therefore the establishment of CLS Boards in each of the pilot areas (as illustrated in Figure 10.24) is seen as the way to establish ownership and monitor performance and continuous improvement ideas through to implementation.

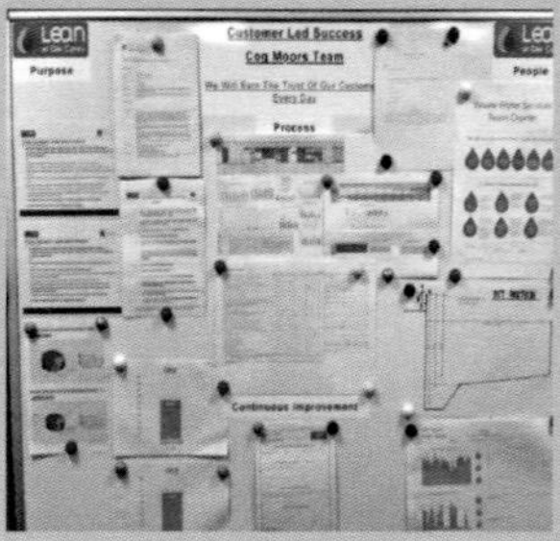

Figure 10.24: The CLS board at Cog Moors

The deployment of the CLS boards runs right through the organisation top down like a golden thread, as illustrated in Figure 10.25.

The CLS board ensures that everyone understands the process and buys in to how they can influence the company objectives on a day-to-day basis for the benefit of the customer. It was critical to successful ownership and engagement that the boards were built by the WWT plant teams and articulated in their own words. For example the team charter and purpose statement: rather than having it imposed upon them, the team had to think about what it is that they are here to do in order to contribute to the company strategy of 'We will earn the trust of our customers every day'. They came up with seven 'We will' statements. For every 'We will' statement, there had to be a statement in the process section which would measure and monitor performance of that commitment. For example, if the 'We will' statement said that they would 'Protect the environment for the customer', the measurement might be compliance of the final effluent going out to sea or to water courses.

Figure 10.25: CLS cascade

Five Fords WwTW CLS Measures			
Objectives	Goals	Strategy	Measures
Health, Safety & Wellbeing	Zero LTI's	Induction/ sign off for all visitors to site	100%
		Reduce risk of slips, trips & falls	Monthly 5S Audits
		Lone Working use	10 Log In's per month
		Lone Working Log Out	0 Alarm Out's
		Positive Interventions	100% closed within x
		Near Misses	100% closed out by x
		Safety Conversations	
Achieving all regulatory requirements	100% Compliance	Combined final effluent quality within parameters	Below x
		Ammonia within parameters	Below x
		Digester Temperature	Greater than 35 degrees C
		pH levels	Greater than 10
		Mixed Liquors within parameters	Between 2500 & 4500
		DO Levels within parameters	Between 1 & 3
		Record/ Monitor Digester Fatty Acids	tba
		Record/ Monitor Digester Alkalinity	tba
		Record/ Monitor Digester pH	tba
Optimising processes & reducing costs/ waste & maximising energy production			
CHP Target is achieved	Over £329.31 per day	Maximise OEE from Belt Thickeners	x%
GGS to exceed target	Over £2805.06 per day		
		Digester Temperature	Greater than 35 degrees C
		Available Screened Tank Level	Between x metres
		Available Thickened Tank Level	Between x metres
		Available Reception Tank Level	Between x metres
		Level Loading of Digesters	
Availability of Sludge Centre	100% Availability	Stock Check of Critical Spares	Weekly Check & Order Process
		Reduced planned maintenance backlog	Month on month reduction
		Jetting of lines to thickened Sludge tank	Quarterley/ 6 Monthly routine?
		All assets online?	No. Assets offline?
AGA Data	None over 10 days old	None of person vs age of data	No Jobs over 10 days old
Customers	0 contacts	No. of Customer contacts	Have we any and where are we at?

Figure 10.26: An example of the CLS deployment from Five Fords

Figure 10.26 shows the format of objectives, goals, strategy and measures cascade (OGSM). For example, it was key to ownership that the WWT plant team members understood the reason why they needed to optimise the belt thickening process. The top-level objective was to reduce cost across the sludge value streams and this was cascaded down to each WWT plant. The agreed strategy was to improve sludge thickness, with the appropriate measure being the required percentage dry solid content of the sludge off the thickener belt. The measure ultimately became the OEE of the belt thickener that incorporated sludge thickness (quality), availability and performance.

Lean principles

The work around creating the CLS board and the associated measures all tie in with our five Welsh Water lean principles:

- **Understand customer value** – What our internal and external customers value about what we do, so implementing measures to ensure site capacity for our tankers to offload (internal customer) and compliance on final effluent (Natural Resources Governance – the external customer) or maximising energy production and reducing costs (working towards potential reduction in customer water rates)

- **Engage colleagues** – The team on site know the processes better than anyone so it is they who know what we need to be looking at in terms of measures to ensure site success

- **Understand end-to-end process** – Through value-adding activities that meet our customer and business needs

- **Create flow and pull** – By implementing leading measures we are ensuring we eradicate potential bottlenecks before they occur; monitoring tank levels and ensuring capacity by targeting low levels so that we can facilitate an influx of tankers at any given time

- **Excellence in everything we do** – By having regular meetings and always monitoring our measures, as well as actioning emerging issues, we are constantly trying to be better at what we do!

Leadership and behaviours – step 10

Although the Asset Optimisation journey is not fully completed at Cog Moors, this is because it is a three- to four-year maturity journey where three of the eight equipment-based steps continue as part of the CI journey. The reality is that both WWT plant teams have made significant improvements on site and have progressed to achieve the Milestone 2 level audit (see Figure 10.27).

From a leadership perspective it has been recognised that it is very important to celebrate success during lean deployment when significant milestones are achieved and to recognise the contribution and continuous improvement effort the teams are delivering. It is also vital that managers support their team's success and celebrate with them. A number of site visits and feedback sessions with the senior sponsors, stakeholders and leadership team have taken place at both WWT plants where the leaders were able to view progress for themselves and congratulate the team members in person.

This type of visible, proactive engagement is crucial to our development as a lean company. In previous engagement surveys, staff perception had been that management were distant and they never saw them; this perception is now changing. The Cog Moors site has also become an active member of a best practice sharing networking organisation and has hosted an open day for other network organisations to come and share their story. This has in turn been reciprocated and given team members an opportunity to go and see best practice in other industries other than utilities and it is thus becoming a learning organisation.

Visual management is also a central part of our philosophy to make it easier to do a good job and catch issues and resolve them as part of daily routine through Customer Led Success.

Evidence-based audit and review process – step 11

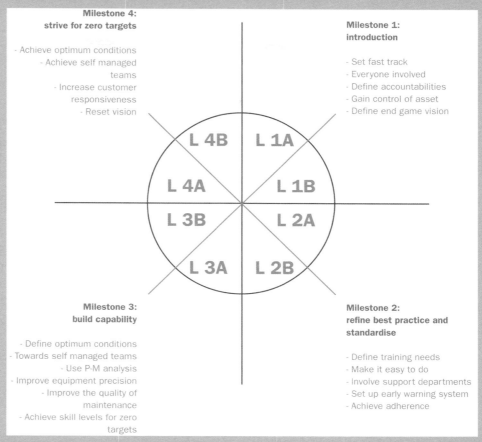

Milestone 4:
strive for zero targets

- Achieve optimum conditions
- Achieve self managed teams
- Increase customer responsiveness
- Reset vision

Milestone 1:
introduction

- Set fast track
- Everyone involved
- Define accountabilities
- Gain control of asset
- Define end game vision

L 4B   L 1A

L 4A   L 1B

L 3B   L 2A

L 3A   L 2B

Milestone 3:
build capability

- Define optimum conditions
- Towards self managed teams
- Use P-M analysis
- Improve equipment precision
- Improve the quality of maintenance
- Achieve skill levels for zero targets

Milestone 2:
refine best practice and standardise

- Define training needs
- Make it easy to do
- Involve support departments
- Set up early warning system
- Achieve adherence

Figure 10.27: AO audit milestone review process

Operational trends are reviewed and reported on the daily dashboard. The progress of the AO is managed through a robust audit and feedback milestone review process (Figure 10.27). Individual projects are also monitored via the lean deployment CLS board, where they are reviewed monthly and assigned a red, amber or green status to prompt action if necessary.

Competency, culture and transfer of ownership to the site teams are monitored through a bespoke lean maturity structure. If a site is moving forward successfully on its maturity journey following the true lean curve, there will be regular actions in the emerging issues, and escalation of ideas along with ongoing CI projects. The sites will be monitored and supported in the use of this part of the board and in problem solving, until it becomes 'business as usual'.

It's our people at the sharp end who make the difference

Extract of an article that was published in Welsh Water's Dŵr monthly magazine in December 2017:

The Cog Moors waste water treatment works team has been busy engaging with the roll out of "Lean Exemplar". We wanted to know what is involved, and how it affects people's day to day jobs so we interviewed John Bowd the site supervisor and operator Rhodri Williams to get their views.

What was your initial reaction and how did you feel when you were told lean was coming to your site?

John: 'Apprehensive at first and not sure how this would be of benefit to me or my site.'

What is different about your site now that lean has been embedded into your working culture?

John: 'Massive optimisation control and sludge processing improvements.'

Rhodri: 'We all take a pride in organising our workplace which reduces Health & Safety risks for everyone on site. For example, cleaning for inspection has enabled polymer leaks to be identified and repaired quickly, resulting in a significant H&S improvement.'

John: 'Also, reduced use of chemicals to treat raw sewage and less breakdowns and parts replacement.'

What are the main positives of the asset optimisation process for you?

Rhodri: 'As the machinery on site now runs far more efficiently with fewer breakdowns, my work/life balance has improved significantly and I am far less likely to be called into work during evenings and at weekends now.'

John: 'A great benefit is that Health and Safety risks are reduced in the workplace.'

Rhodri: 'I now know how, why and what I do in my role will affect how well my site performs, and when important tasks need to be carried out to maintain the smooth running of the site, I feel far more in control now. Everyone on site has a say in lean deployment. We are all experts in our roles and have an important part to play in making lean work as a team.'

John: 'Performance results are now helping us identify where we need to make investments on site to maintain and improve our performance.'

What would you say to someone who is about to have AO rolled out in their area of the business?

Rhodri: 'Initially taking time out to address issues and plan a strategy of improvement can be difficult. It's hard to find the time to dedicate to lean if you are working flat out to maintain the site because it isn't running as efficiently as it could.'

John: 'Short term pain for long term gain – embracing lean, engaging with the deployment specialist and making a valid contribution to that deployment will pay dividends and make our working life a lot easier in the long run.'

We also caught up with lean deployment specialist Jackie G to ask her about her experience at Cog Moors. She told us:

'My objective was to embed the lean deployment vision – improve culture, capability, and systems of work. The team was very enthusiastic about helping me to understand the processes carried out at the site but they were a little apprehensive at first to engage with lean deployment. I gave the team a thorough understanding of our lean principles and how continuous improvement would help transform their site. We were able to identify who their customers were in the treatment process chain on site.

As we started to identify quick wins by focusing their expert knowledge and ideas, engagement built and the team were enthused and now have an excellent continuous improvement culture. Success can be demonstrated by the fact that the team are now delivering continuous improvement initiatives in the workplace which are outside of the original focus areas we identified. They have achieved their initial objective which was to work smarter not harder, with less reactive work.'

Summary of our AO progress

Since November 2015 we have grown our own in-house lean/continuous improvement capability and delivered significant benefits on projects completed to date. The culture and behaviours of the business are changing as they transition from the limited adoption of lean/CI thinking into the wider embedding of 'business excellence' across the whole organisation. In the case of Operations where our physical assets are based, we have adapted the well proven TPM philosophy with essential tailoring to suit our asset optimisation system of working.

Each focused improvement OA project results in a summary of benefits based on the 5Cs that are critical for the business:

- **Cost** impacts are significantly positive since tracking benefits (even accepting that many variables can preclude clarity of cost benefit)
- **Compliance** improved safety performance and reduced H&S incidents
- **Customer** improved internal and external customer service/value/relationships
- **Capacity** increased installed productive capacity by up to 20% in Waste Water Operations and reduced ramp-up lead time on Capital projects
- **Colleague** improved lean/CI capability, competence and growing confidence across the business.

This tailored approach to OA has been fundamental in our cultural transition and – we believe – will also continue to deliver both the 'hard' and necessary end customer 'value for money' business benefits as well as a culture of ownership and CI at the sharp end of the business.

10.4 Warwick Chemicals' TPM experience

By John Jones, Operations Support Manager

Warwick Chemicals is a leading manufacturer of speciality chemicals for the detergent industry. It has around 200 employees running a highly regulated (COMAH) site in North Wales.

The business case revolved around the pressing need to improve the effectiveness of a new – just three years old – chemical plant producing sodium acetate (SA). Customer demand was such that the company was constrained by the SA plant as the 'pinch point' in their end-to-end value stream output.

Warwick carried out a comprehensive diagnostic exercise and scoping study to establish where they were and where they needed to get to. This showed a very unstable current average OEE generally below 40%. Future demand (the next 12 months) showed clearly that the OEE needed to be at a consistent 60%, which would represent a 50% real improvement in the SA plant's current productive capacity.

The challenge was straightforward in the sense that there was a choice to either unlock the installed productive capacity of the SA plant or face the prospect of replicating current capacity through capital expenditure. The former was a possibility, the latter extremely unlikely!

The company decided to implement a TPM training programme and methodology focused on the SA plant that was designed to encourage close, cross-functional teamwork to effectively manage the plant and its equipment through the operators and maintainers responsible for that asset.

Following the diagnostic exercise, Warwick ran a one-day site leadership team TPM awareness workshop to secure their commitment and 'buy-in' to a properly resourced and visibly supported TPM system of work.

One of the key outputs of the session was to invite the site leadership team to answer the question: 'From what we have learnt today, what is TPM going to give us that we are not already doing?'

To facilitate this exercise the leadership team was split into to two groups of five and invited to list out all the business drivers and then rate each one against TPM's potential ability to deliver those business drivers. The result of the combined feedback and discussion is shown in Table 10.3.

This recognition of a 78% potential significance of TPM to help deliver the business imperatives was a major step in giving confidence to all employees that the TPM programme would be correctly resourced from the outset, in spite of likely painful refurbishment costs to restore the equipment to 'as new' condition.

Table 10.3 The potential impact of TPM on business drivers

Business drivers	Potential impact of TPM
Improved profitability	3
Increased sales	3
Customer credibility	3
Staff involvement & engagement	3
Safety performance	3
Environmental conformance	2
Diversification	1
Stakeholder value	2
Reduction in asset maintenance cost	1
TOTAL	21/27 = 78% significant

Rating scale: 0 = No impact, 1 = Some impact, 2 = Significant impact, 3 = Major impact

This positivity was transferred to the TPM pilot project launch in the SA plant with a four-day TPM practitioners' hands-on workshop, where the operators and maintainers also set out their 'end-game vision' for where the TPM process needed to take them, which they articulated simply as:

- we will ensure a commitment to a positive safety culture via fit-for-purpose equipment and workplace organisation
- where we can plan weekly production rates with 100% confidence
- and consistently achieve our planned production on time in full
- together with consistent 100% right first-time quality
- through a commitment to **total asset care** (FLOAC, CBM & PM schedule adherence).

Achieving the vision will require striving towards our four zeros of

- zero accidents and emissions
- zero breakdowns
- zero minor stoppages/interventions/interruptions
- zero defects.

A further important part of delivering the necessary end-game vision was to present TPM as a partnership between production and maintenance, which they expressed as shown in Figure 10.28.

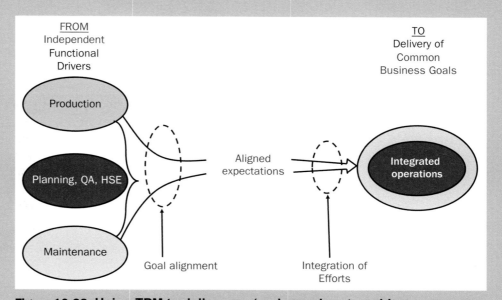

Figure 10.28: Using TPM to deliver our 'end game' partnership

After the four-day TPM practitioners' workshop, where each of the eight equipment steps is worked through as a 'learn by doing' experience on the actual plant, the company launched TPM activity days once every two weeks, organised by shift-based improvement areas, to progressively work through each of the three equipment cycle steps in all their necessary detail.

The impact over the first 14 weeks was dramatic, as shown by the trends illustrated in Figure 10.29 for availability, performance rate when running and quality rate produced.

The OEE results over 12 months from kick off show the combined impact of AxPxQ, moving from a volatile and 'out of control' 40% to an 'in control' and improving 74% and hence an ability to 'forecast with confidence'.

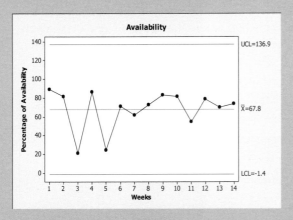

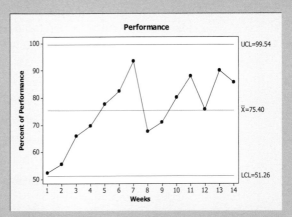

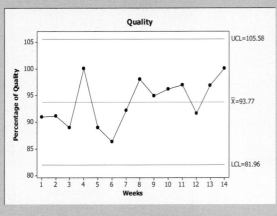

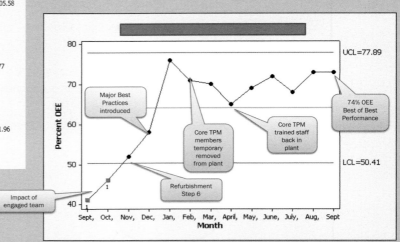

Figure 10.29: Trending the three OEE metrics and (bottom right) OEE trend over 12 months

The before and after photos in Figures 10.30 and 10.31 served as a dramatic reminder of where the company had come from at the start of its TPM journey to where it was 12 months later.

Figure 10.30: Before TPM: OEE 40%

Figure 10.31: After TPM. Equipment is well-designed, fit for purpose, safe, reliable and well-maintained. OEE: 74%

The overall business improvement benefits in plant reliability and predictability showed

- average tonnage increased from 12–14 tonnes per day to 28 tonnes per day
- additional c. $1.5m sales turnover per year
- for a total investment of TPM training and refurbishment costs of $60k
- which on the enhanced net margin of additional sales output represented a six-month pay-back.

Warwick Chemicals was also a very proud winner of the UK National Training Awards for the internal training and development of front-line staff using their 11-step TPM model.

10.5 Three brief case studies

Case Study A is from the pharmaceuticals industry. Case Studies B & C are both from the medical devices industry and both are Shingo Award™ winners.

10.5.1 Case study A: pharmaceutical industry warehouse cranes

Asset care (as in TPM) is one of this company's methodologies for creating an environment to underpin and illustrate their vision of 'This is the way we work here' (see Figure 10.32).

The company already had a number of asset care projects completed and ongoing. Recently, the warehouse and utilities team completed an asset care project for the warehouse cranes, and are now using the asset care philosophy and tools as the routine way of working.

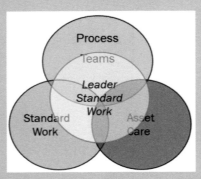

Figure 10.32: The company asset care model

Our challenge

The future vision and challenge, developed through the shift team's involvement in applying relevant measures and TPM-based asset care, is described by the team as follows:

- Operates as it should – with the ASRS (automated storage and retrieval system) part of it as a 'lights-out' operation where alarms are rare
- Operations & maintenance working as one team to self-determined standards and then sustaining those standards over the long term
- Greatly improved understanding of how our physical assets actually work, through relevant training in a safe and fit for purpose environment
- Deliver our internal customer requirements (production) on time in full.

Over six months the team followed the first eight equipment steps of the TPM asset care model:

- Steps 1 to 3, to measure current performance and assess the opportunity for improvement
- Steps 4 to 6, to improve the condition of the equipment and set up new and relevant maintenance checks
- Steps 7 and 8, to standardise the best-practice way to operate and maintain the equipment, to permanently resolve issues and prevent reoccurrence with the '100-year fix' mentality.

The outputs of the TPM asset care project include

- reduced alarms – from over 300 per month, to less than 100 (Figures 10.33 & 10.34)
- no downtime recorded by process teams for 'warehouse downtime' as in product or material starvation to production (their internal customer)
- new maintenance PMs, and operator front-line inspection checks introduced
- less fire-fighting. More proactive and innovative work (for example, mobile lighting on top of crane cab)
- sustaining system in place, using visual controls, process confirmation and leadership support
- successfully passed Milestone 1 (of 4) for evidence-based audit of TPM 'maturity'
- improved teamwork. Problems are now resolved as 'one team working together'.

Asset care now runs as normal business in the warehouse. The team meet once a week to discuss the crane's performance and agree actions to upkeep and improve the crane's reliability.

At the start of the project the team set out their 'end-game vision':

Our asset care vision

'Reliable & safe equipment assets available to run 100% of the time'

We can achieve this by striving for:

- zero accidents
- zero customer complaints
- zero defects
- zero breakdowns
- zero minor stoppages & interventions
- relentless continuous improvement every day

plus... standard (and therefore safe) operating procedures.

Figure 10.33: Improvements through restoration – examples of a crane after refurbishment works (asset care step 5b)

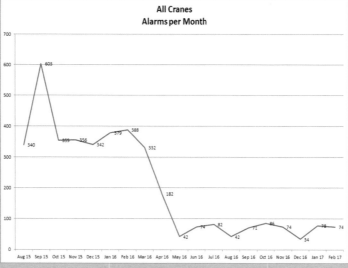

Figure 10.34: Monthly alarms down from over 300 to less than 100

Results have moved from 'warehouse downtime' to 'happy production customers'.

Some 'quotable quotes' from the asset care team

- 'We're being listened to and encouraged'

- 'We're all buying into it'
- 'There's only one best way'
- 'We haven't had to compromise our values'
- 'We not only know the 'What' but also the 'How' and the 'Where to get help'
- 'Who would have thought we could reduce our alarms by two-thirds!'

10.5.2 Case study B: medical devices

TPM's role in its continuous improvement journey

This medical device company began its CI journey in 2003 with a number of kaizen events aimed at removing waste from their processes. As their knowledge of lean manufacturing/CI grew, their focus broadened towards improving all elements of the business in an effort to guarantee customer satisfaction. To support this strategy, in 2004 an operational excellence group was established to ingrain a culture of continuous improvement. Today, lean tools such as TPM, VSM, standard work, and scientific problem solving are practised on a daily basis at a front-line level and the results are visible throughout the plant.

After a series of benchmarking visits during 2005, the company decided that the TPM philosophy and enabling tool could – in the right hands – deliver significant business benefits (through enhanced asset/equipment-based reliability and performance predictability) and also be the enabler to deliver the inclusive culture change they aspired to.

One important message that the benchmarking visit hosts stressed was the need to not only follow a clearly defined TPM process, but to also have a clear series of engagement steps to ensure ongoing sustainability:

- An initial one-day site leadership team 'buy-in' session to the TPM process to support the delivery of their business drivers and future vision, based on an initial diagnostic study
- A series of TPM practitioners' 'hands-on' four-day training workshops
- TPM pilot project launches and progress tracking over four maturity milestones
- Middle and senior management TPM 'pillar champion' coaching
- Focused improvement activities such as 5S workplace organisation, precision changeovers, standard work and early equipment management
- Regular evidence-based top-down and bottom-up TPM audit and review processes
- TPM roll-out planning and programme governance.

One of the initial TPM pilot projects was in the coil-winding facility comprising 23 machines. Following a four-day TPM practitioners' 'hands-on' workshop, the four shift-based TPM teams were launched in 2005. The teams progressively worked through the equipment steps using the 11-step TPM model.

Each shift team initially had dedicated weekly TPM activity sessions over a 14-week period before passing the Milestone 1 audit process tagged as 'Introduction – getting everyone involved'. Following the success at Milestone 1, the TPM process moved from a project-based approach to one of a regular weekly PDCA routine process review at the TPM visual management board for their specific group of assets in order to

- review action list from condition appraisal
- review and progress new ideas
- discuss OEE from previous week to focus this week's priority
- agree on corrective actions
- agree on work to be done before the next review session.

They also

- held two-hour twice-weekly sessions with the full time TPM facilitator to review progress
- held a 15-minute update presentation to the site leadership team every three weeks
- had daily discussion at the morning meeting on OEE and TPM activities
- logged all ideas on the TPM master list.

All of this was aimed at improving the initial TPM routines towards achieving Milestone 2.

Improvement: Design and fit Tool Shadow Boards in Coil Winding.
Benefits: All tools at hand when required.
Operators recognise immediately when tool is missing.
Improved machine uptime and facilitates quick change over.

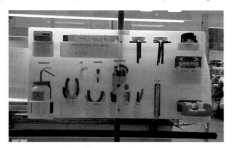

Cell Shadow Board

Layout designed by the Operator .

CP2-Are Equipment Standards Established?

Front Line-Operator Asset Care Examples

On the 'start of shift checks' section
☐Operator is asked to visually confirm guards are in place.
☐We will be adding these visual aids to the check list.

On the 'Once a shift checks' section
☐Operator is asked to visually confirm that dampeners and O rings are correct.
☐Operator is asked to visually confirm Shoes are useable.
☐Operator is asked to visually check that the air pressure gage is 80psi.

On the 'Friday morning check' section
•Strip box cleaned
•Pulleys clean
•Machine cleaned
•Table cleaned
•Oil level checked

CP4-Are All Areas Clearly Labelled ?

Machines &
Maintenance Trolley

Improvement: Additional Pulley to reduce roughness at 24k rpm
Benefit: RPM increase from 18k to 24k with no roughness issues. 10% increase in output.

Before   **After**

Milestone 2b-CP6-Are unit costs reducing?

Coilwinding Area   18% sustained increase in OEE

30% increase in Labour Efficiency

- Headcount reduced by 25% and redeployed and re-trained to start a brand new product area
- Production rates have increased by 10% plus on 5 x major products

Milestone 2b-CP 10-Are there Defined Action Plans in Place?

- Evidence –based TPM initiatives include
  - Safety
  - Set points
  - Re-engineering
  - Availability of materials :-

Arbor Kan Ban   Kit Box cage   Milk Run

Figure 10.35: Milestone 2 evidence

Figures 10.35 shows some of the highlights of what the coil-winding shift teams presented to the site leadership team and the TPM auditors in order to pass Milestone 2 – 'Refine best practice and standardise'.

These audits are 'Go see' evidence-based comprising 20 checkpoint (CP) criteria at each of four 'maturity' milestones. In this case they achieved these Milestone 2 results just six months into their TPM application journey.

Summary of TPM-related highlights

The company increased the standard coil-winding capacity by 10% to 33% depending on machine type. This included converting standard machines to accommodate a wider product range, with a saving of $120k per machine and with no additional floor-space requirement.

Based on their successes in coil-winding, the company rolled out the TPM philosophy over the next few years to all parts of their facility, including the manufacturing support functions, and also used the EEM pillar of TPM for new capital projects.

The company's TPM journey has brought other benefits, including reducing their maintenance inventory costs by 25%, and as part of the TPM system a comprehensive review of preventative maintenance routines and systems resulted in the removal of 1,750 hours per year of non-value-adding work, releasing those same hours for additional production and/or continuous improvement activity.

Having started TPM back in 2005 the company now clearly recognises that TPM – in the sense of getting operational basics in place – has allowed them to gain the confidence to continuously strive towards operational excellence and hence the Shingo Award recognition for their efforts.

Perhaps most importantly, because of consistent leadership and direction, TPM has allowed the company to take its vision and values off of the noticeboard and hand it to its employees, and say with conviction: 'Here you are; with this TPM process you can make a difference and be able to continuously challenge and improve the way we do things here.'

10.5.3 Case study C: medical devices

TPM's role in its continuous improvement journey

This company is a subsidiary of one of the world's largest and most diverse healthcare corporations, manufacturing hip, knee and shoulder replacements, comprising over 1500 stock keeping units. The processes are organised into value streams based on the product type. There are five main value streams on the site.

In 2003 the company began to introduce lean tools such as Kanban systems, OEE, VSM and supplier integration.

This led to some significant lead-time reduction and cost improvements, but there was acknowledgement that this tool-based approach was not sustainable or culturally ingrained.

In 2005 there was an unexpected increase in demand which the plant was not in a position to respond to. This highlighted the need for a more responsive and flexible manufacturing facility. To succeed in this new environment the company needed to build a high-performance culture based on continuous improvement. In 2006, the plant began a cultural, physical and organisational transformation. The company created a vision for 2010 based on doubling capacity, while maintaining the same headcount and floor space. The transformational map was constructed under four work streams – a lean programme, change management, new product introductions, and compliance excellence.

In 2007 machines were physically moved from grouped processes to a value stream (VS) layout to promote flow and enable pull within each area. This involved the relocation of over 400 pieces of equipment.

During this transitional phase the organisation structure was changed from functionally based to a value stream structure. This meant the creation of a VS manager with overall responsibility for the VS and a support team with shared objectives. The support teams were then relocated into custom-made 'pods' – office units for manufacturing support staff located within the VS. The space for these pods was created from the space saved through the lean layout. As the VS structure progressed this led to aligned goals and objectives and a profit and loss account by value stream, which enabled better decision making.

In 2008 the plant introduced a TPM-based approach that they chose to call 'Total asset care' (TAC) to highlight the teamworking aspects between the maintenance engineer and the front-line operator.

After scoping the initial application of TAC to their critical assets in terms of the people, money and time resources compared to an expected realistic business result, the company held a one-day TAC 'buy-in' session with the site leadership team. This session concluded with an exercise to pinpoint the potential contribution of TAC to help deliver their business drivers. The result of 81% significance shown in Figure 10.36 gave the necessary momentum to launch the TAC programme with a series of TAC pilot projects focused on business-critical 'pinch-point' assets.

Business Drivers	Potential Impact of TAC
Zero Accidents	1 to 2
Zero Close Calls / Recalls (Quality)	3
Productivity (15% up Yr on Yr)	3
100% Adherence to Plan	2 to 3
Reduced Overall Plant Operating Cost	2
Reduced Inventory	2
Teamwork / Engagement (Credo Results)	3
Total Score	**17 / 21 = 81%**

0 = None   1 = Some   2 = Significant   3 = Major

Figure 10.36: Ensuring ongoing commitment from the site leadership team

In preparing all employees to take the TAC philosophy on board as a critical part of the business transformation strategy, Figure 10.37 was used as the centrepiece to highlight these six points in a series of site-wide TAC awareness sessions:

- We cannot become a sustainable organisation without having operational basics in place
- This requires standardisation, 5S, process control, reliable data collection and workplace design to give reliable equipment
- The TAC approach partners closely with 5S, OEE and health & safety
- TAC is a basic foundation for creating sustainable and reliable FLOW
- The three-cycle approach taps into the expert knowledge that exists throughout our workforce
- TAC establishes the correct relationship between people and their equipment to create 'ownership'.

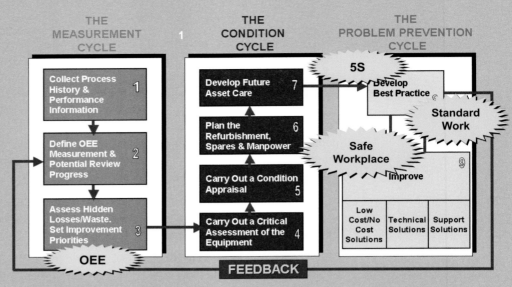

Figure 10.37: The three-cycle TAC process

Summary of TAC-related highlights

As shown in Figure 10.38 the initial TAC pilot projects to Milestone 1 maturity delivered significant financial benefits of c. $600k plus a new furnace capital cost avoidance of c. $1m. After two years, through Milestones 2, 3 and onwards towards Milestone 4, the validated cost benefits had accumulated to over $5m.

TPM Pilot Benefits after 9 months (and at c .2 years)

- Reduced Maintenance spend $ 68,000
- Reduced Non core Hours Over Time $ 238,000
- Less Consumables $ 57,000
- Additional Annualized Savings $ 241,000

- TOTAL $ 604,000

- Plus Cap Ex Cost Avoidance $1,074,000

After c.2 years ,accumulated cost avoidance = $5.37 million

Figure 10.38: Benefit accrual from TAC system application

One of the company's key ongoing learning points was to better understand the dynamics of applying OEE to a series of machine assets in a particular value stream, and hence to appreciate the dynamics of a moving 'pinch point' as improvements are implemented daily. The improved understanding and learning experience of OEE is illustrated and described in Figure 3.4 in Chapter 3.

Glossary

Asset care programme

A systematic approach to keeping equipment in 'as new' condition. This consists of carrying out three routine activities :

- Cleaning and inspection (carried out by the operator and referred to as front-line operator asset care – FLOACS – or autonomous maintenance – AM)
- Checking and monitoring as preventative maintenance (usually called condition-based monitoring – CBM)
- Fixed interval servicing (usually referred to as planned maintenance (PM) carried out by the maintainer).

Availability

The actual run time of a machine as a percentage of its planned run time.

Best of the best

An OEE figure calculated by multiplying the best weekly availability achieved, the best weekly performance rate achieved and the best weekly quality rate achieved for a specific machine, typically over a reference period of at least one month.

Changeover time

The elapsed time between the last good unit/piece of Product A to first good unit/piece of Product B at the standard production rate.

Condition appraisal

The assessment of the condition of a machine's components as a preparation step to undertaking the refurbishment plan and hence improving the OEE. This also involves carrying out an initial deep clean as part of the assessment. Sometimes referred to informally as 'spot the rot'.

Condition cycle

The second stage of the TPM improvement plan, which includes the criticality assessment, condition appraisal, refurbishment plan and the future asset care programme to keep the machine in that restored condition.

Core TPM team

These are the shift-based teams comprising operators and maintainers and a team leader, supported by a TPM facilitator. The teams work through the first eight equipment steps of the TPM improvement plan on their TPM pilot projects, typically over a 16–20 week period, ahead of it then becoming a routine plan, do, check, act (PDCA) cycle.

Criticality assessment

An evaluation of each of the machine's component parts against set criteria and their likely impact on safety, productivity (as measured by the three elements making up the OEE), environment, ease of operation, inherent reliability, maintainability and cost.

Door-to-door losses

These are losses that indirectly affect the value stream in which the physical manufacturing assets reside, but are not one of the six classic equipment-based losses. These losses are based on management decisions and typically include labour co-ordination losses (for example, no labour or incomplete team – or maintainer diverted to other priority), upstream product starvation, no planned production, no packaging materials, consumable stock-outs, awaiting QA clearance instructions, team meetings, shift handovers & rest breaks – all of which require the equipment to be stopped.

Eight-step TPM improvement plan

This is a set of logical steps the core teams progressively go through when applied to a specific physical asset in their TPM application area. It enables the team to understand the equipment functionality, measure the opportunity for improved asset performance, resolve those problems and prevent recurrence. Also by appraising the condition of the equipment, restoring it to an 'as new' condition, and keeping it at that level by applying the agreed future total asset care regime, the teams will not only improve the equipment, but more importantly they will discover the real reasons why the equipment is in the condition in which we initially find it and hence why it's not performing in the way we would want. Some of these issues can be fixed quickly and some are more long term. Only the critical plant and equipment will be subject to the 8-step TPM improvement plan.

5S

The English version of the Japanese 5Ss which are: Sort out, Set limits & locations, Shine, Standardise, Systemise to Sustain.

Five whys

The technique of asking 'why?' five times in order to get to the root cause of the problem.

Four milestones

This is the progression the organisation goes through over a period of approximately three to four years as they embark on the TPM process (see 'rollout' below). These have been recognised as discrete maturity phases that organisations go through as they transform themselves.

The four milestones are: MS1 Introduction; MS2 Refine best practice and standardise; MS3 Build capability; MS4 Strive towards zero losses.

At each milestone evidence-based audits are carried out to establish current capability in transforming the business and to focus further planning to take into account the future changes required to meet customer and market needs, as well as the organisational needs. For each milestone the management team pillar champions will have defined goals and targets that need to be realised having reached each of the milestone stages.

Gemba walk

A Gemba walk is an essential part of the operational excellence philosophy. Its primary purpose is to allow managers and leaders to observe the actual work process in the physical work place and to engage with employees, gain knowledge about the work process, and explore opportunities for continuous improvement.

Improvement zone (IZ)

This is a physical geographic area where the first line managers and their teams apply the techniques of TPM and 5S. This area is a manageable but representative portion of the process or plant which, when improved, will provide an important contribution to the business.

Key contacts

These are support personnel, usually representatives from the functional departments like finance, design, engineering, laboratory, or individuals with specialist knowledge. They will become involved either with an improvement project for themselves or using their specialist knowledge to support a TPM improvement team. Their aim is to support organisational learning and problem resolution using the tools of TPM.

Leader standard work

Leader standard work is a system that ensures that leaders develop the right culture by undertaking the right activity in the right style by
- understanding the roles and responsibilities of leaders at all levels
- checking that activity is taking place to ensure business success
- recognising people's contribution to success
- identifying coaching and development opportunities so that
- the whole organisation engages its people with the members taking initiative

so that all employees become more readily involved through coaching to improve the likelihood of a successful and sustainable transition and outcome.

Maintainability

This refers to how easy it is to gain access to the equipment and the particular skills needed to diagnose and resolve a problem.

Measurement cycle

The first stage of the 11-step TPM improvement plan, consisting of collecting equipment history, calculating the OEE and assessing the six classic equipment-based losses' impact on the productivity of the specific machine asset under review.

Minor stoppage

When a machine has to be stopped for a relatively short period (for example, to clear a blockage) and then re-started without the need for any significant repair. A minor stop therefore causes an operator to have to interfere with the process, but does not require the attendance of a maintenance technician in which case it would be classified as a breakdown.

OEE

The key measure used in TPM to calculate the percentage effectiveness of the equipment. Taking into consideration the availability of the equipment, the performance rate when running, and the quality rate of the manufactured product produced, it is measured over a period of time (typically per shift, day, week or month). The difference between the current OEE and its maximum potential is the current cost of non-conformity. Sometimes referred to as the 'hidden factory'.

Operational improvements

Improvement activities which result in increasing the equipment's reliability when implemented by the TPM core team. The objective is to make it easy to do things right and difficult to do things wrong through the use of appropriate visual indicators and visual management techniques.

Pillar champions

There are classically nine capabilities that need to be embraced if TPM is to flourish and then be sustained for the future. These are:
- Continuous improvement in overall equipment effectiveness (OEE)

- Front-line operator asset care (FLO'AC)
- Planned maintenance & quality of maintenance (PM & QM)
- Skills development (SD)
- Early equipment management (EEM)
- 5S workplace organisation (5S)
- Publicity & communications (P&C)
- Supply chain management (SCM)
- Health, safety & environment (HSE)

Because these nine pillars of TPM are so important we assign their development and consistent deployment to a relevant member of the management team. Each pillar champion, as they are referred to, creates the necessary environment at the plant by changing the way they manage, to enable everyone to contribute to these principles and the TPM process. Their key role therefore is to develop the policy for the particular pillar and then ensure its consistent deployment.

Pilot projects

Initial TPM pilot projects are learning experiences for the core teams to work through the eight equipment steps within the TPM improvement plan. They are small but representative 'chunks' of plant that enable us to flush out the management processes and habits that need to change if we want TPM to flourish across a plant or site.

P-M analysis

A problem-solving tool and mind-set used in TPM which uses a mnemonic of four Ps and five Ms:
- There are Phenomena occurring which are Physical in nature and which cause Problems that can be Prevented.
- Which are related to the 5 Ms of Machines, Manpower, Methods, Materials & Mother Nature.
- In order to fully understand the interdependencies and interrelationships of the 4Ps and 5Ms there is the need for the vital 6th M of Measurement.

Performance rate

The actual performance rate of a machine or process when running a specific product, expressed as a percentage of the planned standard performance rate.

Problem prevention cycle

The third stage in the 11-step TPM improvement plan, when the TPM core team concentrates not only on solving immediate problems but also on preventing problems from recurring in the future through adopting best practice, and defined as standard work.

Rollout

This is where we start implementing the TPM techniques across the whole site. This is so that we can begin to get everyone involved and contributing to the TPM process. This also has a number of stages (see 'four milestones' above), so that we implement TPM at a sustainable rate.

Quality loss

Lost production due to the manufactured product not being produced right first time at the required level of quality. It will therefore need to be either re-worked or scrapped.

Quality rate

The right first time OK product, expressed as a percentage of the total units manufactured or processed in the time period under review.

Reduced-speed loss

Production lost due to running equipment at a speed lower than its intended or validated standard performance speed (see also performance rate above).

Refurbishment plan (sometimes called restoration plan)

Identifying all the activities that need to be undertaken in order to restore the equipment to an 'as new' condition. This includes a detailed estimate of the cost, manpower resources, agreed priorities, timing and responsibilities.

Scoping study

A scoping study – sometimes referred as to as a front-end diagnostic study – provides information and evidence to justify and support the development of the TPM implementation programme. This will include a cost/benefit appraisal. It also identifies any potential roadblocks and provides an indication of the workforce's perception, feelings and readiness for the TPM programme.

Setup and adjustment losses

Production time lost because a machine is being set up or adjusted at the start of a production run, often following a planned changeover.

Six losses

These are the categories of losses the TPM teams use to identify and measure the classic equipment-based losses, so that they can prioritise and progressively reduce or eliminate them. These are the categories that affect your 'floor-to-floor' overall equipment effectiveness (OEE) score. The six losses are:
1   Breakdowns
2   Excessive setup and changeover

These two losses affect whether the machine is available to produce or not. This is why we use this as the availability percentage within the OEE calculation.
3   Idling and minor stops
4   Running at reduced speed

These two affect the performance rate of your machine when running. This is the percentage rate within the OEE calculation.
5   Reduced yield (scrap & rework)
6   Start-up loss

These two affect the quality of the product produced on the machine. This is the quality rate percentage within the OEE calculation.

Standard work

A detailed definition of the most efficient method to produce a product (or perform a service) as a series of specific work tasks to achieve a desired output rate. This is achieved by breaking down the work content into elements, which are sequentially organized and repeatedly followed. Often presented in the form of standard operating procedures as a series of highly visual single point lessons linked to a training accreditation/tracking process.

Startup loss

Lost production due to defects which occur at the start or restart of a run often following a changeover, breakdown or minor stop.

Support improvements

Improvements to equipment efficiency that can only be achieved through changes implemented in other parts of the organisation.

Support team

The members include representatives from each support function such as health, safety & environment, finance, design, engineering, sales and marketing, human resources, training, production control, quality control, supervision, employee union. Also sometimes referred to as key contacts, they may also be specific pillar chamions.

Takt time

The average time between the start of production of one unit and the start of production of the next unit, when these production starts are set to match the rate of customer demand. As such, takt time simply reflects the rate of production needed to match the demand – whether it takes four minutes or four years to produce the product, the takt time is based on customer demand. If a process or a production line are unable to produce at takt time, either demand levelling, additional resources, or process re-engineering is needed to correct the issue.

Technical improvements

Improvements to equipment effectiveness that require specialised technical analysis of problems before they can be implemented as a sustainable improvement.

TPM

TPM is the abbreviation of Total Productive Maintenance. It is a comprehensive strategy that supports the purpose of equipment improvement to maximise its effectiveness, efficiency and product quality. Many TPM practitioners prefer to call it Total Productive Manufacturing in order to highlight the need for team work as an equal partnership between production and maintenance.

Visual management (including visual indicators)

A powerful means of communicating, sharing information and making it easy to do things right and difficult to do things wrong. Techniques include TPM activity boards, charts and graphs, photographs, floor markings, equipment-based colour coded indicators, which give the status of the condition of a physical characteristic or phenomena such as temperature, pressure, velocity, alignment and positioning within clear limits.

Workplace organisation

Closely aligned with the principles and practice of 5S. The aim is to create flow (as opposed to simply 'good housekeeping') .This is achieved by creating a safe and fit for purpose workplace where everything is to hand, with a right place for everything and everything in its place in the right quantity at the right time,. Also physical layouts to minimise walking, storing, wasted effort and any other non-value adding activities and events are all central to the goal of creating and sustaining a 'world class' workplace.